INFERENTIAL STATISTICS in the BEHAVIORAL SCIENCES

Sheldon G. Levy
University of Michigan

HOLT, RINEHART AND WINSTON, INC.

New York / *Chicago* / *San Francisco* / *Atlanta*
Dallas / *Montreal* / *Toronto* / *London*

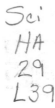
Figures 5.3 and 7.2 are taken from *Elementary Statistical Methods in Psychology and Education* by P. Blommers and E.F. Lindquist, by permission of the publisher, Houghton Mifflin Company. Figures 5.14 and 9.15 are taken from *Introduction to Probability and Statistics, Third* Edition, by Henry L. Alder and Edward B. Roessler, W.H. Freeman and Company. Copyright © 1964. Figure 9.16 is taken from *Elementary Statistics* by Paul G. Hoel, by permission of the publisher, John Wiley & Sons, Inc.

PREFACE

With so many texts of elementary statistics now available, one ought to have sound reasons for placing another into circulation. Whether or not the following are sound enough will be determined through experience.

This text is intended to serve as a one-semester introduction to statistics. Although it may be oriented toward psychology in some ways, it is hoped that it will find use in other fields, such as sociology, business, and education.

Perhaps the greatest difficulty with which students must cope in the introductory course is the learning of the concepts of inferential statistics. These ideas include, among many others, those of sampling, setting up a model of the population, determining the sampling distribution, and testing the null hypothesis. For many students, the amount of time spent in this area is too short. Even among those students who find the descriptive part of the traditional course relatively easy, many cannot adequately cope with and understand the latter half of the course.

With the feeling that one of the major difficulties is a lack of time devoted to the inferential section, this text has been so organized that it begins with several concepts of inferential statistics. Descriptive statistics is brought in only as is necessary to continue the inferential argument. In addition, the examples given to illustrate the descriptive ideas are not limited to distributions of individual scores. Distributions of various values of a sample statistic are also used. The purpose of this is to acquaint the student with the concepts relevant to the idea of a sampling distribution as early as possible. After the formal models for the z and t tests for the true mean and difference between means have been presented, as well as the ideas of confidence intervals and of one-tailed tests, additional descriptive material is examined. At this point, however, the concepts of inferential statistics can still be "sinking in." Thus, students who are having some difficulty have an opportunity to reflect on this material while the descriptive material is presented. Then, when a return is made to the remaining inferential tests (correlation, the binomial, χ^2 goodness of fit and association, z and t tests based on matched groups, and analysis of variance), there is some hope that the student will yet grasp the basic ideas before the course "credit doors" close. The z and t tests for matched groups as well as the F test for the one-way analysis of variance have been included at the end of the text rather than earlier primarily for review purposes. These tests allow a review of the earlier tests that deal with population means. The matched group tests also allow a review of Pearson's r.

Emphasis is also given on the translation of the real world situation into mathematical statements and the reinterpretation of the mathematical conclusion in terms of the real world. Although this discussion is implicit in many texts, a deliberate attempt is made to formalize the relationship. Further, a fairly detailed examination of probability is included so that the computations that are eventually performed in the formal statistical tests will not appear cook-bookish.

Another major aim of the text is to make it as understandable as possible for the reader. However, this in no way implies any intention to have the text replace the teacher. What is hoped for is an instrument which allows a fair amount of self-study. Hopefully, then, less class time could be devoted to formal lectures and more time to both questions and answers and the working of problems.

Whether all or any of these goals have been reached is not known. Some will object to the reorganization of the traditional approach to the course. Others may object to the verbal treatment of fairly complex mathematical ideas, which of necessity results in a loss of precision.

However, if the approach incorporated here helps students in the social sciences and related fields achieve a better grasp of the rationale of inferential statistics, at least the author will feel that the addition of another text has not been a negative event.

Although this book grew out of notes for an elementary statistics course, I am indebted to teachers, students, and colleagues for the final effort. Among my teachers and now colleagues who contributed to an education far beyond that represented in this text are Professors John Milholland, William Hays, Warren Norman, Clyde Coombs, and Robert Hefner. In addition, Professors Robyn Dawes, Myron Wish, and E.

Lowell Kelly read the manuscript with great care and contributed much in the way of helpful suggestions, wise advice, and needed encouragement.

I am indebted to the Literary Executor of the late Sir Ronald A. Fisher, F.R.S., Cambridge, and to Oliver & Boyd Ltd., Edinburgh, for their permission to reprint the Table of *t* from their book *Statistical Methods for Research Workers.*

Professors Bob Hoch and Wilbert McKeachie also deserve my thanks, the former for indicating that statistics taught backwards might be a publishable idea (in a perishable world) and the latter for expressing surprise that I would complete the job in a year (which is one reason why it took two years instead of three).

I am grateful to my wife Mary Lois for her editorial skill, typing efforts, and her exhaustible but not yet exhausted patience.

In ways that are difficult to specify though they are concrete, I am indebted to my classes in statistics for what I trust has been a mutually rewarding learning experience.

ANN ARBOR, MICHIGAN
JANUARY, 1968   *S.G.L.*

INTRODUCTION

The field of statistics serves two very important functions: one is to describe and organize large amounts of quantitative information; the other is to allow inferences to be made about a group based on information about relatively few members of the group. The area of descriptive statistics deals with the first function; the area of inferential statistics with the second.

For example, information about a large number of dwelling units could be obtained in terms of the number of rooms each had, or the cost of construction, or the living area, or the height from the floor to the ceiling. In another case, information about many people might be in terms of their IQ's, or their weights, or their degree of aggressiveness. Data of this nature can be utilized in two ways. In one, the quantitative information is organized to present a clearer picture of the attribute of the group that has been measured. The utilization of data in this way is the function of descriptive statistics. In the other, the data is used to make judgments about the nature of a larger group that has not been measured on the particular attribute, such as the group of all dwelling units in a particular city, or all adults in a particular country. The function of inferential statistics is to make this judgment possible.

This text will combine both aspects of the field, since they are in fact highly related. This relationship occurs because in order to make inferences about the larger group, it is first necessary to describe efficiently many pieces of information about observed members of that group.

CONTENTS

INFERENTIAL
STATISTICS in the
BEHAVIORAL
SCIENCES

1

THE LOGIC OF INFERENCE

INTRODUCTION

A major part of inferential statistics deals with statements about large numbers of cases, or populations, not all members of which are examined or measured. In such a situation the statements cannot be taken as facts but are instead generalizations which become hypotheses or assumptions.

In order to determine if the statements are reasonable ones, a relatively small number of cases, or sample, is selected from the large set of cases, or population, in such a way that it is considered representative of this population.

The information in the sample is then examined to determine whether it is consistent with the hypotheses about the population. If it is, then the hypotheses are not rejected. If, however, the sample results are inconsistent with the hypotheses then the conclusion is made that at least one hypothesis must be false.

In the following sections of this chapter, a more complete and precise examination of the logic of hypothesis testing will be given. Succeeding chapters will then slowly, but inexorably, chip away at the problem of determining, in an objective way, when the results of the sample may be said to be consistent with the hypotheses and when they may be said to be inconsistent.

MODELS, THEOREMS, AND EVIDENCE

The Real World and the Abstract World

The idea of testing hypotheses is probably not an unfamiliar one. All of what is generally referred to as science uses the notions of theories, hypotheses, deductions, and predictions. To examine theory formulation in general and its relationship to statistical models, a distinction between the real world and the abstract world must be made. The real world is the

1

observable world of people, events, rivers, and stars. The abstract world, as it will be considered here, consists of the conceptual world of logicians and mathematicians. The problem under consideration is the relationship between the real world and the abstract world. Statistics, considered as a field, deals with one portion of the real world and the abstract world and the relationships that have been developed between them. Statistical models or theories are one kind of abstract world.

The Development and Use of Models

Science has three primary goals. The first is to be able to understand what is observed in the world. The second is to be able to predict the events and relationships of the real world. The third is to control aspects of the real world. The factor of control is not inherent in all scientific investigation. Astronomers are usually content merely to understand and predict to particular aspects of the universe. Clinical psychologists on the other hand generally are not content with only understanding abnormal behavior. The treatment that is given to patients is itself an indication that they wish to change or redirect the behavior that is observed.

One way that science proceeds toward these goals will be described below. This description is not of the actual procedure that occurs but is an idealization of the process and may easily be related to the special case of statistics.   .

Investigators generally start with observations. Even in those cases where the observer has a hunch or hypothesis, the development of that hypothesis is usually based on some observations. These observations lead him to formulate generalizations about the events he has observed. For example, if a ball is rolled off a table, it will fall. Over and over again the same phenomenon occurs. A generalization might then be formulated that if the support of an object is removed, it will fall. Another example might be the observation that if a person wants to get from one side of the street to the other, he will cross at a corner. This particular phenomenon may be frequently observed. Again a generalization might be formulated, although in this case it would not be quite as precise a description of the world as in the first case.

At some point in the process of model building, recourse is made to logical systems. These may be verbal or mathematical. The main attempt is to develop abstractions about the elements (such as tables and balls) and relationships among the elements that exist in the real world. In addition, logical rules are incorporated that tell one how these elements and relationships may be dealt with so that new relationships may be deduced.

Some of the rules of logic are based on general intuition. For example, three basic rules of thought that have frequently been accepted as "correct" regardless of the system of logic that is being used are:

1. *Identity*. If a statement is true then it is true.
2. *Contradiction*. No statement can be both true and not true.
3. *Excluded Middle*. Any statement is either true or not true.

These are not the only rules of logic which are important, and at almost every point in the development of a logical system there is disagreement among logicians about what is "basic" and what is not. Nevertheless, an abstract system of logic consists of the three components — the elements, the relationships among the elements, and the rules of logic. Usually the basic rules of logic are implicit and the elements and their relationships form the axioms or postulates or hypotheses of the system. The set of elements and the axioms or hypotheses may then be called the *model*, or theory.

As an elementary example, Euclidean plane geometry might be considered. One could imagine observations in the real world that would lead one to conclude that parallel objects, such as buildings, trees, or roads, never meet, or that the shortest distance between two places is a straight path. At this stage these observations would be classified as generalizations about the real world.

Shortly (in perhaps a few centuries), an abstract system is developed that no longer can be said to consist strictly of generalizations about the real world. In this system there are elements like lines that have no width and points that have neither length nor width (which means that they can only be seen by the mind's eye — and then not too clearly). Further, the generalizations have also been abstracted and become the axioms of the system; such as, parallel lines never meet even if extended infinitely far, or, the shortest distance between two points is a straight line. The problem is no longer in the real world. Instead there is an imaginary world of the thinker that, in the above case, consists of points and lines, and axioms that tell how the points and lines are related.

Within this framework there is a logic that allows the thinker to derive or deduce other relationships. These deductions or *theorems* in Euclidean plane geometry include propositions such as, the sum of the angles of a triangle is 180 degrees, or, two lines perpendicular to the same line are parallel to each other. The method for proving that the theorems are correct deductions within the logical system involves applying the rules of logic to the axioms.

The abstract system is wholly contained. It has no necessary relevance to the real world. Its elements, axioms, and rules of logic which lead to the deduction of theorems are complete. The axioms are given as true within the abstract system and the deductions are true if the logic has been correctly applied. The game can be played and the real world does not have to be considered.

For the experimenter, however, the real world does have to be considered. For him, the abstract system is a means of understanding the world. There is still the problem of being able to predict outcomes in the real world. In fact, the prediction is a basic test of this understanding.

The theorems that are derived within the abstract system allow an opportunity for testing predictions about the real world. If there are no mistakes in logic, the theorem will be a correct abstract deduction. But does it fit the real world? Is the sum of the angles of triangular objects really 180°? If two planks are laid in a floor and both are perpendicular to one side of the room, will the planks be parallel to each other? (Of course they will.)

The procedure then is to retranslate the elements and relationships of the theorem in terms of the real world and see if such relationships among actual objects do exist.

As with all theories or models, if the theorem fits the real world facts, the theory may be said to be supported but not proven. Additional theorems which are also accurate predictions of the real world further support the theory. But there always exists the possibility that some other model, with one or more axioms that are not the same, could also allow theorems to be deduced that would fit the same real world facts.

On the other hand, if a theorem is derived which does not fit, or which predicts falsely, then there are only two possibilities provided that the theorem itself has been accurately interpreted. Either the logic by which the theorem was derived was incorrectly used, or the theory or model contains at least one assumption that is false *in the sense that it is not an accurate translation of the state of affairs that actually exists in the real world*, that is, it is an inaccurate translation or a translation of a false generalization.

Frequently, the strategy that scientists use to decide between two theories is to perform a critical experiment. The critical experiment represents a situation whose outcome is consistent with the theorem derived from one theory but inconsistent with the theorem derived from the second theory. Obviously, it is first necessary to derive the theorems from which the different predictions are made before the critical experiment is designed. Since an accepted rule of logical thought is that a proposition cannot be both true and not true, the outcome of the critical experiment allows a decision to be made between the two theories. That theory is false which predicted an outcome that is different from the actual occurrence. The remaining theory is substantiated but not proven true.

The steps of the model building process can be diagrammed, in a rather sketchy way. It must be repeated that this situation does not necessarily represent the actual steps that are gone through in any particular real situation but is an idealization of those that are usually performed.

REAL WORLD		ABSTRACT WORLD
Observation		

Observation

↓

Concept formation
    and
Generalization   (Abstraction)   Formalization into models
          ————————→   that consist of elements and
                                        relations among elements
                                        (Elements and Axioms)

                                        |
                                        Deductions using
                                            rules of logic
Observations   (Predictions)   ↓
that either support or   ←————————   Theorems
disconfirm the theory

Statistics is a field that contains certain types of abstract models that allow inferences to be made about populations from samples. The study of these abstract models in this text will include their relationship to the real world of the psychologist and other behavioral scientists.

Examples

In order to illustrate briefly some of the above ideas two examples will be presented. In neither of the following cases is it necessarily true that the models were developed in the way that is indicated. The description is for illustrative purposes only.

Example 1

One can imagine that experience with objects in the real world would lead to some type of number system. The set of integers $(1, 2, 3 \cdots n \cdots)$ may be considered to be one such abstract collection of elements in which the real world property of existence has been abstracted. That is, each object is considered a unit and this is the only property that is being abstracted. Within the abstract number system there are a set of axioms. On the basis of the elements and the axioms deductions may be made within the system. One such deduction is $2 + 2 = 4$.

Now consider a translation from the real world to the abstract collection in which the real world elements are objects like apples and rocks.

Then the deduction $2 + 2 = 4$ could be interpreted as a conclusion about the real world that two apple–objects added to two rock–objects results in four objects. In this case a correct translation from the real world to the abstract world has been made and it is not surprising that the abstract deduction fits the real situation.

Suppose, however, that quarts of liquid are translated to the abstract collection. Now the deduction $2 + 2 = 4$ would be interpreted to mean that two quarts of liquid added to two quarts of liquid will yield four quarts of liquid. Consider an instance in which two of the units are quarts of water and two are quarts of alcohol. If the abstract deduction $2 + 2 = 4$ is interpreted as predicting that two quarts of water added to two quarts of alcohol will yield four quarts of the mixture, this prediction will not be verified. The result will be less than four quarts of the mixture. In this case there is an incorrect translation of units of liquid into the number system of the integers and the axioms about the integers. For solid objects, x of one type added to y of another type will yield $x + y$ objects. But for liquids, x units of one added to y units of the other will not necessarily give $x + y$ units. If they are units of the same liquid of course they will yield $x + y$ units, but if they are different liquids then the units may or may not be additive.

Example 2

Other experiences could be imagined that would lead to the development of the abstract syllogistic logic. An example of the use of this system might be:

All x's have the property y
This q is an x
Therefore, this q has the property y

The conclusion, "this q has the property y," is a correct deduction within the abstract system for the given premises.

Suppose that "cats" is considered x and "three eyes" is considered y and a particular object is considered q. Then the argument could be represented as:

All cats have three eyes
This object is a cat
Therefore, this object (cat) has three eyes

If the deduction is taken as a prediction about the real world and an actual cat is examined it probably will not have three eyes. The conclusion that was deduced within the abstract system, while logically correct, is a false statement about the real world.

The reason is obvious. The "axiom" of the system (all cats have three eyes) is based on a false real world generalization (since the real world generalization is, all Martians have three eyes.)

While these examples are extremely trivial, they do illustrate some of the basic, if not profound, thought that goes into the development of models of the world.

STATISTICAL MODELS

The generalizations that are abstracted into the hypotheses of a logical system frequently are universal statements. These universal statements usually deal with outcomes of observations, all of which cannot be made.

For example, the generalization that balls fall when rolled off a table deals with all rolls of all balls and all tables. Obviously, the complete set of observations about which the generalization deals can never be made. The statement is then one about a universal population of observations which can never be measured in its entirety.

As a second example, consider the generalization that people who want to get from one side of the street to the other cross at the corner. Since this is not always the case, the rule for human behavior should read "usually cross at the corner." Again, however, the generalization may be considered to be about a population of all people, and all streets, which is realistically unmeasurable.

In both of the above cases, the generalization can never be proven to be correct because all of the observations which it covers cannot be made. In the first case, however, the predictions that would be derived from the abstract model of the situation are so explicit that a single observation counter to it would prove the abstraction false. If any sample of even one ball were rolled off any particular table and it did not fall, the generalization would then be said to be not true.

In the second case, the predictions are much more complicated. Suppose, for example, that the generalization were made more precise so that it read "70 percent of the people who cross from one side of the street to the other, cross at the corner." A sample of 100 observations might turn out not in the ratio 70:30, but perhaps 68:32, or 75:25. This does not necessarily mean that the generalization, which is about all observations, is false. The chance factors that operate in selecting only a sample of observations might reasonably lead to 68:32 or perhaps 75:25.

Statistical models deal with the second situation, that is, they are abstractions of populations that have variable or differing outcomes.

The above examples deal with very simple situations. Generalizations of a more complicated sort are frequently made. One such complication deals with relations. For example, in absolute units of force, Newton's second law of motion may be expressed abstractly as $F/a = m$, where a is the acceleration produced by a force of magnitude F acting on a body of mass m. For different values of force that are applied to a particular object and/or different amounts of acceleration that the object undergoes, the law states that the mass remains a constant. However, the law as expressed is precise. For a given force and acceleration there is only one possible value for the mass of an object. Contrast this to a statistical relation that might be based on the statement that the more money people have, the more they spend. The abstraction of this statement could be expressed mathematically as $S = f(H)$, where S is the amount of money spent and $f(H)$ indicates there is a rule, as yet unspecified, that defines the actual value of S for different values of H, where H is the amount of money a person has. In this case, one would not expect to be able to develop for $f(H)$ a specific rule that would allow one to predict precisely the value of S, because there are so many factors that influence S besides H. All of these factors probably could not be determined. In fact, there might be instances in which individuals spent less after increasing the amount of money they had.

Both of these cases can again be interpreted as abstractions about populations of observations which cannot all be made. Again, in one case, a single observation counter to the law would be considered evidence against it, but no number of observations that were consistent could absolutely prove it to be true. In the other case, the situation is ambiguous. Since some observations will be opposite to the prediction because of uncontrolled factors that operate, the generalization cannot absolutely be proven false no matter what the sample result turns out to be.

The development of a model that makes the above types of imprecise deductions is fortunate because many observations in the real world cannot be controlled so that they can be observed with precise regularity. For example, the precise outcome for the toss of a coin cannot be predicted. A particular strain of rats may prefer Type A mash to Type B, but sometimes a fool animal will eat Type B. This type of observation may be contrasted to that of rolling a ball off a table which results in its always falling, or in mixing exactly y cc of a particular acid to neutralize exactly x cc of a particular base, or of observing that gas Q under constant volume increases its pressure exactly R amount when the temperature is raised from 60°C to 70°C. Although both types of observations will vary from one time to the next, the amount of variability in the second set of observations is relatively so small that the relevant factors appear to have been identified. In fact, the variability may be attributed to limitations on the precision of the necessary instrument rather than to the influence of factors operating on the events that cannot be controlled. As a result, generalizations about the observed phenomena frequently take the form of precise statements.

SUMMARY

In an attempt to understand the real world, concepts are developed and generalizations are made about the happenings in the world. The generalizations about the real world may be considered to deal with populations of observations, all of which cannot be made. From these an abstract model of the population is formed that consists of hypotheses that are abstracted from the generalizations and that concern the elements of the population and their relationships. A primary purpose of the model is to allow deductions to be made in such a way that:

a) investigators will generally agree that the deduction is a correct one within the system, and
b) investigators will generally agree about the type of real world observation that is consistent with the deduction.

Using rules of logic and the hypotheses in the model, deductions are made. Generally, these deductions concern samples of observations. Although these samples are groups of abstract elements, a relationship can be made between the abstract sample and a real world sample. The deduction then becomes interpreted as a prediction about the real world and is related to the actual observation.

The basic difference between the deduction in the statistical model and one in, say, classical mechanics or Euclidean geometry, is that the statistical deduction is an imprecise statement. It does not state that, given the hypotheses, certain results will always occur. Rather, it states that given the hypotheses, results will vary and will have specified probabilities associated with the various possibilities.

In the statistical case, as in others, if the model is an accurate translation of the characteristics of the unmeasured real world populations, then certain results for samples are expected. If the observed sample is consistent with the expectations, then none of the hypotheses can be said to be false, although they have not been proven true. If the observed sample is not consistent with these expectations, then the conclusion is that at least one hypothesis of the model was an inaccurate translation of the real state of affairs. This is with the understanding, of course, that the deduction about the results that were expected was made through a correct use of the logic.

By virtue of the statistical nature of the model, no result is totally impossible under the hypotheses. Some arbitrary decision must be made about when an observation is so unlikely under the hypotheses, that a reasonable conclusion is that at least one of them is false, that is, the true state of affairs is different in at least one respect from those that were abstracted into the model. The field of statistics consists of both the abstract models and the relationships that exist between the real and the abstract worlds.

2
BASIC CONCEPTS

INTRODUCTION

In order to understand the relationship between description and inference, a distinction must be made between the two basic types of information that are dealt with. One type concerns a number of individuals; the other concerns a number of groups. To understand this differentiation, it will first be necessary to discuss *populations* and *samples*. Some methods by which data description is accomplished will then be presented. After these procedures are understood for both of the basic types of information, it becomes possible to investigate the relationship between description and the use of limited numbers of individuals to make inferences about larger groups.

POPULATIONS AND SAMPLES

Populations

Usually, populations consist of large groups of people. In statistics, however, several refinements of this concept must be made before the idea of a population can be usefully employed. First of all, a population may vary in size from one situation to the next. It may consist of one hundred individuals or one million, or, in fact, an infinite number. (Generally, the mathematical conclusions that will be presented are based on the assumption that the population consists of an infinite number of individuals. Although this will not always be the case, the conclusions will still be valid provided the population is large.) Secondly, the individuals do not have to be people; they can be mice, or events, or some other collection of units. Since people are not the only things that can make up a population, a more neutral term, *elements*, will be used to describe the units in a population. Thirdly, a common attribute must be specified on which the elements are to be measured and given scores or values.

Of course, the elements in a collection have a variety of attributes on which they may receive values, and in different studies one or another of them may be specified. These attributes, or traits, may already be in existence, for example, height or weight of adults in the United States. Or they may be created, as in an experiment, for example, the distance jumped by white mice when shocked in a totally dark cage or the length of time that ball bearings of a certain size last when made out of a new plastic. The investigator is concerned with the specific attribute of the collection of elements and the scores they receive. Thus, although the elements of the population may be looked upon as consisting of the group of objects that make it up, the scores that the elements receive on the attribute describe the population. Of course, a score is always attached to an object or element.

Formally, a population will be defined as *a specific collection of distinguishable elements that receive scores on a given common attribute or trait.* In delineating a population in a study it is necessary to define not only the elements that are in the collection but also to specify the attribute on which the elements are to be scored.

The following examples demonstrate the meaning of the *statistical* word population. Note how the number, nature, and measured attribute of the elements may differ:

1. All of the people living in the United States with respect to their heights.
2. All of the females above 18 years of age in the world with respect to the length of their eyelashes (genuine only).
3. Sophomore students taking elementary statistics in psychology at United States universities this semester with respect to their IQ scores.
4. All possible throws of a coin with respect to the side on which each falls.
5. Cancer patients given x-ray treatment with respect to how long they live.
6. All mice raised only on milk with respect to the speed with which they run a given T maze.

One might note from example 4 that the elements in a population may be hypothetical, and their number may be infinitely large.

Samples from Populations

It is usually not possible to measure every element in a given population. It would take a long time to measure all of the possible throws of a six-sided die. Similarly, one could probably not measure the heights of everyone in the United States because by the time everyone had been measured some would have died, others would have been born (others grown, perhaps a few shrunk, and so forth). Even in cases when it might be possible to measure all of the elements of the population, it is generally not efficient to do so. If one wanted to measure the average weekly alcoholic intake of senior women in United States universities during the fall term it would be a rather large task. (It would be difficult enough just to measure the women.) In most cases, it is not necessary to measure all the elements in a population. Instead, a *sample* of elements is selected and measured. Inferences about the population are then made on the basis of this information. Since the scores are attached to the elements, the procedure involves sampling a representative group of elements. Their scores are then taken to be representative of the scores of the total population, and inferences are made about the total group *with respect to the given attribute.* Therefore, the population must be clearly specified with respect to the attribute, and it must be clearly defined; that is, every element in the population must be known so that a sample can be selected.

Types of Samples

In the statistics that will be discussed in this text, samples will be considered representative of the population only if they are based on elements that are selected randomly and independently.

Random selection is a process by which every element in the population has an equal chance of being chosen in the sample. Generally, this concept of selection is called *simple random sampling.* This text will use the words random selection or random sampling to mean simple random sampling. In order to accomplish random selection, it must be possible to enumerate every element of the population. This requirement is another way of saying that the population must be clearly defined.

For sampling to be independent, the selection of any element must not influence the selection of the next element, nor must it have been selected because of some previously chosen element. For example, if one desires to study married couples, the couples might be selected randomly and independently. However, if one were interested in studying some aspect of married men and women as individuals, but every time one person was chosen the partner was also, then the individuals would not have been selected independently. Similarly, if one were interested in studying automobile drivers involved in accidents, the drivers selected might not be independent of each other. This could come about if the sampling of one driver resulted in the inclusion of the other drivers involved in the same accident. (If accidents as a unit were chosen, or if the selection were done so that one element did not determine that another element would be chosen, samples in which the observations were made randomly and independently could, of course, be obtained.) Another way to express the above sample requirements is to state that for sampling to be random and independent, it is first necessary that each element have an equal chance of being included in the sample (randomness), and that the selection of one element still leave the remaining elements with an equal chance of being included in the sample (independence).

Many Samples from a Single Population

When an investigator decides to select a sample from a population, he realizes that the sample he selects is only one of a large number that might have been chosen. If the population consists of only three elements, any one of three different, or *unique*, samples of size two might be selected. (One sample is considered to be different from another or unique if at least one element in one of them is not found in the others.) If the elements of the population are called *A*, *B*, and *C*, then the three unique samples of size two are *A* and *B*; *B* and *C*; and *A* and *C*. As can readily be seen, all of the individuals in one sample are not also found in another.

The number of possible samples of a particular size rapidly increases as the size of the population increases. For example, in a population of five elements, there are ten unique samples of size two. (Work this out by letting the elements be *A*, *B*, *C*, *D*, and *E* and then choosing two at a time in such a way that the exact same two are never selected.) If instead of samples of size two, those of size four were considered, then there would be only five unique samples. (Each sample would consist of all of the elements in the population but one, and a different one could be left out each of five times.) As another example, consider samples of size two in a population of size ten. In this case, there are 45 unique samples. There are 4950 in a population of size 100; and 499,500 *unique* samples of size two that might be selected from a population of 1000 elements. For samples of size five, the number of unique samples from the above populations would be 252; 75,287,520; and 8,250,291,250,200, respectively.

Three obvious conclusions stand out from the above examples. The first is that the number of unique samples that are possible depends on the size of the sample and the size of the population. The second is that the number of unique samples of a particular size rapidly increases as the size of the population increases. Finally, and very importantly, the number of unique samples is usually far greater than the total number of elements in the whole population. This last conclusion means that if one were to study all of the unique samples of a particular size from a population, the elements would have to be used over many times. Remember, the only requirement for a sample to be unique is that not *all* of the elements in one sample also occur in another.

Since populations may often consist of millions of elements (pollsters often take samples from all of the adults in the United States, who number about 100 million), it is not reasonable to study the entire population. The amazing usefulness of the field of inferential statistics is that it allows one to make intelligent inferences about the larger group based on only a *single* sample of limited size, *as long as the elements in the sample are obtained by random and independent selection.*

DESCRIBING A SINGLE GROUP

Measures of Central Tendency and Variability

The previous discussion of sampling should not be taken to imply that total populations are never studied. A teacher may be interested in how his class is doing and include everyone taking the course when he evaluates exam grades. He tries to come to conclusions about how the entire group is performing. A superintendent may be interested in comparing the effectiveness of different teaching methods in the sixth-grade classes in his school system (although he probably would be doing this to generalize about future classes). Colleges are usually interested in the relationship between entrance exam scores and grades of each student who enrolls (although, here again, it is very likely that inferences about this relationship would be made concerning future incoming students). However, whether the group being studied is the whole population or only a sample from the population, the first important interest is to describe the scores of the individuals or elements in the group in some concise way.

Therefore, suppose that a group of 500 students have been measured for their rate of reading, in words per minute. This group may consist of a sample drawn from a population or may constitute a population, such as the students in a particular school. In any event, these 500 students are each given a score. The problem is to describe their scores.

One possibility would be simply to list each student and his reading rate score. Then, all the information would be included but it would be hard to interpret. A second step might be to rearrange all of the scores from highest to lowest. This would give a better picture but it might still be difficult to interpret the information. Certainly the amount of information would not yet have been reduced. There were 500 scores to start with and there are still 500 scores.

About the best one could hope to do would be to describe the whole group by a single number. The question then is, what is the best single number to use. Obviously, no single number can describe everyone exactly, unless everybody had exactly the same score, which in this case would mean that everyone read at exactly the same rate.

Any single number used to describe the entire group would therefore be in error by a certain amount; it then seems reasonable that the best number would be the one that resulted in the least error. This sounds extremely simple.

However, statisticians are subtle. So they ask, "What kind of error do you want to make small?" This gives everyone a chance to express opinions.

There are good arguments for several definitions of error. If the wish is to be right most often, then the best single number to describe a group would be that number which occurs most often. Instead of using all 500 scores, ten reading scores will be used to illustrate the principles. They are presented in Table 2.1.

Table 2.1

Reading Rate Scores for Ten Individuals

Person No.	Reading Rate (words/minute)
1	125
2	257
3	172
4	175
5	262
6	512
7	257
8	304
9	309
10	400

In this case, if one wished to select a number such that it would precisely represent the largest number of people in the group of ten, the number 257 would be selected. This is because two people received a score of 257, whereas the greatest number of people in the group that received any other score is no more than one.

This most frequently occurring score is called the *mode*. The series of scores is called the *distribution* of scores. The mode of a distribution of scores is defined as the most frequently occurring score in that distribution. This measure, the mode, reduces error to a minimum, *when error is defined as the number of scores that are different from the selected number*. The amount of error is then taken to be the number of scores that are different from the mode. The average error per person is then obtained by dividing the total amount of error by the total number of scores in the distribution. If A represents the average error per person, E the number of scores different from the mode, and N the total number of scores in the distribution, then

$$A = E/N$$

Another way to express this formula is to let the number of scores that are exactly the same as the modal score be represented by m. Then the total, N, is equal to $E + m$. This means that

$$N = E + m$$

So $E = N - m$ and the average error per person can also be represented by

$$A = \frac{N - m}{N} = \frac{N}{N} - \frac{m}{N} = 1 - \frac{m}{N}$$

A second concept of error is the difference between a score in the distribution and the number chosen to represent the whole distribution. Thus, the total amount of error is the sum of all the differences of the scores from the representative number. This concept of error treats a plus error the same as a minus error. For example, the error involved with respect to person ten, if the number 255 is arbitrarily chosen to represent the distribution, is the amount by which this person's score differs from 255. This is 145 words per minute. On the other hand, the amount that person one differs from 255 is 130 words per minute. Notice that the important thing is how much each person differs from the chosen number *without regard to the direction of the difference.*

By using two vertical lines, differences can be represented without regard to direction. Thus, the distance between 15 and 10 is $|15 - 10| = 5$. The two vertical lines indicate the *absolute value*, or the distance between without regard to direction. Thus the absolute distance between five and ten is $|5 - 10| = 5$. This is the same as $|10 - 5| = 5$.

Now it becomes necessary to develop a shorthand way of writing a large group of numbers. The problem is not so difficult when there are only a few, but it is quite severe when there are many numbers (such as 500). In order to represent everyone's score in a distribution the capital letter X is used. This letter represents a variable because it changes its value from one person to the next. In order to specify which individual score is being considered, a label or subscript is attached to X. Thus, X_1 means person one's score. In Table 2.1, $X_1 = 125$. (What is X_8 equal to?) If a specific person is not to be referred to, then the subscript that is used is i. Thus, X_i means the score of the ith person. In Table 2.1 this could be anyone from person one to person ten.

The next symbol looks complicated but once it is understood it makes life (for a statistician) a lot easier. The symbol represents an operator. An operator tells one what operation to perform on some numbers. For example, $\times$ is the symbol for the operation "times," which is shorthand for "multiply this number by that." It is much easier to express the multiplication of two numbers by the $\times$ operator, as in "5 $\times$ 6," than it is to express this as "multiply the number 5 by the number 6" or to say "add five to itself six times." Similarly $-$, $+$, $\div$, and $|\ |$ (absolute value), are each a symbol for an operation. The operation that is shorthand for several additions at the same time is represented by Σ. This symbol is called the summation sign and is the Greek letter, capital sigma. Suppose that there were four numbers to be added. If the numbers are labeled X_1, X_2, X_3, X_4, then the long way to write that these numbers should all be added up is $X_1 + X_2 + X_3 + X_4$. To use the shorthand system, the symbol X_i is used. The general label, i, can be used to denote any of the individual scores. The specific score is not known, of course, until i is given some number. Consider the mathematical statement,

$$\sum_{i=1}^{4} X_i$$

This says, "Add up all of the X_i scores when i goes from 1 to 4." This is the same as saying $X_1 + X_2 + X_3 + X_4$; that is,

$$\sum_{i=1}^{4} X_i = X_1 + X_2 + X_3 + X_4$$

Similarly,

$$\sum_{i=1}^{9} X_i = X_1 + X_2 + X_3 + X_4 + X_5 + X_6 + X_7 + X_8 + X_9$$

and

$$\sum_{i=3}^{5} X_i = X_3 + X_4 + X_5$$

One can see why the shorthand system is so useful when one considers

$$\sum_{i=1}^{500} X_i$$

This discussion has led to a method for writing the amount of absolute error in a shorthand way. Table 2.1 gives the labels that will be used to describe the ten scores. Since error is from some point, suppose the point 255 is used. Then the *absolute* error involved in using the number 255 to represent the first person is $|X_i - 255|$ which, in this case, is $|125 - 255| = 130$ words per minute (wpm or w/m). To represent the score of any person in general, X_i is used as the symbol so that the error for the "*i*th" score is $|X_i - 255|$. It follows that the *total* amount of absolute error for the distribution of ten scores is

$$
\begin{aligned}
\sum_{i=1}^{10} |X_i - 255| &= |X_1 - 255| + |X_2 - 255| + \cdots + |X_{10} - 255| \\
&= |125 - 255| + |257 - 255| + \cdots + |400 - 255| \\
&= 130 + 2 + \cdots + 145 = 809 \text{ w/m}
\end{aligned}
$$

(You should work this out to make sure that you understand how the number was obtained.) This represents the total amount of distance that the numbers are from the number 255. But the number 255 was just arbitrarily chosen. The number of interest is whichever one will make the total distance the least. This might not necessarily be an actual score in the distribution, often it will not be.

It turns out that the best number to use, that is, the one that makes the total distance of all of the numbers from it a minimum, is a number in the middle of the distribution when the numbers are arranged from low to high. For the ten reading scores, this arrangement is 125, 172, 175, 257, 257, 262, 304, 309, 400, 512. Any number between 257 and 262 would be in the middle of the distribution because it would divide the scores so that half of the scores fall below it and half fall above it. To avoid confusion, the number used is that which is in the middle between 257 and 262. This is 259.5 (since $(257 + 262)/2 = 259.5$). This middle number is called the *median* and will be symbolized by *Md*. The median, then, is the number which is the closest to all the other numbers or that number *from* which the other numbers have the least amount of total absolute error.

If there is an odd number of scores then the middle number is the median. For example, if there were only nine reading scores (say 125, 172, 175, 257, 262, 304, 309, 400, and 512), then the median would be the middle score, or 262. In this case, the middle score is considered to be split in half so that exactly 4½ scores fall below it, and exactly 4½ scores fall above it. Therefore, it fits the definition of the median. The formal definition of the median is: *A point such that exactly half of the scores in a distribution fall above it and exactly half fall below it.*

A reexamination of the error problem indicates that the least total absolute error is equal to

$$
\sum_{i=1}^{10} |X_i - Md|
$$

This is

$$
|125 - 259.5| + \cdots + |400 - 259.5| = 801 \text{ w/m}
$$

This will be symbolized as

$$T_{ab} = \sum_{i=1}^{n} |X_i - Md|$$

Then the average error for a group of scores is

$$A_{ab} = \frac{\sum_{i=1}^{n} |X_i - Md|}{n}$$

where n is the number of scores in the distribution. (In the example given, $n = 10$, and $A_{ab} = {}^{801}\!/_{10} = 80.1$ w/m.)

To summarize: the point in a distribution which minimizes the average error of all of the scores from that point is the median, *when error is defined as the absolute distance of a score from a given point*. In order to compare the error among distributions with different numbers of scores, average error is used rather than total error.

For the next two types of error (the most important one is saved for last), consider first the case where a point is chosen and the errors are taken as plus or minus, depending on whether the score is above the point chosen ($+$) or below it ($-$). When the signs are kept the errors are called *algebraic* errors. (Algebraic simply means that the sign is kept. Therefore one can have algebraic scores, algebraic sums, and so on.) In other words, instead of throwing away the direction of the error, the direction is kept. The point that minimizes error when it is defined this way is the *mean*. The mean is the sum of all of the scores divided by the number of scores. Using mathematical notation, the mean is symbolized by $\bar{X}$ (X-bar) and

$$\bar{X} = \frac{\sum_{i=1}^{n} X_i}{n}$$

Then the total algebraic error is

$$T_{alg} = \sum_{i=1}^{n} (X_i - \bar{X})$$

and the average algebraic error is

$$A_{alg} = \frac{\sum_{i=1}^{n} (X_i - \bar{X})}{n}$$

This may also be written

$$A_{alg} = \frac{\sum_{i=1}^{n} x_i}{n}$$

where $x_i = X_i - \bar{X}$ and is the deviation of a score from the mean. Frequently (x_i) is used instead of $X_i - \bar{X}$. Notice that the vertical lines are no longer used since the direction of the error is to be kept. For the ten reading rate scores,

$$\bar{X} = \frac{\sum\limits_{i=1}^{10} X_i}{10} = \frac{125 + \cdots + 400}{10} = \frac{2773}{10} = 277.3 \text{ w/m}$$

Then

$$A_{\text{alg}} = \frac{\sum\limits_{i=1}^{10} (X_i - \bar{X})}{10} = 0 \text{ w/m}$$

If error in a distribution is defined as the directed or algebraic distance from a point, then the point that minimizes the error is the mean. However, the amount of error will always turn out to be zero. This measure, then, is not very useful. (Some of you might want to argue that the error is not really 0 since the mean does not represent everyone exactly. That is, it is just the point at which the plus errors exactly balance the minus errors. This is correct, but by defining error as a directed distance, that is by keeping the sign, the total amount of error does turn out to be zero, even though the mean does not represent everyone precisely. Thus a minus error was allowed to "cancel" an equal plus error. If you owe someone ten dollars and someone else owes you ten dollars, the net amount that you owe is zero dollars. Further, when direction is considered, a minus error does not mean less error, it simply means a particular direction to the error, whereas zero error does mean *no* error.)

One way to get rid of the minus signs is to take the absolute value. This was done in the second definition of error. Another way to define error is to *square* all of the deviations of a score from a point. This also makes all of the scores positive. All of these manipulations may look positively foolish to you, especially this last one. In fact, this last definition of error has been found to be the most useful one. The point that will make the squared errors a minimum is also found to be the mean. The total error is then

$$\sum_{i=1}^{n} (X_i - \bar{X})^2$$

and the *average* squared error, which is called the *variance* and is symbolized by SD^2_X, is equal to

$$\frac{\sum\limits_{i=1}^{n} (X_i - \bar{X})^2}{n}$$

The square root of $SD^2{}_X$, the variance, is SD_X and is called the *standard deviation*. Thus,

$$SD_X = \sqrt{\frac{\sum\limits_{i=1}^{n} (X_i - \bar{X})^2}{n}} = \sqrt{\frac{\sum\limits_{i=1}^{n} x_i{}^2}{n}}$$

This completes a presentation of types of error. Statistical work generally involves use of the variance and standard deviation.

The mode, median, and mean are called measures of *central tendency* and they are all averages. Each reflects, in a different way, the "most representative" score in the distribution.

The various types of error that have been discussed above are all measures of *variability*. Each reflects how much the scores, on the average, differ from each other.

Obviously, a very informative way of describing a distribution briefly is to give not only the value of the measure of central tendency but also the value of the error that is minimized by this measure. For example, one might attempt to describe a group of scores efficiently by giving its mean. However, if one also knew the variance or standard deviation of the distribution, a great deal of additional information would be gained concerning the group. For this reason, a distribution of scores is frequently described by giving both its mean and its standard deviation.

Units

Because the elements are scored on an attribute, the numbers that are attached to them and the error measures as well, will be in terms of some unit. If heights are being measured the unit may be inches or feet. If reading rates are being measured the unit may be words per minute. In most cases then, numbers that are operated on by addition or multiplication or by some other operation represent numbers of units, and these units also may be affected. For example, if weights are being measured, then 7 lbs − 3 lbs = 4 lbs. In this case the number was changed but not the unit. Subtraction or addition are operations which do not affect the units. Multiplying or dividing by pure numbers (that is, numbers that do not have a unit) also does not affect the unit. Thus, the average weight of two objects weighing 7 lbs and 3 lbs respectively is (7 lbs + 3 lbs)/2 = 5 lbs. In this case the 2 did not have units attached to it. Similarly, the total weight of 8 objects each of which weighs 3 lbs is 8 (3 lbs) = 24 lbs.

However, if two numbers with the same type of unit are either multiplied together or divided, the unit is changed. Four inches times 4 inches is 16 inches². Sixteen inches² times 4 inches is 64 inches³. If division were the operation then 4 inches ÷ 4 inches = 1. This number is a pure number because the units were cancelled out by the division. Similarly 16 inches^2 ÷ 4 inches = 4 inches.

These results are readily summed up by noting that units get multiplied together and divided into, just as numbers do. If one of the numbers in the multiplication is a pure number, then, of course, this does not affect the unit. Just as obviously, the operations of addition and subtraction must involve either pure numbers or numbers which all have the same unit. It works quite well to treat the unit as a quantity. For example, 4 w/m + 12 w/m = w/m (4 + 12) = w/m (16) = 16 w/m. In this example, words per minute was factored out. However, 6 w/m − 3 (as a pure number) or 7 w/m − 4 inches leaves us baffled.

This discussion is important as it relates to the variance and standard deviation as measures of error or variability. In the case of the variance, a number of units was subtracted from the average number of units; then this answer was squared. This yielded squared units. For example, (4 w/m − 5 w/m)^2 = 1 w^2/m^2 (that is, 1 word squared per minute squared). The other operations which are performed to compute the variance are addition and then division by a pure number, neither of which affects the units. Sometimes these units are hard to interpret. Inches^2 is easy enough, but how about lbs^2 or IQ units^2? One advantage of taking the square root is to return the units to those in which the original measurements were taken. Hence, $\sqrt{\text{lbs}^2}$ = lbs and $\sqrt{\text{w}^2/\text{m}^2}$ = w/m. (Remember to operate on the units as if they were a quantity.) These results follow just as it follows that the square root of x^2 is x.

Although both the variance and the standard deviation are useful as measures of error, *one advantage of the standard deviation is that it is in terms of the original units of measurement, and thus easier to interpret than the variance which is in terms of those units squared.*

Scores and Intervals

It is probably apparent that in order for elements to receive scores on an attribute some instrument must be used to make the measurements. For example, if a table is being measured to determine its length, a ruler might reasonably be the measuring instrument. If a person's weight is being measured, a scale would seem to be an appropriate instrument.

However, the scores that are assigned to the elements are always approximate because of the measuring instrument. If the ruler is only accurate to inches, the table might be measured as being 27 inches long. This would really mean that the table was between 26.5 and 27.5 inches. If a more precise ruler were used, say one that read to tenths of inches, the table might have been measured as being 27.2 inches in length. Even this measure is not perfectly accurate. The true length of the table is between 27.15 and 27.25 inches. All that is meant by saying that the ruler measures to the nearest tenth of an inch is that the instrument will allow one to determine which tenth of which inch the length of the object is *closest* to. To say that the table is 27.2 inches long merely means that the table is nearer to 27.2 inches than to 27.1 inches or 27.3 inches. Hence, it can be anywhere between 27.15 and 27.25 inches and be closer to 27.2 than to any other tenth of an inch.

Similarly a very accurate scale might measure a person's weight as 145.264 lbs. This scale allows one to determine weight to the nearest thousandth of a pound. The true weight of the subject is between 145.2635 and 145.2645 lbs.

Every score may be considered to represent an interval within which the true value for the element falls. The concept of a score as representing an interval allows an easy transition from *distributions* of scores to *frequency distributions* of scores.

A frequency distribution is simply a listing of scores and the number of elements that received that score. For a small set of elements there will often be only one case at each score. For example, the set of ten reading rate scores presented in Table 2.1 could be presented as a frequency distribution as is done in Table 2.2. The symbol X represents the score and the symbol f represents the frequency or number of cases at that score.

Table 2.2

Frequency Distribution of Ten Reading Rate Scores

X	f
125	1
172	1
175	1
257	2
262	1
304	1
309	1
400	1
512	1

Since scores represent intervals, the frequency distribution is an abbreviated form of the actual measurements. To be precise the listing should have been the one given in Table 2.3.

The distribution in Table 2.3 is a condensation of the whole distribution in the sense that all of the intervals for which there were 0 cases have

Table 2.3

**Frequency Distribution of Ten Reading Rate
Scores in Terms of Intervals**

X	f
124.5–125.5	1
171.5–172.5	1
174.5–175.5	1
256.5–257.5	2
261.5–262.5	1
303.5–304.5	1
308.5–309.5	1
399.5–400.5 ·	1
511.5–512.5	1

been omitted. Generally, the tables are presented as in Table 2.2 with the understanding that the indicated score represents an interval.

Many distributions of scores involve large numbers of elements. For example, the 500 students mentioned earlier might all have been measured with respect to their reading rate. In this case, a frequency distribution might have been formed but it might not be reasonable to list each score separately along with the frequency of cases at that score. Instead, the scores might have been grouped into intervals that were larger than 1 unit. In fact, it might be reasonable to group the scores in intervals of 50 units. The frequency distribution then might be represented as indicated in Table 2.4.

Table 2.4

**Grouped Frequency Distribution of 500
Reading Rate Scores**

X	f
101–150	60
151–200	67
201–250	78
251–300	106
301–350	90
351–400	42
401–450	31
451–500	20
501–550	6

This table also is not precise. That is, Table 2.4 indicates that 78 people received a score of between 201 w/m and 250 w/m. This really means that the 78 scores fell between 200.5 w/m and 250.5 w/m.

For many computations the individuals are considered to be spread evenly throughout the interval even if there is only one case in the interval. Thus the 78 individuals would be considered to be spread evenly between 200.5 and 250.5. While this is not always the case, it seems reasonable to use this as a working assumption. Obviously, some working generalization is needed because the original information about the scores has been lost when they are grouped in intervals of any length larger than the original measurements. However, as was stated earlier, the grouping of the scores does have the advantage of making the data more comprehensible than it would be if all of the separate scores were listed.

ELEMENTS OF POPULATIONS

To this point examples of the elements of a population have been people, or rats, or flips of a coin, that is to say, in terms of some type of "individual" as the unit. Another very important type of population is one in which the elements are groups of individuals rather than the individuals themselves. A population might consist of five individuals as the elements. However, it would be possible to talk about another population, such as the population whose elements consist of all of the unique samples of size two from the population of five. As pointed out previously, there are ten such samples. Therefore this new population has ten elements, but the elements are no longer individuals. Instead they are groups of two individuals at a time. Just as it was possible to select individuals from a population of individuals and describe the group selected, it is possible to select a set or collection of samples from a population. Further, it should be possible to describe this collection.

In order to be able to do this, it is first necessary to know the attribute on which the elements are scored. If individuals are measured on height the groups as a whole should also be scored on height. If IQ scores have been given to the individual elements, then the score for the group should also be on IQ. But the group consists of more than one individual. How can it be described?

Obviously, treat each group as an individual and give it an individual score. What score? The score that best describes the group. What one is that? Well, that depends on the definition of error that is being used. It might be the mode, or the median, or the mean.

To differentiate the score that measures an individual from that which measures a sample, the measure of the sample is called a *statistic*. *A statistic is a measure used to describe a sample of elements*. The mean is one such measure; so are the mode and the standard deviation of the sample.

A most important set of elements that is studied in the field of statistics is that consisting of *all* of the unique samples of a particular size that could be selected from a specified population. The "new" population in this case is, as before, the set of elements and the scores that they receive on the common attribute. However, the elements in the new population are groups of individuals, and the scores are the various values that the statistic receives. The common attribute is the same as before, such as height, IQ, or distance jumped.

To illustrate the two cases, consider individuals first. The type of statement that might be made in this instance is that out of all of the individuals in the population, person number 72 had a history exam score of 92.0. Mathematically, this would be expressed $X_{72} = 92.0$. In the second case the statement might be that out of all of the unique samples of size 50, sample 216 had a mean history exam score of 88.7. Mathematically this could be stated $\bar{X}_{216} = 88.7$.

Just as it was possible to sample individual values or scores from the population of all individuals, so it is possible to sample values of the statistic from the population whose elements are all of the unique samples of a particular size.

An Example

In order to illustrate in more detail the previous discussion as well as the presentation of the types of error, consider the following example. Instead of using scores for individual elements in this example, several different samples will be used.

Suppose several samples, each of size ten, had been taken from the United States adult population and each person had been asked ten questions about foreign affairs. The score for each person was the number of questions he answered correctly. The score for the *sample* was the mean (that is, $\bar{X}$) as obtained from the formula,

$$\bar{X} = \sum_{i=1}^{10} X_i/10$$

(since n for each sample was ten). Table 2.5 gives the results (after re-arranging the means of the samples from the lowest mean to the highest).

Altogether then, 15 different samples each of size ten were collected, and the mean for each of the samples was computed. Thus 15 means were obtained. Each of these means was labeled. Notice that the labels for the means of the samples are $\bar{X}_i$'s whereas the labels for individual scores are X_i's (without the bar). There is no difference in any of the computations, each is a score whether it is based on a whole sample or on just a single person. All the label does is tell one what kind of score is being evaluated. Of course, since each of the samples consisted of ten persons, the mode, median, and the various errors could be computed

Table 2.5

**Values of the Sample Mean for 15
Samples of Size 10**

Sample	Label for the Sample Mean	Value of the Sample Mean
1	$\bar{X}_1$	3.5
2	$\bar{X}_2$	3.5
3	$\bar{X}_3$	4.0
4	$\bar{X}_4$	4.5
5	$\bar{X}_5$	4.5
6	$\bar{X}_6$	5.2
7	$\bar{X}_7$	5.6
8	$\bar{X}_8$	6.6
9	$\bar{X}_9$	6.7
10	$\bar{X}_{10}$	6.8
11	$\bar{X}_{11}$	7.0
12	$\bar{X}_{12}$	7.1
13	$\bar{X}_{13}$	7.2
14	$\bar{X}_{14}$	7.4
15	$\bar{X}_{15}$	8.2

within each sample just as the mean was. This is what was done with the reading rate scores earlier in this chapter.

In this case, however, these various measures of central tendency and the errors associated with them will be computed *between* various sample means. That is, the measures will be computed on a set of values for a sample statistic.

At this point, care must be taken not to get confused. The example that is to be worked is also based on a sample of scores. However, the observations in this sample are sample means rather than individual scores. Thus, this sample has 15 observations. The questions are the same as previously: what is the mode, median, mean, and the minimum errors for these measures? What does differ in the two cases are the populations from which the elements in the sample have been selected. This sample consists of elements each of which is a group of ten people rather than a single person. The population in this case is the set of values for the statistic across all of the unique samples of size ten that exist for the adult population of the United States. (The number of unique samples would be almost infinitely large. That is, if you consider a number larger than 10^{70} as "almost infinitely large.")

It is readily seen from the distribution that the sample mean that occurs most frequently is both 3.5 and 4.5, since each occurs exactly twice. In this case the distribution has two modes and is called *bimodal*. Either one of these values will result in a minimum amount of error when error is defined as the number of wrong guesses. The total amount of error will then be 13 and the average amount of error will be $A = E/N = {}^{13}\!/_{15} = 0.867$ wrong guesses. The median of the observations is the middle of the scores when they are arranged from lowest to highest. This is the eighth score, $\bar{X}_8$, and is 6.6.

Since the median is 6.6, then the average absolute error from this point is a minimum and is

$$A_{ab} = \frac{\sum\limits_{i=1}^{n} |X_i - Md|}{n} = \frac{\sum\limits_{i=1}^{15} |X_i - 6.6|}{15} \text{ questions}$$

(Work this out and see if you get the answer, $A_{ab} = 1.25$ questions.)

Finally, to compute the mean of the sample means, it is necessary to find

$$\bar{X}_{\bar{X}} = \frac{\sum\limits_{i=1}^{n} X_i}{n} = \frac{\sum\limits_{i=1}^{15} X_i}{n} = 5.853 \text{ questions}$$

(which will be rounded off to 5.9).

The variance of the sample means when taken around their overall mean is found from

$$SD^2_{\bar{X}} = \frac{\sum\limits_{i=1}^{15} (X_i - \bar{X}_{\bar{X}})^2}{15} = \frac{\sum\limits_{i=1}^{15} (X_i - 5.9)^2}{15} = \frac{33.45}{15} = 2.23 \text{ questions}^2$$

The symbol $\bar{X}_{\bar{X}}$ will be used to denote the mean of a sample of means just as $\bar{X}$ or $\bar{X}_X$ is used to denote the mean of a sample of individual scores. Then the standard deviation is $SD_{\bar{X}} = \sqrt{2.23} = 1.5$ questions. (If you don't believe any of this, work it out. Even if you do believe it, you should work it out.)

To summarize, the above problem has been to describe a sample in which the observations in the sample happened to be means of samples of size ten. The most frequently occurring sample value, that is, the mode of the sample means, was computed as was the median of the sample means and the mean of the sample means. For each of these statistics of the sample, the error that was a minimum around these values was also computed. Care was taken to express the results in terms of the appropriate units.

STANDARD SCORES

Before the discussion is extended to the testing of hypotheses, a method for standardizing or comparing scores in various distributions will be presented. Consider Table 2.6 which represents two sets of scores for a group of students — perhaps the results of two exams which a group of students have taken.

Table 2.6

**Scores on Two Exams for
a Group of Students**

	Scores	
Student	I	II
1	5	15
2	3	6
3	2	5
4	1	5
5	4	9

How can the score for a student in one distribution be compared to his score in the other? The actual scores are not very good for comparison since person two, for example, scored higher on the second exam than on the first but he obviously did better, *relative to the group*, on the first exam. One reason you can see that this method might fail is that the scoring procedure may differ from one exam to the next. On the first exam a person may only have been able to get a score between 0 and 5, whereas on the second exam he may have been able to get anything between 0 and 15. For the same reason, the number of points above or below the group mean may not be sufficient to make the comparison. That is, person number five is only one unit above the mean in group I ($\bar{X}_I = 3$) and he is also one unit above the mean in group II ($\bar{X}_{II} = 8$) but, *relative to the group*, he did better in group I than in group II. This follows because in group I everyone is very close together, so one unit must indicate more than one unit in group II where the scores are spread apart.

To adjust for these problems, that is, to standardize from one distribution to another, it would appear reasonable to divide the distance that a score is from the mean by a measure of how much the individuals in the group, on the average, vary about their mean. A measure that does this is the standard deviation. To obtain a standard score, the mean of the distribution is subtracted from the score and this result is divided by the standard deviation of the distribution.

to translate to another

Symbolically,

$z_x \left(\frac{x_x}{s.px} \right)?$

$$z_X = \frac{X - \bar{X}}{SD_X}$$

z_X, the standard score, will be positive for a score if it is above the mean, and negative if it is below the mean. (What is the z score for the mean of any distribution?) The z score thus represents the number of standard deviations that the score is above or below the mean.

Thus person five has a z score of $z_{5_I} = (4 - 3)/1.4 = 1/1.4 = +0.7$ in the first distribution but only $+0.26$ ($z_{5_{II}} = (9 - 8)/3.8 = 1/3.8 = +0.26$) in the second. Hence, the intuitive interpretation that person five did better in group I is borne out. Similarly, you should do the computations for person two to show why he can be said to have done better in group I than in group II even though his score in group II was higher.

The idea of relating scores to the variability of the distribution, as is done with standard scores, is a very important concept. Further, standard scores can be computed for any distribution of scores. All that is needed is a score in the distribution and the mean and standard deviation of the distribution.

Of course, z scores are also valuable in relating individuals within the same distribution to each other, since the z score gives both the direction from the mean and also the number of standard deviations from the mean in that direction. It is apparent that any time z scores are computed, their sign ($+$ or $-$) must be included.

Finally, since z scores can be computed for distributions of scores based on elements or compound elements, it does not make any difference whether these scores are of individuals or are values for a sample statistic.

Two important characteristics of the z scores within any distribution should be noted. First, the mean of the z scores is always 0, that is,

$$\bar{z} = \frac{\sum\limits_{i=1}^{n} z_i}{n} = 0$$

Secondly, the variance and standard deviation of a set of z scores of a distribution is always 1, that is, $SD_z^2 = SD_z = 1$.

Some time has now been spent in describing a set of scores, be they values for different individuals or values representative of different samples. The two purposes of this description were first, to enable one to meaningfully reduce a large amount of information. A second purpose, and one that is to be discussed more fully next, was to set the background for the testing of hypotheses about a population by the selection of a single sample.

HYPOTHESIS TESTING

Very early, information was presented that indicated that the number of possible samples that one might draw from a population of a particular size was usually far greater than the total number of people in the population. Since the population itself was too large to be efficiently studied completely, all the samples could not be either.

The big puzzle that perplexes most people is how one can come to any sort of conclusion about the population by drawing a single sample. After all, there are so many possibilities for a sample, and only one is drawn. Since the observations are randomly and independently drawn, it is just by chance that one sample is obtained rather than another one of the millions or trillions possible. If the sample were only of size 100 from a population of thousands or millions, it would appear to be difficult to say much. That much can be said will be shown shortly.

By now it must be realized that the total population from which the sample is to be drawn is not studied. Since this is so, the nature of the population is not known. Thus, the best that one can do is guess about the population from which one is to draw the sample. This guess, which may be complex, is called the *model* and was defined extensively in Chapter 1. Remember that the model consists of the hypotheses that have been made about the population and about the way in which the sample is drawn.

What the investigator does then is to create a model, or a set of hypotheses, about the real world. He assumes, to start with, that his actual sample will be drawn from a world with the hypothesized characteristics. Then he asks, "If the world is as I have hypothesized, what kind of sample would I expect to obtain?" Of course he realizes that even if the hypotheses are all correct, samples will differ from the expected just due to chance. Even so, if the hypotheses are correct, samples like the observed one should occur fairly often, even if that sample is not exactly as was expected. One problem then is to calculate the likelihood or probability of samples like the observed one, assuming the hypotheses are correct.

Since the probability or likelihood of a sample occurring changes depending on the kind of population from which it was selected, one specific state of affairs or set of hypotheses must be assumed in order to make the calculations. After the calculations are made, the experimenter makes a decision. The basis for the decision is as follows: If samples like the one he observed were frequently expected from the assumed population, then not much can be said. The experimenter cannot say that his assumptions are false, because the evidence is not against the hypotheses. In fact, if the hypotheses are true, then samples like his were fairly probable. On the other hand he cannot say that he has proven the hypotheses to be true, because although a sample like his was likely to occur if these hypotheses are true, it is also possible that it came from a population other than the hypothesized one. (See Chapter 1 for a complete discussion of this.) Thus the experimenter can never *prove* from a sample what the nature of the population is. The only way to do this would be to measure the whole population.

Suppose, however, that the investigator finds that samples like the one he drew are very unlikely to occur from a population like the one he assumed. Then he concludes that it came from some other population. Which one it did come from he cannot, of course, say with certainty. This is so, because from a sample one cannot prove the nature of the population from which the sample was selected. However, he can, in this case, be pretty sure about the population from which the sample did not occur. Therefore, he can conclude that at least one of the assumptions about the population is false. Of course, he might still be making a mistake. After all, the sample might have come from the assumed population. All that he determined was that it was *unlikely* to have come from the assumed population, not that it actually did not.

The above points are a sketch of what is involved in inferential statistics. They will be discussed in much greater detail later. For now, the outline and gist of the problem should be studied carefully and understood thoroughly. One important realization that must occur is that no matter what decision the experimenter makes, he runs the risk of making an error. Suppose, for example, that the probability of obtaining samples like the observed one is high. This means that samples like the observed one often occur when the assumed conditions are really true. Under these circumstances, the experimenter will not reject the assumptions. But he may be failing to reject something that really is not true, because the sample may have come from some other population. On the other hand, if samples like the one he observed were very unlikely to have occurred, then he will reject his assumptions about the population. There is, however, a small chance that he may be rejecting something that is really true, since his sample could have come from that population. Before throwing up your hands, understand that inferential statistics is a field that allows one to make decisions in the face of uncertainty. While there is always a possibility that the wrong decision will be made, making those errors can be greatly reduced by the appropriate application of statistical procedures.

3

SOME MATHEMATICAL
BACKGROUND NECESSARY
FOR TESTING HYPOTHESES

INTRODUCTION

The outline of the problems involved in testing hypotheses has been given in Chapter 2. The goal of this chapter is to develop precise concepts and techniques for solving these problems. In order to do this it will first be necessary to define the expected sample. Then it will be necessary to determine for a particular set of hypotheses or *model* what that expected sample is. In addition, the probabilities of the various values of the statistic will be deduced from the hypotheses. From this deduction the probability for obtaining just by chance samples that are like the observed one will be determined. Consequently, the concept of probability will have to be examined in detail as will the notion of samples that are like other samples.

STATISTICS AND PARAMETERS

Before the topics just introduced are considered, a closer examination of the statistic, its relationship to the population, and the hypotheses is warranted. A statistic is some particular measure of a sample. One measure is the mean, another the standard deviation, another the mode, and so on, with each sample giving a value to the statistic. There are also many measures for the whole population. Thus, there is a population mean, a population standard deviation, a population mode, and so on. The measures of the population are called *parameters*. For each statistic that will be discussed, there is an analogous parameter. If the statistic is a mean, then the analogous parameter is also a mean. Naturally, since the population is not measured in its entirety, the actual value of the parameter is not known. Generally, one of the hypotheses in the model concerns the value of the parameter. Thus, in drawing a sample, one obtains a value of the statistic. The sample is assumed to have been drawn from a population with a hypothesized value for the parameter, although this is only one of the hypotheses about the population.

The Expected Value of a Statistic

It is now possible (and necessary) to refine the concept of an expected sample. As stated previously, a statistic is a measure of a sample. Each sample gives a value to the statistic and this value may be used to describe the sample in a concise way. The hypotheses about the population lead to expectations about the value of the statistic. This is what is meant by the idea of the expected sample.

A precise definition of the expected value of the statistic still must be given. For almost any population there is an extremely large number of unique samples that might be taken. Of course, every unique sample will not give a different value to the statistic because different elements will sometimes have the same score. (Samples are said to be unique if they do not have all of the same elements, but it is still possible that two samples might have the same scores.) Frequently, however, various unique samples that might be selected will have values of the statistic that differ from each other. Therefore, the expected value of the statistic cannot be the value of the statistic that one will always obtain from a particular population. Instead, the expected value of the statistic will have to be one that is representative of all of the values of the statistic that might occur from all of the unique samples of a particular size from the population.

The problem of choosing a representative number has been investigated previously. The possible choices examined were the mode, the median, or the mean of the distribution. However, by definition, the expected value is taken to be the mean of the distribution. Therefore, the expected value of the statistic is defined as: *The mean of all of the values of the statistic based on all of the unique samples of a particular size from a specific population.* The symbol that will be used to represent the expected value of the statistic is E(stat). If the statistic is the sample mean, this symbol becomes $E(\bar{X})$. $E(\bar{X})$ is simply the mean of all of the sample means based on all of the unique samples of a particular size from the given population. Likewise, $E(SD_X)$ is the mean of all the sample standard deviations.

Unbiased Estimators

As discussed previously, every statistic or measure on a sample has an analogous parameter for the whole population. The measure on the population results in a single value (although this value may not be known). Since the population consists of a clearly defined set of elements, this single value is fixed for that particular collection of elements with respect to the attribute specified.

A statistic is said to be an unbiased estimator of the population parameter when its expected value equals the value of the parameter. The sample mean is such a statistic. The expected value of the sample mean equals the value of the population mean.

That not every statistic is an unbiased estimator of the population parameter is well demonstrated by the standard deviation. The expected value of the standard deviation is the mean of the *SD*'s of all of the unique samples from the population (by definition of the expected value). But this expected value for the sample statistic is not equal to the population standard deviation. Hence, the sample standard deviation is not an unbiased estimator of the population parameter.

Sub-Summary

The notion of the sample that is expected under the hypotheses has been made precise by defining it in terms of the expected value of the statistic. Some statistics are unbiased, that is, their expected value equals the value of the parameter, and others are biased, their expected value does not equal the value of the analogous parameter.

Notation

In order to distinguish the measures of a population from those of a sample, lower case Greek letters will be used for parameters, and italic capital Roman letters for statistics. Thus, SD_X is the standard deviation of a sample of scores, $SD_{\bar{X}}$ is the standard deviation of a sample of sample means, σ_X (lower case Greek sigma) represents the standard deviation of a population of individual scores, and μ (lower case Greek mu) represents the mean of a population of individual scores.

PROBABILITY

Before being able to make deductions from the model of the population it will be necessary to examine the concepts of probability and the computations that result from these ideas. This section may well be the most difficult in the text because of the many unfamiliar and precise concepts. However, its complete understanding is essential to the rest of the material.

The Sample Space

Probability notions develop from an idea called a *sample space*. The sample space consists of the *outcomes* of a *conceptual experiment*. These outcomes are separate and distinguishable so that each trial of the experiment results in only one outcome.

Simple Experiments

The best way to obtain familiarity with these ideas is through examples. Consider the conceptual experiment of tossing a coin. For specificity, let the coin be a Lincoln penny. The outcomes of this experiment consist of the two distinct sides of the coin. These distinct outcomes could be labeled side one and side two, but generally they are labeled heads and tails. The whole sample space can be listed very easily. It consists of the following outcomes (the brackets are used to set one outcome apart from another):

$$\{H\} \qquad \{T\}$$

The experiment described above is called a *simple* experiment because its outcomes cannot be further reduced to component outcomes. Thus, in the tossing of a coin, the sides are irreducible. For example, the side labeled by the outcome "heads" cannot be reduced. (The fact that the side of the coin consists of the nose, eyes, ears, and so on, of Lincoln does not mean that it can be broken down into these component outcomes. It is not reasonable to flip a coin, even conceptually, and get just Lincoln's ears or his nose. The side of the coin is an irreducible outcome of the experiment.)

Another example of a conceptual experiment is tossing a die. The outcomes of this experiment are the distinct sides of the die and these sides are usually labeled either a one, two, three, four, five, or six depending on the number of dots on the side. This experiment is also a simple experiment because the outcomes cannot be further reduced. The sample space can be represented as follows:

$$\{1\} \quad \{2\} \quad \{3\} \quad \{4\} \quad \{5\} \quad \{6\}$$

As a final example, consider the experiment that consists of selecting an individual element from a population. Each distinct element selected may be considered an outcome. The outcome might be labeled by assigning a different integer to each element or by assigning the score that the element receives on the attribute that is being considered. Generally, the latter procedure is used. For a population of N elements, the sample space can be represented as follows:

$$\{X_1\} \quad \{X_2\} \quad \{X_3\} \cdots \{X_N\}$$

where X_i is the score of the ith element or outcome.

It is apparent that for all of the above conceptual experiments, real experiments are possible. One can actually toss a penny, or toss a die, or select an element from the population. This is not always so. Conceptual experiments can be created that have no real counterparts. Obviously, the scientist, as a scientist, is not interested in abstract experiments alone. Rather, he is interested in relating the ideas and conclusions that are arrived at in the abstract case to the real world so that he can better understand the real world. Thus, populations can be considered, in the abstract, to consist of collections of distinguishable elements or outcomes. But in any real case, these elements are people or mice or counties, or almost anything, and the outcomes are denoted by the scores the elements receive on some measurable attribute. It is in the inferences to real populations and their attributes that the investigator is interested.

Complex Experiments

Experiments can be imagined where the outcomes would be reducible. For example, consider an experiment that consists of two tosses of a coin. There are four outcomes to this experiment. The sample space is as follows:

$$\{H,T\} \qquad \{H,H\} \qquad \{T,H\} \qquad \{T,T\}$$

Each of these outcomes can be reduced to the separate or component outcomes that occur on each of the separate tosses or trials of the experiment. That is, the outcome $\{H,T\}$ consists of the outcomes "heads" on the first trial and "tails" on the second trial.

Similarly, a pair of dice may be tossed resulting in 36 outcomes. Thirty-six outcomes exist because for every side that may occur on the first die any one of six sides may occur on the second die. Again, each of these outcomes may be reduced to the outcome of each separate die. The sample space of this experiment may be represented as in Figure 3.1.

As a final example, consider the outcomes of an experiment that consists of selecting samples of size four from a population of size six.

The possible outcomes of the experiment are the unique samples of size four. The sample space is given as follows:

$$\{X_1,X_2,X_3,X_4\} \qquad \{X_1,X_3,X_5,X_6\}$$
$$\{X_1,X_2,X_3,X_5\} \qquad \{X_1,X_4,X_5,X_6\}$$
$$\{X_1,X_2,X_3,X_6\} \qquad \{X_2,X_3,X_4,X_5\}$$
$$\{X_1,X_2,X_4,X_5\} \qquad \{X_2,X_3,X_5,X_6\}$$
$$\{X_1,X_2,X_4,X_6\} \qquad \{X_2,X_3,X_4,X_6\}$$
$$\{X_1,X_2,X_5,X_6\} \qquad \{X_2,X_4,X_5,X_6\}$$
$$\{X_1,X_3,X_4,X_5\} \qquad \{X_3,X_4,X_5,X_6\}$$
$$\{X_1,X_3,X_4,X_6\}$$

Each of these outcomes is reducible to its component outcomes based on each of the separate elements. In this example the outcomes have

been defined just in terms of the elements in the sample and not in terms
of their order. The selection of samples from a population, indicated in
Chapter 2, was also done without regard to order. That is, the experiment

Sides of First Die   Sides of Second Die

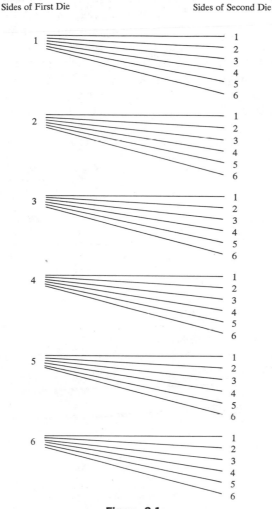

Figure 3.1

of selecting unique samples is one in which the outcomes differ with
respect to the actual elements selected, not in terms of the order in which
they were selected.

It would, of course, be possible to specify an experiment that would
consider different orders to be different outcomes, such as the experiment
described earlier of tossing a coin twice. If order were considered in the

sampling experiment above there would be many more possible outcomes. In fact, for every outcome given above, there would instead be 24 outcomes that contained the same elements but differed only in order. To see why this number is 24 consider a particular set of four elements, for example $\{X_1, X_4, X_5, X_6\}$. If the order in which the elements occur is important then it is possible to have selected any one of the four elements first. For each of these possibilities, any one of the three remaining elements might have been selected next and for each of these three either one of two elements might have been selected next and for each of these two only one element could have been selected last. This gives $4 \times 3 \times 2 \times 1 = 24$ possibilities. They can be diagrammed as in Figure 3.2.

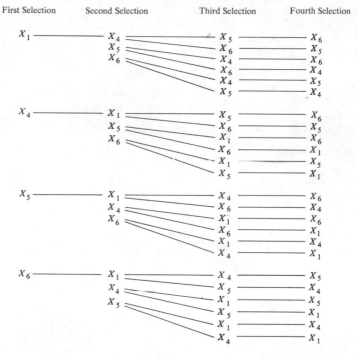

Figure 3.2

Events

Events are defined as collections of outcomes. Since a collection may have only one outcome, events may be the same as outcomes. Because the collection of outcomes can be defined in any one of a number of ways, the notion of an event is best explained through examples.

Consider first the sample space of the experiment that consisted of two tosses of a coin. One possible event is the event that consists of a head on the first toss and a tail on the second toss. This event only has one outcome in the collection of outcomes that define it, namely $\{H,T\}$. Consider the event which only is defined by the outcome on the first trial such as a heads on the first of two tosses of the coin. For this event there are two possible outcomes in the sample space, either $\{H,H\}$ or $\{H,T\}$.

Experiments in which the outcomes are the unique samples from a population can also be grouped into collections which form events. Since the interest is usually in the scores that the individuals receive, events are defined in these terms. Suppose, for example, that the six individuals in the population described above had scores as follows:

$$X_1 = 2 \qquad X_4 = 7$$
$$X_2 = 3 \qquad X_5 = 2$$
$$X_3 = 7 \qquad X_6 = 1$$

One possible event is the event defined by the outcomes (samples of size four) in which at least one person has a score of 1. If the samples are relisted using the actual scores instead of the X_i labels they become:

$$\{2,3,7,7\} \qquad \{2,7,2,1\}$$
$$\{2,3,7,2\} \qquad \{2,7,2,1\}$$
$$\{2,3,7,1\} \qquad \{3,7,7,2\}$$
$$\{2,3,7,2\} \qquad \{3,7,2,1\}$$
$$\{2,3,7,1\} \qquad \{3,7,7,1\}$$
$$\{2,3,2,1\} \qquad \{3,7,2,1\}$$
$$\{2,7,7,2\} \qquad \{7,7,2,1\}$$
$$\{2,7,7,1\}$$

It is now easily seen that there is a collection of ten outcomes in the sample space for which it is true that at least one individual has a score of 1.

For the event consisting of outcomes such that at least one individual has a score of 7, there are fourteen outcomes.

Other events could be defined. For example, events could be defined in terms of operations on the scores contained in a particular outcome. The event consisting of outcomes in which the sum of the scores is equal to 19 consists of two outcomes, $\{2,3,7,7\}$ and $\{3,7,7,2\}$. Generally, the events of interest in inferential statistics are those consisting of all of the outcomes that give the same value to a particular statistic. Thus, in the above experiment, the event that consists of outcomes which have $\bar{X} = 2$, has only one outcome $\{3,2,3,1\}$ in the collection. It should be obvious that if events are defined in terms of values of the statistic, the outcomes will not always consist of elements with the same scores. From a larger population samples of size four could be selected and the event, $\bar{X} = 2$, might include outcomes such as $\{2,3,2,1\}$, $\{2,2,2,2\}$, $\{5,1,1,1\}$, and so on.

In summary, the unique samples of size n may be considered outcomes to an experiment. These outcomes constitute the sample space of the experiment. The values of the statistic may then be considered to be one way of defining events with each event consisting of a collection of the outcomes that give a particular value.

Mutually Exclusive Events.   Events that are defined in such a way that they cannot simultaneously occur are called mutually exclusive. In the experiment that consists of a single toss of a coin, the event, a heads, and the event, a tails, are mutually exclusive since they cannot both simultaneously occur. A more precise definition could be given by defining two events to be mutually exclusive if they have no outcome in common.

In the experiment that consists of selecting samples of four individuals, the unique samples are events all of which are mutually exclusive, since if one combination of four is selected it excludes the possibility of some other combination of four being simultaneously selected. The two examples just presented include definitions of events that contain only a single outcome. Events that include more than one outcome may also be mutually exclusive. In the experiment that consists of tossing a pair of dice, the event, the sum of the two dice is odd, and the event, the sum of the two dice is even, are mutually exclusive — both events cannot occur at the same time.

However, in the above experiment the event, a seven, and the event, the sum is odd, are not mutually exclusive since the collections of outcomes that define each event include many of the same members. For example, $\{6,1\}$ and $\{3,4\}$ are outcomes that are members of each collection. However, $\{6,5\}$ is an outcome that is only a member of the second event.

It should be apparent that not only may the unique samples define events that are mutually exclusive but so may the values of the statistic, since outcomes giving one value of the statistic cannot simultaneously give another value to the same statistic. In any experiment, if the events are defined so that each event consists of a single different outcome of the experiment, they are mutually exclusive. This is a consequence of the previous definition of the experiment as one that consists of separate and distinguishable outcomes only one of which can occur on each trial.

Independent Events.   When the occurrence of one event in no way affects the occurrence of another event, the two events are said to be independent. In the experiment of tossing a coin twice, the event, heads on the first toss, and the event, heads on the second toss, are independent. The occurrence of the first event does not affect the second. Similarly, the elements that are sampled from a population are independent events. Selecting one element does not affect the one that will be selected next.

Mutually exclusive events of necessity cannot be independent, since the occurrence of one event prevents any one of the others from occurring.

Thus far the attempt has been to develop concepts and ideas which form a basis for the development of probability calculations. The next section, therefore, will form the foundation for evaluating the probability of obtaining, just by chance from some hypothetical population, values of the statistic like the observed one.

Defining Probability

Subjective Definition

To define probability it will be best to start with general ideas that have occurred to people based on their experience.

It may be apparent that the ideas of the sample space are themselves based on experience. The outcomes of the conceptual experiments that have been discussed are abstractions that frequently represent outcomes to real processes. In fact, it is possible to define events in such a way that any real experiment of the type presented would have mutually exclusive events that would exhaust the possibilities. Tossing a coin, or a die, or selecting a person from a population are real experiments that are of this nature.

It is from experience with experiments like the above that notions of probability develop. The question of how likely an event is, when that event is defined by a single separate and distinguishable outcome of an experiment, has to do with how often one would expect it to occur. How often one expects something to occur is frequently related to how often it has occurred in the past.

It might seem, therefore, that the probability for mutually exclusive events should be defined as the number of times that a particular event has occurred out of the total number of times any of the possible events has occurred. This notion will not work. To see why, consider a coin. Suppose that the coin is tossed 100 times and the number of times that it comes out heads is 48. Then the probability of heads would be $48/100 = 0.480$. However, one more toss of the coin would change the probability of heads occurring. If this toss resulted in a heads, then the new probability would be $49/101 = 0.485$ and if it did not result in heads the new probability would be $48/101 = 0.475$. The next toss would again change the probability as would succeeding ones. Further, different coins would have different probabilities depending on their "personal" experience.

Obviously, then, simple relative frequency is not quite what is meant by probability. First of all, again using the coin as an example, a probability is assigned ahead of time, even before the coin has been tossed once. Secondly, this probability is a specific and constant value. In the case of the coin it is 1/2 for either a heads or a tails because there seem to be two reasonable outcomes, and each seems no more likely than the other if the coin is tossed in such a way that the trials are independent of each other and only chance factors operate. Similarly, 1/6 seems appropriate as the probability for a side or face of a die and 1/N as the probability for selecting a person by chance from a population of N people. These probabilities do not represent actual results but rather the results that are expected if the experiment is repeated many, many (many) times (and more).

Thus, probability concepts are developed out of experience with real processes and events but then become abstract notions about long-run expectations. In order to be precise these abstract ideas are developed in terms of conceptual experiments and events that consist of outcomes to the experiment. The next section will develop more precisely the mathematical idea of probability.

Defining Probability—A Precise Definition

Probabilities are numbers that are associated with events. In order to define probability, it will first be necessary to examine the idea of an elementary event. *An elementary event is an event consisting of a single outcome of a simple experiment.* All other events are *compound events.* Elementary events are always mutually exclusive. If an irreducible outcome occurs, no other irreducible outcome can simultaneously occur. (If it could, then the occurrence would consist of two irreducible outcomes. It could then be reduced to these outcomes. Therefore, it could not originally have been irreducible.)

Consider again a conceptual experiment consisting of elementary events. (Conceptual experiments are quite easy. Much easier than running rats down mazes for example, because all you have to do is *think* about running rats down the mazes. This of course makes it a lot easier on the experimenter, as well as the rats. All types of conceptual experiments can easily be run, some of which couldn't possibly be actually tried.) The experiment consists of tossing a coin (which you are no doubt familiar with doing by now, at least conceptually). Think about tossing the coin over and over again. Sometimes it will come out to be the elementary event defined by the outcome heads and sometimes that defined by tails. (It might even stand on its edge but since this is a conceptual experiment this possibility can be eliminated.) The probability of an elementary event is then defined as the number of times that the particular event occurs, divided by the total number of times that any elementary event occurs, *over the long run.* When this proportion is equal for all of the elementary events, the events are then said to be *equally likely* or *equally probable.* The idea of a "fair" coin or die means that the elementary events are all equally likely. In defining probability this way, the number of trials of the experiment that determine the proportions for each event is infinite. Over the long run is over a very long run.

To summarize, the probability of an elementary event is the relative frequency with which that event occurs over an infinite number of trials.

It is not necessary to limit this definition only to elementary events. That is, the events that are each defined by a single distinguishable outcome of an experiment (like one consisting of two tosses of a coin) may or may not be equally likely. Still, the probability of their occurrence may be taken as the relative frequency with which they will occur, over the long run.

Of course, the idea of an infinite number of trials must remain a conceptual or imaginary process. Thus, the probabilities are not statements of what has happened, but are interpretations of what would happen if an infinite number of trials were taken. To restate this notion: in a conceptual experiment the assignment of probabilities to the events may be considered equivalent to a statement about the relative frequencies with which each event will occur if an infinite number of repeated trials of the experiment are considered. If 0.5 is assigned to each event in the experiment that consists of tossing a Lincoln penny, then this may be considered to be a statement that an infinite number of repeated trials of the above conceptual experiment will result in one-half of the outcomes being heads and one-half being tails.

Symbolically, the probability of an event can be represented by letting n_{E_i} represent the number of times that the ith event occurs and N represent the number of times that any event occurs. Then $P(E_i) = n_{E_i}/N$ where $P(E_i)$ is the probability of the ith event.

This formulation of probability results in probabilities being limited to values between zero and one, $0 \leq P(E_i) \leq 1$. This conclusion follows since no event can occur more often than all of the time or less than none of the time. In the first case, $n_{E_i} = N$ so that $P(E_i) = N/N = 1$ and in the second case, $n_{E_i} = 0$ so that $P(E_i) = 0/N = 0$. (The sign $<$ means "less than" and the sign $\leq$ means "less than or equal to." Similarly, $>$ and $\geq$ mean "greater than" and "greater than or equal to." The signs can be read from either direction; $a < b$ can be read as, a less than b, or as, b greater than a. Thus, $-2 \leq x \leq 20$ means that -2 is less than or equal to x and x is less than or equal to 20. This statement would usually be read x is greater than or equal to -2 and less than or equal to $+20$. If x were a variable, the above statement would indicate that it was limited to values between -2 and $+20$ inclusive.)

Further, the events defined by a single outcome of the experiment are exhaustive; they cover all of the possibilities. Every trial of the experiment must result in some event defined by an outcome in the sample space. Thus, the probability that a trial will result in one of these events is 1, or certainty.

The investigator is not only interested in the conceptual experiment. The events of the conceptual experiment are generally related to real occurrences. Similarly, the probabilities that are assigned to the events are also supposed to represent probabilities for actual occurrences, usually with the condition that the trials of the actual experiment are independent of each other and are influenced only by chance.

Experimentally, however, only a finite number of trials can be taken. The actual relative frequency in any real set of trials will usually not be precisely that which is expected on the basis of the abstract probabilities. Fortunately, an important theorem of Bernoulli relates the relative frequency after a finite number of trials to that which is expected over the long run. The theorem states that if p is the probability of an event, then the more trials that are taken the closer should the relative frequency be to that which is indicated by the probability p.

In the case of the Lincoln penny, it might be imagined that the probabilities that should be assigned to each of the two elementary events is 1/2. If these probabilities are appropriate, then the more that a real penny is tossed, the closer should the observed relative frequencies be to 1/2. As a matter of fact, this is not what occurs. Tossing the coin over and over results in probabilities that are slightly different from 1/2. This is due to the fact that a penny is not an unbiased coin. One side is slightly heavier than the other. This, of course, does not prevent one from having a concept of an unbiased coin, that is, one which if tossed an infinite number of times would turn out to have equal relative frequencies for each of the two events. In statistics, the ideas are models of the world. These ideas lead to expectations about the results of real experiments. The real experiments then give results which indicate whether the abstract ideas are reasonable ones to have about the real world. ·

Probability Computations

Probabilities for Mutually Exclusive Events

If a set of events are mutually exclusive, then by definition no more than one of them can occur on a particular trial of an experiment. If $\cap$ (cap) is the symbol used to represent *and*, then the probability of events A and B can be represented as $p(A \cap B)$. If A and B are mutually exclusive, then $p(A \cap B) = 0$, by definition. The symbol used to represent *or* is $\cup$ (cup). The probability of either event A or event B occurring when A and B are mutually exclusive is given as follows:

$$p(A \cup B) = p(A) + p(B), \text{ if } p(A \cap B) = 0$$

This follows from the definitions of mutually exclusive and of probability that have been given. If A and B are mutually exclusive, then the probability of either one occurring is the number of times that either one occurs out of the total number of times any event occurs. Thus, for mutually exclusive events,

$$p(A \cup B) = (n_{E_a} + n_{E_b})/N = n_{E_a}/N + n_{E_b}/N = p(A) + p(B)$$

The general rule for mutually exclusive events is given by the following. *For a set of N mutually exclusive events* $A_1, A_2, \cdots, A_N$, *the probability that any one of a set of n* $\leq$ *N will occur is the sum of the separate probabilities.*

For example, consider the sides of a fair die. Each outcome may define an event. These events are mutually exclusive. If one side of the die is face up, say the 4, then another side cannot simultaneously be face up. Consider the compound event, an even number. This event consists of the elementary events $\{2\}$, $\{4\}$, and $\{6\}$ which are mutually exclusive.

In this case, $N = 6$, and $n = 3$, so obviously $n \leq N$. The probability that any one of the three events will occur on a toss of the die is the sum of the separate probabilities. Therefore,

$$p(A_2 \cup A_4 \cup A_6) = p(A_2) + p(A_4) + p(A_6)$$
$$= 1/6 + 1/6 + 1/6 = 1/2$$

An equivalent way of looking at the problem is to use the idea that for any set of mutually exclusive and exhaustive events that are equally likely, the probability of a compound event consisting of any one of a specified number of these is equal to the number of these in which the compound event occurs divided by the total number. This easily follows because equally likely events are interpreted to mean events whose long-run relative frequencies are equal. Thus for mutually exclusive and equally likely events $A_1, A_2, \cdots, A_K$, the relative frequencies may all be represented by n/N. If there are k mutually exclusive events then the probability that any one will occur is equal to 1, that is, $n/N + n/N + \cdots + n/N = kn/N = 1$. Thus, $kn = N$. Therefore, the probability of any one event can be equivalently represented as either n/N or $n/kn = 1/k$. Suppose then that a new compound event is defined which consists of 5 of the original set of mutually exclusive and exhaustive events. Again, the probability rule for mutually exclusive events gives as the new probability $1/k + 1/k + 1/k + 1/k + 1/k = 5/k$. Thus, the probability of the compound event under these conditions equals the number of original events (5) divided by the total number of events (k). For the problem of the die discussed above this again leads to the result of $3/6 = 1/2$.

Similarly, the probability for a particular value of the statistic may be looked at either way. Since all of the unique samples that give a particular value to the statistic are mutually exclusive, the probability of the value of the statistic is the sum of the separate probabilities. That is, if A_1, A_2, $\cdots$, A_n are the outcomes (unique samples) that result in a particular value of the statistic, say S_i, then,

$$p(S_i) = p(A_1 \cup A_2 \cup \cdots \cup A_n) = p(A_2) + \cdots + p(A_n)$$

However, since the unique samples all are equally probable, then, $p(S_i) = $ *Number of unique samples that equal S_i/Total number of unique samples.*

Probabilities for Independent Events

For a set of N independent events, the probability that all of a set of $n \leq N$ events will occur is the product of the probabilities. Symbolically, if A_1, A_2, A_3, $\cdots$, A_N are all independent, then $p(A_1 \cap A_2 \cap A_3 \cap \cdots \cap A_N)$ $= p(A_1)p(A_2)p(A_3) \cdots p(A_N)$. For example, the probability of a heads and then a tails on two tosses of a coin is equal to $p(H \cap T) = p(H)p(T)$ $= 1/2 \times 1/2 = 1/4$.

Probability computations rapidly become more complicated. For example, the probability of a seven on the single toss of a pair of dice requires the use of the rule for mutually exclusive events as well as the one for independent events. Each way of getting a seven consists of two independent events. For example, if a 6 and a 1 were obtained, then $p(6 \cap 1) = p(6)p(1) = 1/6 \times 1/6 = 1/36$. However, there are many other ways of getting a seven, for example, a 3 and a 4. Altogether there are six different ways of getting a seven (see Figure 3.1). By the rule for independent events each of these ways has a probability of $1/36$. However, all of the ways are mutually exclusive. If a seven occurs by one pair of numbers, it excludes the possibility that it will simultaneously occur by another pair of numbers. Therefore, by the rule for mutually exclusive events, $p(7) = 1/36 + 1/36 + 1/36 + 1/36 + 1/36 + 1/36 = 1/6$.

Finally, the rule for independent probabilities may be used to examine the probabilities for the unique samples of a particular size. A particular unique sample consists of a set of random and independent selections. This means that at each stage of sampling, each element in the population has an equal chance of being selected into the sample. If there are N elements, then each one has a probability of $1/N$. Suppose the sampling is sequential and an element that is selected is not returned to the population before the next one is selected. Then the probability for the first element is $1/N$, and the probability for the second is $1/(N - 1)$ because the population has been reduced by one as a consequence of the first selection. The next selection would have a probability of $1/(N - 2)$, and so forth. If the selections are independent of each other, then a unique sample of size n has a probability of occurrence that is determined by the product of the probabilities, $(1/N)\ [1/(N-1)]\ \cdots\ [1/[N-(n-1)]]$. No matter which unique sample of size n actually is selected, each possible one has this same probability.

The above sampling procedure is called *sampling without replacement*, and is the type of sampling that most frequently occurs in behavioral science studies. If the elements were returned to the population after each selection, the process would be *sampling with replacement*. Then the probability at each stage would remain $(1/N)$ so that the probabilities for the unique samples, if the selections are independently made, would all be equal and would have a value of $(1/N)^n$. For large populations, $1/[N-(n-1)]$ is almost the same as $1/N$ so that the probabilities for the unique samples are approximately equal under either procedure. (For example, if the sample size is $n = 100$ and $N = 1,000,000$, then $1/[N-(n-1)] = 1/999,901 = .00000100001 \approx 1/N = 1/1,000,000 = .00000100000$. The symbol $\approx$ is used to indicate that one value is approximately equal to another.)

Summary

It is perhaps appropriate at this point to review the essential problem whose solution is being sought. Real world problems frequently involve determining some aspect of the nature of large populations. Because of various considerations it is not usually reasonable or sometimes even possible to measure the whole population. This means that the exact nature of the population cannot be determined. Instead, the best that can be done is to hypothesize about the population and then draw a sample to see if the results in the sample are consistent with the hypotheses. However, due to chance processes, sample results vary from one time to the next. Therefore, it is not reasonable to expect samples that are consistent with the hypotheses always to give the same result. Another way to state this is to say that, even if the hypotheses about the population are correct, samples will vary from each other just due to chance.

To determine if the sample result is consistent with the hypotheses, several refinements were needed. First it became necessary to define the *parameter* and the *statistic*. Next, it became necessary to indicate that one of the deductions that could sometimes be made from the model was the expected value of the statistic. Because of the variability that occurs in the values of the statistic merely due to chance, the determination of the consistency of the observed value of the statistic with the expected value had to be based on the likelihood, or probability, that values like the observed one would occur if the hypotheses were in fact correct. If the likelihood were large then the observation could be considered consistent with the hypotheses and if it were small it could be considered inconsistent. However, in order to determine likelihoods, the whole notion of probability had to be carefully examined.

Further subproblems remain before a solution to the problem of the consistency or inconsistency of the sample result can finally be given.

First, it would be helpful if all of the possible values of the statistic, *and the probability of each*, could be determined. Then, if the concept of the values of the statistic that are like the observed one were developed, the problem of determining the likelihood of values like the actually obtained one would be straight-forward. The order in which these topics will be investigated is, first, the listing process. Then in Chapter 4, the concept of values of the statistic like the observed one will be examined and a model, or set of hypotheses, about a population will be presented. Finally, the method of deducing the expected value of the statistic as well as the probabilities associated with the values of the statistic will be given.

The student should understand that although the basic problem was presented quite early, extensive development is required before it can be solved. Each of the ideas that has been presented must be understood before the succeeding ones can be grasped. Further, the whole sequence and its logic must be thoroughly learned before the solution that is provided can make sense. Therefore, because of the lengthy development that is presented, it may be necessary to review several times different aspects of the argument in order that the logic of the whole sequence be kept in mind. One reward of success at this venture will be the relative ease with which the remaining ideas can then be understood (although, of course, they will still not be easy in an absolute sense).

LISTING THE VALUES OF THE STATISTIC AND THE ASSOCIATED PROBABILITIES— PROBABILITY DISTRIBUTIONS

The Discrete Case

The problem of specifying all of the possible values that the unique samples of a particular size might give to the sample statistic (and the probabilities associated with these values) when they are drawn from a specified population is not a simple task. Obviously, a complete listing of the samples is not possible. Fortunately, some samples will have exactly the same values as other samples. Two samples may be unique, that is, they may not have all of the same individuals, yet they might have the same value for a particular statistic. For example, their medians might be the same, or their means might be the same. Thus, at each value of the statistic, there would be expected to be many unique samples that would give that value.

In order to arrive at the probability of getting values of the statistic like the observed one, a concise way is needed to describe the probabilities associated with each value of the sample statistic. Obviously, even though there are many samples that would have the same value, there are still so many different values that would occur that to specify the probability of each would take an eternity (which, even if one were to have, would most likely not be the preferred way to spend one's time). To pictorially represent more concisely the values that the sample statistic might take, an axis is needed. In order to indicate the probabilities for each of these values another axis is needed. These two needs produce a picture like that in Figure 3.3.

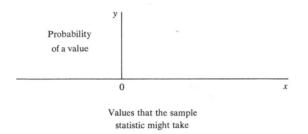

Figure 3.3

Since a statistic may have negative values, there is the possibility that values will be below zero as well as above it. For example, if people are scored as to how much money they have, and a minus number represents how much they owe, a particular group might have a negative mean. However, probabilities cannot have as wide a range of values. The smallest probability is 0 and the largest is 1. That is, the number of favorable outcomes can never be less than 0 of the total number and the maximum value can never be greater than all. Since the probability is obtained by dividing by the total, the range of values must be between 0 and 1.

Figure 3.3 does not really indicate anything. There must be points in the diagram. Each point will then signify two things. First, it will represent a value for the statistic. This will be indicated by the distance that the value is to the right or left of the probability axis. Secondly, the point will have a probability of occurring. This will be indicated by how far above the "values" line (this is the horizontal or x axis, while the vertical axis is called the y axis) the point is. If there are a finite number of points this means that there are only certain values that the statistic can have. For example, Figure 3.4 represents a discrete distribution based on values of the sample mean for samples of size one. (A distribution is considered to be discrete between two values if, in that interval, there are only a finite number of points to the distribution. In order for a distribution to be continuous in an interval, there must be no missing points at all for it.)

Figure 3.4 is a diagram of a *probability distribution*, that is, a distribution of a set of values and their associated probabilities. The values do not

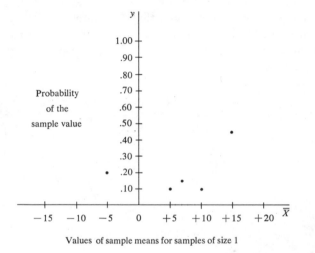

Values of sample means for samples of size 1

Figure 3.4

necessarily have to be values of a statistic; they could also be values assigned to individuals or *elements*. In this case, the only values for the sample means that could occur would be -5, $+5$, $+7$, $+10$ and $+15$. This, of course, means that only people having these scores are in the population, since selecting a sample of size one is the same as selecting some individual. It is also seen from the diagram that the probability of getting a sample of size one, or an individual, whose mean is -5 is equal to 0.2. The shorthand way to write this is $p(\bar{X} = -5) = 0.2$. This statement says, "the probability of the sample mean having a value of -5 is 0.2". Then it is seen that $p(\bar{X} = +5) = 0.1$, $p(\bar{X} = +7) = 0.15$, $p(\bar{X} = +10) = 0.1$ and $p(\bar{X} = +15) = 0.45$. Note that the probability of a sample of size one having either a value of -5 or $+5$ or $+7$ or $+10$ or $+15$ is 1.0. In other words, it is certain that a sample of size one selected from the population will have some one of the above values. Of course, the probability that the sample of size one will have values other than those above is 0, since there are no such samples possible. You may have noticed that the probabilities for each of the values were added together to obtain the total probability. This was done because the events were *mutually exclusive*. That is, if a sample of one value were drawn, then it could not have happened that the same sample had some

other value. Since the probability for the occurrence of any one of a set
of mutually exclusive events is the sum of the separate probabilities, the
probability that a sample of size one would be selected and have either a
mean value of -5 or a mean value of $+5$ is $0.2 + 0.1 = 0.3$, as long as
the selections were randomly and independently made. In the shorthand
notation one would say,

$$p[(\bar{X} = +5) \cup (\bar{X} = -5)] = p(\bar{X} = +5) + p(\bar{X} = -5)$$

$$= 0.2 + 0.1 = 0.3,$$

if

$$p[(\bar{X} = +5) \cap (\bar{X} = -5)] = 0$$

It must be apparent that if samples of size two, three, or some other
size were taken from the above population, many other possible means
might occur. For example, if samples of size two were considered, a
sample mean of 0 might occur $[(+5 + -5)/2 = 0]$ or of $+1$ $[(-5 +7)/2 = 1]$, and so forth. Further, it should be apparent that as the
size of the sample increases, more and more possible values will occur.
In fact, from a large enough population it would be expected that every
value from -5 to $+15$ would occur, although a large sample would be
very unlikely to have a mean of -5 or of $+15$ since every element in the
sample would have to have exactly the same score. Nevertheless, occasionally one would expect samples with means of -5 or of $+15$.

To illustrate this a little further, consider again samples of size two. In
the original distribution there were five different values for the elements,
$-5, +5, +7, +10$, and $+15$. If samples of size two are considered then
any element having any one of the five values could be selected second.
This gives 25 combinations. Thus, samples of size two from the above
population have 25 combinations whereas there were only five possible
combinations for samples of size one. Not all of the 25 combinations
of two give different means. For example, $[(+5) + (+15)]/2 = [(+10) + (+10)]/2 = \bar{X} = 10$. Nevertheless, there are many more values of the
mean for samples of size two than there were for samples of size one. If
samples of size three were taken there would be $5 \times 5 \times 5 = 125$ combinations of the values. Again, not all of the means would be different,
but there would be many more values of $\bar{X}$ for $n = 3$ than for $n = 2$.
(For example, $n = 3$ could yield $\bar{X} = (-5 + 5 + 7)/3 = 7/3$. This
value of $\bar{X}$ is not possible for $n = 2$ from the above population.) For a
sample of size 30, the number of combinations is $5^{30} \approx 931,000,000,000,000,000,000$ (931 quintillion).

Although many of these samples would have identical means, it should
be clear that there would still be an extremely large number of values
for $\bar{X}$ based on samples of size 30. Of course, all values of the mean will

not be equally probable. Samples of size two offer a brief illustration of this. Consider a process whereby each of the two elements is selected randomly and independently from a large population. The random process gives each element an equal chance of being selected. This, of course, does not mean that each *value* has an equal chance of being selected in the above population because 15 percent of the elements have a score of -5 but 45 percent have a score of $+15$. Therefore, if a sample space is defined in which the outcomes are the values of the individual elements, and events are defined as collections of all those outcomes having the same value, each sample of two consists of two independent events. Therefore, the probability of a particular two is the product of the probabilities. Then, $p(-5 \cap -5) = p(-5)p(-5) = (.15)(.15) = .0225$ and $p(+15 \cap +15) = p(+15)p(+15) = (.45)(.45) = .2025$. In the first case the mean is equal to -5 and in the second it equals $+15$.

The Continuous Case

In most populations, of course, the individuals may have any one of a great number of scores and hence the statistic based on samples of a particular size from that population may also have any one of a great number of values. To list the probability of each of these values of the statistic would be impossible. Instead, a shorthand way of writing the probability distribution has been devised based on the fact that a very large number of values can be represented by a continuous distribution. Consider Figure 3.5.

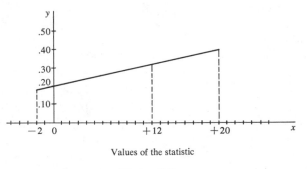

Values of the statistic

Figure 3.5

Notice that instead of a discrete number of points, as were presented in the first example, there is a line. This line is composed of an infinite number of points. Thus, all possible values for the statistic between -2 and $+20$ are presented. Each of these values has a probability of occurring. Of course, the probability for any single value of the statistic would have to be extremely small because there are an infinite number of possible values between -2 and $+20$; the probability that any one of these values will occur would have to be very close to 0 since the sum of the probabilities for all of the values must equal 1.0. That is why, in Figure 3.5, the y axis no longer represents the probability of the value of the sample statistic occurring. In order to interpret Figure 3.5 the next section is necessary.

Mathematical Functions

It has been pointed out in the previous discussion that the listing of the probabilities for every possible value of the statistic is not reasonable when there are an infinite or even a large number of values of the statistic. Hence, a procedure has been devised that shortens the listing process. In Figure 3.5, note that for each value on the x axis there is a value of y associated with it. This is written as $y = f(x)$ which simply means that y is a function of x, that is, for each value of x, a unique value of y is determined. The function is determined by a *rule* for specifying y when x is given. In Figure 3.5, the rule only holds when x is greater than or equal to -2 and less than or equal to $+20$. However, the rule has not been specified. In Figure 3.5, $f(x) = x/100 + 0.2$. Thus the rule in this case for obtaining y when the x value is given is to divide the x value by 100 and then add $+0.2$. The full statement for the case presented in Figure 3.5 is then written,

$$y = \frac{x}{100} + 0.2 \quad \text{for} \quad -2 \le x \le 20$$

This rule allows one to determine the y value *for any of the infinite values of x that fall between -2 and $+20$.* You will admit this is easier than a listing.

But what has happened to the probabilities? They are no longer located in the diagram. How are they found? The answers to these and other exciting questions follow.

Probabilities in the Continuous Case

Each value of the statistic can again be considered to be an event defined by those outcomes (unique samples) that give the particular value. According to the probability concepts presented thus far the events each have probabilities attached to them. The actual probabilities, of course, depend on the number of outcomes that give the particular value. However, in continuous distributions there are an infinite number of events. Further, probabilities are still limited to values between 0 and 1. These two facts create difficulties. Obviously, a concept of probability should hold for the continuous case which does not change from one distribution to another. As a result, it is not possible to assign to every one of the infinite events a probability. To understand why this is so consider the case where all of the events in a continuous interval have equal probabilities and each event is defined by the outcomes that give a particular value to the statistic. A possible example of this might be given by the distribution which is presented in Figure 3.6.

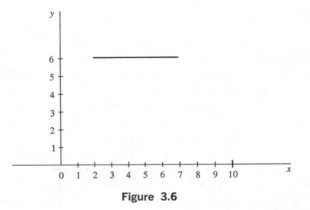

Figure 3.6

This distribution is continuous within the interval from 2 to 7 although the rule is quite simple. All $f(x)$ states is that for any value of x in the given interval, y is to receive the constant value, 6. It is still true, however, that within the interval there are an infinite number of values or events. Suppose each event is assigned a probability of 0. Since the events are mutually exclusive, the probability that any one of them will occur is the sum of the separate probabilities. This sum must equal 1 because it is certain that one of the values will occur. However, that all of the probability values must be equal is indicated by the fact that the height of the y axis is the same for every value of x. But if each value equals 0 then their sum also equals 0, that is, $\infty \cdot 0 = 0$. (The symbol ∞ represents the concept infinity. Thus, $\infty \cdot 0$ indicates that 0 is being added to itself an infinite number of times.) Suppose then that each event has a constant probability c where $c > 0$. Then the sum of all of the probabilities is $c \cdot \infty$, and this will be greater than 1. Thus, the probability for each of the infinite number of events can neither be 0 nor greater than 0.

In order to avoid throwing many statisticians out of work, a solution to this problem had to be found. The essence of the resultant efforts is described below.

Since probabilities cannot be defined for each of the events, this attempt was abandoned. But the sum of the probabilities, however they are defined, must still equal 1. Therefore, instead of computing probabilities based on individual values, probabilities are now based on areas under the curve between two points. Because the probability that some one of the events will occur is still certain, the total area under the curve is taken to represent a probability of 1. Probabilities are then no longer defined in terms of individual values but in terms of intervals. The probability for an event which is defined by the collection of outcomes in an interval is then the *proportion* of the total area under the curve that falls between the two end points of the interval. The probability of getting any value between the lowest value and the highest one is 1.0, since that is the proportion of the total area between these two points.

For example, in Figure 3.5 the probability of obtaining a value of the statistic between -2 and $+20$ is equal to 1.0 since the whole area under the curve is included from -2 to $+20$. On the other hand, the probability of obtaining a value for the statistic between $+12$ and $+20$ is only about .45.

Since some readers may be interested in how this value is obtained, a sketch of the argument will be presented. The probability for an event occurring between two values in a given probability distribution is the portion of the total area of the curve that is under these two values. For a single specific value for the statistic, like 12.7, what is the probability of exactly 12.7 occurring? Since all of the area under the curve between 12.7 and 12.7 is a straight line, and since a straight line has no width and an area of 0, the portion of the total area of the curve under 12.7 is 0.

However, as has been discussed previously, if single values are considered and each has a probability of 0, the probability for any set of these values will still be 0. This would be so even if the set included all of the values, that is, $\infty \cdot 0 = 0$. Since an event that has a probability of 0 is an impossible event, but some event does occur, the mathematics involved in finding a probability only considers actual intervals, that is, the lowest and highest values are not the same. The mathematical field of calculus solves the problem of computing the probabilities by considering infinitesimally small strips (which are pretty small but do have some width). Then by adding all of these strips together the total area is found. This is essentially what was done to arrive at the value .45 obtained for the statistic between $+12$ and $+20$ in Figure 3.5.

You will recall that Σ was used to represent the addition of a finite number of terms. In calculus, the $\int$ (integral sign) is used to indicate adding up an infinite number of infinitesimally small strips. In order to find an area, limits are placed on the integral sign. Thus, to compute the area between $+12$ and $+20$, $\int_{+12}^{+20}$ had to be found.

However, the area will differ depending on the kind of function $f(x)$. The reason for this should be obvious. When y is a function of x the height of the curve is determined by the rule for determining y when x is given. As the height of the curve varies, as it will for different rules, different proportions of the area will be between the same two values. For example, consider the following two cases. It is apparent that the proportion of the total area that is between the values 10 and 20 is greater in graph A than in graph B. It is also clear that, although the precise rules have not been given, $f(x)$ in case A is different from $f(x)$ in case B.

In the example that is being considered, $f(x) = x/100 + .2$. Therefore the complete job was to find $\int_{+12}^{+20} (x/100 + .2)\, dx$. The symbol dx indicates

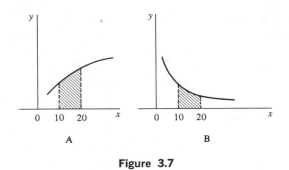

A   B

Figure 3.7

that it is the area underneath the function that is to be found. The formula then is the mathematical way of saying, find the area under the curve represented by $y = x/100 + .2$ which is between the values $+12$ and $+20$. This area was divided by $\int_{-2}^{+20} (x/100 + .2)\, dx$ which represents the total area under the given curve. The fraction was then the probability of obtaining a value between $+12$ and $+20$ *for the given probability distribution*. It should be apparent that for any probability distribution, the probability of an event defined by an interval approaches 0 as the distance between the highest value in the interval and the lowest value in the interval approaches 0.

You will not be expected to be able to do the computations; instead, tables will be provided which do the job for you. But it does seem reasonable to expect you to understand the kind of reasoning that goes into the computation. Hopefully, the numbers will then make a little more sense.

To summarize, a probability distribution is a distribution of a set of values and their associated probabilities. These distributions may come from any one of a number of fields of investigation such as physics, chemistry, gambling, sociology, business, education, or psychology. The primary emphasis in this text is on the application of these ideas to values of a statistic where the attributes being measured come from the behavioral sciences.

Probability distributions may be discrete or continuous. For relatively few values, discrete distributions are used with the values indicated on the x axis and the probabilities represented on the y axis. The separate and distinguishable outcomes of an experiment may each define an event. Compound events may then be defined that consist of a number of these events. In either case, the probability of an event is the number of times that event occurs out of the total number of times any event occurs in the long run, provided the events are mutually exclusive and exhaustive. In the special case where a set of mutually exclusive and exhaustive events are equally likely, the probability of a compound event consisting of a specified number of these events is the number of events in the compound event, divided by the total number of events in the set.

For large numbers of values, or an infinite number of values, continuous curves are used to represent the probability distribution. The shape of the distribution is determined by the rule that relates values on the x axis to values on the y axis. In this case, probabilities can only be assigned to intervals in which the highest value of the interval and the lowest value are not identical. The probability then becomes the proportion of the total area under the curve that is contained under the portion of the curve indicated by the interval. Obviously, the proportions for the areas differ depending on the rule that relates the values on the x axis to the values on the y axis.

The extended development of the listing process allows the introduction to a very common continuous probability distribution called the normal curve. This particular distribution will recur throughout the remainder of the text. The next section will introduce this curve as well as the method for computing probabilities based on it.

The Normal Curve

Figure 3.8 presents a diagram of a normal curve. The diagram has a y axis and an x axis with the x axis again representing scores. These scores

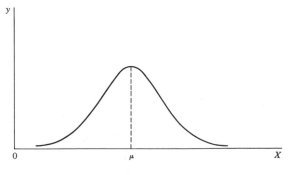

Figure 3.8

may be of individuals or of a statistic, such as the values of sample means. The normal curve is a *theoretical* distribution which the distribution of some important real world attributes approximate. The curve is such that it extends infinitely far in either direction. The further away the curve gets from the mean, the closer it gets to the x axis. Therefore, since the area under the curve within an interval represents the probability, the further away from the center of the curve events are, the less likely they are to occur.

The normal curve is a curve that has specific characteristics. It is these specific characteristics that allow one to obtain the probabilities between two values. For one thing, the curve is symmetric. Also the mean, median and mode are all at the same place. As in the previous examples, the normal curve is determined by a rule which assigns, for every value of x, a particular value of y. Thus, the curve is also specified by a rule of the form $y = f(x)$.

In this case,

$$f(X) = \frac{1}{\sigma_X \sqrt{2\pi}} \, e^{-(X-\mu)^2/2\sigma^2} X$$

where $(X - \mu)$ is the deviation of the score from the mean and σ_X^2 is the variance of the distribution. Since

$$y = \frac{1}{\sigma_X \sqrt{2\pi}} \, e^{-(X-\mu)^2/2\sigma^2} X$$

every value of X determines a value of y. e is a constant which approximately equals 2.71828, just as π is a constant which approximately equals 3.14159. Of course σ^2_X and μ will be a constant for any particular distribution.

The student might note that the equation for the normal curve can also be written in terms of z scores. That is, the definition of z was the deviation between a score in a distribution and the mean of the distribution divided by the standard deviation of the distribution. In the above case $z = (X - \mu)/\sigma_X$. Thus, $(X - \mu)^2/\sigma^2_X = [(X - \mu)/\sigma_X]^2 = z^2$.

Then, since $\sigma_z^2 = 1$, the normal curve equation can also be written $y = f(z) = (1/\sqrt{2\pi})e^{-z^2/2}$. In this case, each value of z would determine a value of y. The result would be a *transformed distribution* of the original scores, the scores having been transformed from X scores to z scores. This transformation is a linear transformation on the X scores and will not affect the shape of the distribution. (Linear transformations will be discussed in the next chapter.) However, the mean and the variance of the distribution will be changed to 0 and 1 respectively. This follows from the fact that the mean of any distribution that has been converted to z scores ($\bar{z}$) is always 0 and the variance of the distribution of z scores

(SD_z^2) is always 1. Obviously, the case where the z scores happen to be normally distributed is only a special case of this general conclusion.

The resulting normal curve is diagrammed in Figure 3.9 and is called the *unit normal curve*. z scores from a unit normal curve are called *normal deviates*.

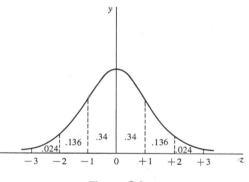

Figure 3.9

Every normal distribution can be standardized by transforming the scores to z scores. This results in a unit normal curve with a mean of 0 and standard deviation of 1.

For the normal curve all the probabilities have already been computed. It turns out that the probability of a case falling between a z score of 0 and a z score of +1 is .34 *in a normal curve*. Since the curve is symmetric, it must also be true that the probability of a score *in a normal distribution* falling between the mean and one standard deviation below the mean is also 0.34. To write this in mathematical notation one writes $p(0 \le z \le +1)$ = 0.34 and $p(-1 \le z \le 0)$ = 0.34. Other facts are $p(+1 \le z \le +2)$ = 0.136 and $p(+2 \le z \le +3)$ = 0.021. What is $p(-3 \le z \le -2)$? And $p(z \le 0)$? What about $p(z \ge -1)$?

You should now relax with this thought in mind. The normal curve is essentially no different from the curve first presented which was $y = f(x) = x/100 + 0.2$. The only thing that has changed is the rule. Obviously, a change in the rule will alter the portion underneath the curve in a particular interval. For the normal curve, tables are available which tell the portion of the curve in any interval from the mean to some point (in terms of z scores). (See Table I in the Appendix.) Because the curve is symmetrical, obviously only half of the values need to be given. The student will realize that there are an infinite number of z scores above a z score of 0. Not all of these are usually listed in the tables. Generally, the z score is only given to the nearest 10th or 100th.

Because of the importance of the normal curve, two examples will be given to demonstrate its characteristics and its use. The first example will concern a distribution of scores for individuals, and the second example will deal with a distribution of values of a sample statistic.

Example 1.   Suppose a group of 1000 male adults are measured on the variable of height. Assume that the mean value for the heights is 69 inches and the standard deviation is 3 inches. Assume also that the scores have a normal distribution. Then the scores may be represented as in Figure 3.10. (The broken line of the *x* axis near the origin indicates

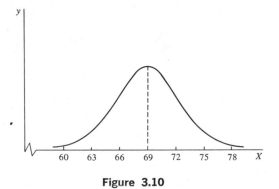

Figure 3.10

that there are missing values on the axis. These values are frequently omitted when the distribution of scores ranges around large values.)

Since the normal distribution is a *continuous* distribution, the diagram indicates that there were some scores at every possible value. This cannot possibly be true because this would indicate that an infinite number of scores were obtained and it is known that only 1000 were, many of which had the same value. A more accurate presentation would have been to draw a discrete distribution. However, if scores are just about normally distributed, the difference between the actual case and the ideal case is so slight that the advantages of using the ideal representation lead one to it.

The problem to be considered is the evaluation of the probability of getting individuals within some specified range of height. For example, what is the probability of obtaining, randomly, a person whose height is greater than 75 inches. Mathematically, the question is, what is $p(X \geq 75)$ where X is the score on the height variable.

If you were to look in the tables for the normal curve, you could search far and wide and still not find a table for the normal curve with a mean of 69 and a standard deviation of 3. This is because every distribution of scores that is normal can be reduced to the unit normal curve of z scores in which the mean is 0 and the standard deviation is 1. (If the original distribution were not normal, it could also be reduced to a z score distribution of mean $= 0$ and $SD = 1$, but the resulting z distribution would not be normal.) The diagram will then look like Figure 3.8.

The reason for this can be seen by remembering that a z score is obtained by $z = (X - \bar{X})/SD_X$. Thus, every score is not only a certain number of units above or below the mean but is also a certain number of standard deviations above or below the mean. *In a normal distribution,* there is always the same probability of getting a z score above a certain value, below a certain value, or between the same two z values. This follows simply from the definition of the normal curve which says that the curve always gives the same probability of occurrence to z scores between the same two specified values. If a curve is such that it does not give the required probability then it cannot be a normal curve, also by definition.

The question originally asked was, what is $p(X \geq 75)$ in the above distribution? Since the distribution of scores was normal, the answer can be obtained by looking at a normal curve table. But the table only gives the answer for z scores; therefore, it is necessary to find the number of standard deviations above or below the mean that the score of 75 is. This is the same as finding the z score, which is $z = (75 - 69)/3 = +2$.

The normal curve table gives the probability of obtaining a z score greater than or equal to $+2$ as equaling .0227 (that is, $.5000 - p(0 \leq z \leq +2) = .0227$). If one were interested in finding out the probability of a person being between a height of 67 inches and 73 inches, the steps would be as follows:

The interval is 67 to 73 inches. For 67 inches, $z = (67 - 69)/3 = -\frac{2}{3}$ and for 73 inches, $z = (73 - 69)/3 = +\frac{4}{3}$. In order to reduce the amount of confusion, a diagram should always be drawn, the axes labeled, and the numbers filled in. For this reason, confusion-reducing Figure 3.11 has been included.

The problem then reduces to one in which the probability for the

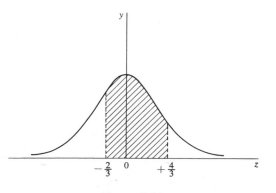

Figure 3.11

shaded portion is sought. This will be the portion of the total curve that is in the interval between $-\frac{2}{3}$ and $+\frac{4}{3}$.

By the use of the normal curve table (which is now becoming an easy job), it is found that $p(-\frac{2}{3} \leq z \leq 0) = .25$ and $p(0 \leq z \leq +\frac{4}{3}) = .41$. Therefore, the shaded area must equal $.25 + .41 = .66$. Hence, the probability of obtaining a height between 67 inches and 73 inches is .66 *when the heights are normally distributed with a mean of 69 and an* SD_X of 3.

Example 2.   In the first example, a group of scores was presented in which each of the scores represented an individual. In the next example, a group of scores will be given in which each value is of the sample statistic. For specificity, the mean will be the statistic.

Consider again the example presented in Table 2.5, where means of various samples were computed. The mean was the average number of questions that were answered correctly in the sample. For purposes of this illustration, samples of size 40 will be considered so that each mean is based on the average number of questions correct when $n = 40$. Further, the situation will be modified so that each individual will have been asked 15 instead of 10 questions.

For reasons that will be presented later, the probability distribution of the means based on all of the unique samples of size 40 from this population may be treated as a normal distribution. If a normal distribution is assumed with $E(\bar{X}) = 6$ and $\sigma_{\bar{x}} = 1.5$, probability calculations can be easily demonstrated. The distribution of sample means under these conditions would be diagrammed as in Figure 3.12.

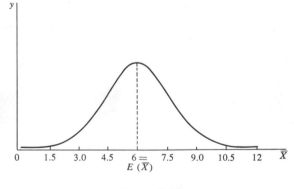

Figure 3.12

Obviously, the normal distribution is only an idealization for at least two reasons. The first is that the number of unique samples is finite and the normal distribution is continuous. This is no real problem because the number of unique samples of size 40 that could be taken from the adult population of the United States is larger than 10^{250}. This number is larger than the number of particles in the universe. As a result it would be impossible to list all of the unique samples separately because it would take more than a particle of the universe to list each sample and thus the universe would get used up long before the listing process was completed. This would obviously be a waste of a good universe. The student can appreciate the concern that mathematicians had for the universe when they developed the idea of a continuous distribution in order to avoid using it up.

The second reason that the above distribution is an idealization is that the normal curve theoretically stretches infinitely far in either direction. The situation that has been presented prevents a sample mean from having a value less than 0. That is, the worst that all of the individuals in a sample could do is answer no question correctly. In this case $\bar{X} = 0$. However, in a normal distribution with $E(\bar{X}) = 6$ and $\sigma_{\bar{X}} = 1.5$, only six cases in 100,000 would have a value less than 0. Thus, if the values from 0 and above are approximately normally distributed with a mean of 6 and a standard deviation of 1.5, the theoretical normal distribution would be a very reasonable probability distribution to use.

With these minor considerations in mind, probability calculations can readily be made using the normal curve table.

For example, what is the probability that a randomly and independently drawn sample of $n = 40$ would have a mean less than 1.7, that is, what is $p(\bar{X} < 1.7)$?

Again, the calculation must be based on the transformed distribution. In this case the scores for the means are transformed to z scores by the usual procedure. That is, the mean of the distribution, $E(\bar{X})$, is subtracted from each value of $\bar{X}$, and then the difference is divided by the standard deviation of the distribution which is $\sigma_{\bar{X}}$. Symbolically, $z = [\bar{X} - E(\bar{X})]/\sigma_{\bar{X}}$. Since $E(\bar{X})$ and $\sigma_{\bar{X}}$ are constants, the transformed distribution will remain normal, but with a mean of 0 and a standard deviation of 1. All unit normal distributions are the same, by definition. Thus, to find $p(\bar{X} < 1.7)$, $\bar{X} = 1.7$ must first be converted to a z score. This gives $z_{\bar{X}=1.7} = (1.7 - 6)/1.5 = -4.3/1.5 = -2.87$. The normal curve table indicates that $p(z < -2.87) = .002$. Therefore, in the problem presented $p(\bar{X} < 1.7) = p(z < -2.87) = .002$.

As a final example, suppose one wanted to find $p(|\bar{X} - E(\bar{X})| \geq 2)$, where $|\ |$ represents the absolute value. In this problem, the probability concerns differences between the sample mean and the expected value that have an absolute value at least as large as 2. Diagrammatically, the problem is to find the proportion of the total area that is in the shaded portion of Figure 3.13.

As before, the problem must be answered by first converting to z

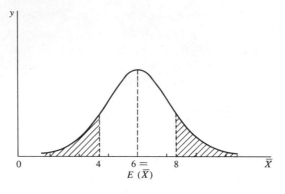

Figure 3.13

scores. If $\bar{X} = 4$, then the corresponding z score is $z = (4 - 6)/1.5 = -1.33$. If $\bar{X} = 8$, then $z = (8 - 6)/1.5 = +1.33$. In terms of the transformed distribution, the problem is to find the area indicated in the shaded portion of Figure 3.14.

From the normal curve table $p(z \geq +1.33) = .09$. Since the curve is symmetric, $p(|z| \geq 1.33) = 2(.09) = .18$. The complete statement for the probability question originally asked is:

$$p(|\bar{X} - E(\bar{X})| \geq 2) = p(|z| \geq 1.33) = .18$$

In terms of sampling, this means that if a sample of $n = 40$ were randomly and independently selected from the above population, there would be 18 chances out of 100 that the mean of the sample would deviate at least two units from the expected value of the sample means. Equivalently, one could state that there are 18 chances out of 100 that the absolute value of the z score for the observed mean would be greater than or equal to 1.33.

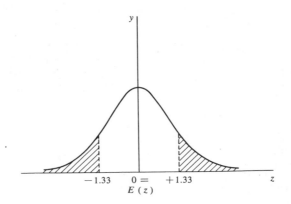

Figure 3.14

4

A SIMPLE STATISTICAL MODEL—
THE z TEST FOR THE TRUE MEAN

INTRODUCTION

Many of the important ideas have been presented upon which the interpretation of the consistency of a sample result with the hypotheses will be based. In terms of the problems that were indicated at the beginning of the last chapter, two remain. One is the definition of what is meant by sample results that are like the observed one. The second is the development of models of the population from which the probability distributions for the statistic may be deduced. When this second step is completed it will finally be possible to determine in a precise way the actual probability for obtaining, just by chance, samples like the observed one when the hypotheses about the population are in fact true. Once this has been accomplished, the remainder of the book will primarily be concerned with translating various real world situations that occur into appropriate statistical models and then determining if the model is an accurate statement of the true state of affairs.

A SITUATION

Suppose an investigator were interested in the average amount of time it took students at a particular university to get to campus. Studies at other similar universities have indicated to him that the mean time for students is 11.2 minutes. Therefore, he decides to take a sample of 35 students from his university to see if 11.2 is a reasonable value for the parameter of the population in which he is interested.

TRANSLATION INTO A STATISTICAL MODEL

The investigator knows that even if the mean time that it takes students to get to campus at the university is exactly 11.2 minutes, a sample of

35 students is unlikely to have a mean of 11.2. That is, the means of the samples will vary from each other just due to the chance factors involved in sampling. Therefore, he predicts that if the value 11.2 is correct he will obtain a sample mean that is consistent with it. By consistent he means that the results like the obtained one will occur frequently (have a high probability) if his hypothesis is correct.

In order to determine consistency, the investigator will first have to be able to determine, from the model of the population, the value of the statistic that is expected. He must also determine the probabilities that are to be associated with the various values of the statistic that will occur if the model is correct.

From the discussion in Chapter 3, it should be apparent that a normal probability distribution with a known mean and standard deviation is one for which probabilities can easily be determined. Thus, the problem of translation becomes much easier if a model of the population can be developed which leads to the logical deduction that the probability distribution of the statistic (in this case the mean) is normal and from which the expected value of this distribution and its standard deviation can also be deduced.

Theorems (Deductions)

Within the system of probability theory there are several theorems that have been deduced. These theorems indicate the conditions under which the normality of the statistic will be guaranteed. From these theorems the expected value and standard error of the statistic may be determined.

Normality of the Statistic

There are two conditions under which the sample means based on all of the unique samples of a particular size will be normally distributed. The first is that the scores of the individual elements in the population are themselves normally distributed. The second is the *Central Limit Theorem* which states that the probability distribution of the means of the unique samples of a particular size approaches a normal distribution as the size of the sample increases no matter what the underlying distribution of individual scores is. Generally, a sample size of at least $n = 30$ is considered necessary to insure that the distribution of sample means will be very close to normally distributed even if the underlying distribution of the population is not.

The process that the experimenter goes through in selecting a particular sample must be one that results in a probability distribution that is equivalent to that obtained by distributing the values of the statistic across all of the unique samples of a particular size. Since this method weights all of the unique samples equally (each unique sample is only counted once), the process of random and independent sampling will give the same results. This process gives each sample an equal chance of occurring. In the long run, therefore, repeated random and independent sampling should result in each unique combination being selected the same proportion of time.

The probability distribution of a statistic is called a sampling distribu- tion. Its formal definition is: *A sampling distribution is a probability distribution of all possible values of a statistic that occur in all the unique samples of a specific size from a specified population. Equivalently, a sampling distribution is a probability distribution of the values of a statistic obtained by repeated random and independent sampling of samples of a specific size from a specified population.*

The Expected Value of the Statistic

If the mean of the population is equal to μ, the expected value of the sample means is given by $E(\overline{X}) = \mu$. The proof of this theorem is one of the deductions in the abstract statistical system.

Standard Deviation of the Distribution

The standard deviation of a sampling distribution is called a standard error. The standard error of the mean is denoted by $\sigma_{\bar{x}}$. Another theorem within the abstract system that has been proven is that $\sigma_{\bar{x}} = \sigma_X/\sqrt{n}$ where σ_X is the standard deviation of the population and n is the sample size.

A closer examination of the above formula is warranted. It would appear reasonable that for a given sized sample the sample means should differ from each other more if the individuals in the population are widely different than if the individuals are close together. The more that the individuals differ from each other the larger will σ_X be and, therefore, the larger will $\sigma_{\bar{x}}$ be. However, it should also be true that the larger the size of the samples, the *closer together* the means of those samples should be for a given σ_X. This conclusion is also included in the formula since larger n increases the denominator of $\sigma_X/\sqrt{n}$ and, therefore, decreases $\sigma_{\bar{x}}$.

The Abstract Model

The abstract model that has been developed as a translation of the situation described at the beginning of the chapter consists of the follow- ing hypotheses about the population:

1) $\mu = a$
2) Sampling random and independent

3) $\sigma_{\bar{x}} = \sigma_X/\sqrt{n}$
4) $\bar{X}$ normal

Under these conditions the sampling distribution of the mean can be deduced. This deduction is diagrammed in Figure 4.1.

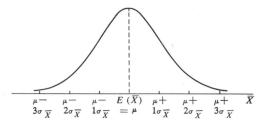

Figure 4.1

This deduction means that 68 percent of the values of $\bar{X}$ will be between $\mu \pm \sigma_{\bar{x}}$ and that 95 percent will be between $\mu \pm 2\,\sigma_{\bar{x}}$. In fact, the probability for any interval of values can be determined by transforming the above distribution to the unit normal curve and using the normal curve tables.

Predictions to the Real World—Samples "Like" the Observed One

If the above model is an accurate translation of the real world, the prediction about the sample that is to be observed should be correct. But what is to be predicted? Samples vary from the expected just due to chance. The basis for the prediction requires a detailed examination to be made precise. The preliminary statement has been made many times. The sample that is predicted is one that gives a high probability to the occurrence of samples like it. The key to making this idea precise is the concept of samples "like" the observed one.

Certain rules based on intuitive considerations may be made concerning the basis for rejecting or failing to reject the model as an adequate translation of the real world.

Consider again the deduced sampling distribution, but in terms of the unit normal curve which is the actual basis for determining the probabilities. For convenience, this distribution is diagrammed in Figure 4.2.

First, it must be agreed that if samples like the observed one have a high probability under the hypotheses, then the hypotheses cannot be rejected, but that if results like the observed one are unlikely under the hypotheses then at least one hypothesis of the model must be considered a false statement about the real world. Further, let it be agreed as a quite reasonable position that the closer the observed result is to the

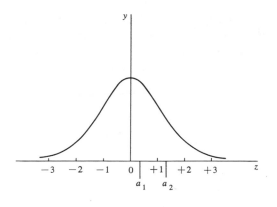

Figure 4.2

expected result, the less likely it should be that the hypotheses are rejected, that is, the more probable results like that should be. Similarly, the further away from the expected result the observed one is, the more likely it should be that the hypotheses are rejected, that is, the less probable results like it should be.

With this as a starting point, the question of which samples are like the observed one can be attacked.

Suppose, first, that only those samples that give exactly the same result as the observed result are considered to be like the observed one. Then the probability of interest is for the event that consists of all of the outcomes (unique samples) that give exactly the observed value of the statistic. As has been discussed previously, this probability is 0. Thus, one would always reject the model even if the observed result were exactly equal to the expected. This obviously does not provide a basis for determining whether the sample result is consistent with the model.

It is apparent that the definition of results like the observed one must deal with an interval. This interval contains a class of events whose probability will be given by the proportion of the total area under the curve defined by the interval. Two possible definitions for the interval might seem reasonable. The first defines results to be like the observed one if they are as close or closer to the expected value as the observed one. However, this definition goes counter to the intuitive basis that was originally agreed upon. To understand this, consider two possible sample results a_1 and a_2 indicated on the unit normal curve in Figure 4.2. a_1 is closer to the expected result of $z = 0$. However, the probability for the class of events that are as close or closer to $z = 0$ as a_2 is must be larger than the probability defined by a_1, because all of the events in the class defined by a_1 are also in that defined by a_2, but a_2 contains many more events in addition. Another way to state this is that the area defined by

a_2 (from 0 to a_2) is obviously greater than that defined by a_1 (from 0 to a_1). In fact, under this conception, the further one gets from the expected value the *higher* the probability and therefore the more consistent would be the result with the hypotheses. Further, observed results that were very close to the expected would have low probabilities and thus would lead to rejection of the model. This is exactly opposite to a reasonable decision-making process.

The solution to this problem is to define results to be like the observed one when they are *at least as deviant* from the expected as the observed one is. Using the values a_1 and a_2 in Figure 4.2 it is obvious that from a_1 to ∞ is an interval that contains a larger proportion of the area under the curve than is defined by the interval a_2 to ∞. Thus, the probability of results "like" a_1 is greater than those "like" a_2. This definition results in decisions that are consistent with intuition. The closer that observed results are to the expected, the higher is their probability under the hypotheses and hence the more consistent they are with the hypotheses. The further away they are the less likely they are and, therefore, the more inconsistent. *The class of events defined by a_1 will be considered to be those in the interval from a_1 to $+\infty$ if $a_1 \geq E(stat)$ and from a_1 to $-\infty$ if $a_1 \leq E(stat)$.*

Since the direction that the outcome will vary from the expected due to chance may be either above or below the expected value and probabilities concern events that have not yet occurred, the probability of events like the observed one must include all of those that are at least as deviant in either direction from the observed. The actual direction of the result is not known except for events that have already occurred. The deviance of the result is then defined not in terms of units away but in terms of probabilities. That is, the smaller the probability for a class of events defined by an observed result, the more deviant they are considered to be. Thus that class of events is as deviant from the expected on the opposite side of it which occurs as infrequently as the class of events defined by the observed one. Suppose a is the expected result and a_1 is the observed result. Further, suppose that the probability given by the interval a_1 to ∞ if $a_1 > a$ (or a_1 to $-\infty$ if $a_1 < a$) is p_1. Then the probability of obtaining by chance events like the observed one is $2p_1$. Thus the probability for results like the observed one is twice the probability of the class of events defined by the observed one.

Decisions about Specific Hypotheses

Although it is possible to make decisions about models, the investigator is usually interested in making a decision about one particular hypothesis in the model. In the situation indicated at the beginning of this chapter the investigator wanted to determine specifically if $\mu = 11.2$ was a reasonable hypothesis about the mean travel time in the population. Suppose that the model that is used as the abstract translation of the real world situation is the following:

1) $\mu = a$
2) Random and independent sampling
3) $\sigma_{\bar{x}} = \sigma_X/\sqrt{n}$
4) $\bar{X}$ normal

However, if all of these remain hypotheses, the experimenter will be unable to make a specific judgment. If the sample result is consistent with the model then none of the hypotheses are unreasonable. However, if the result is inconsistent with the model, no specific decision about which hypotheses are false can actually be made. It may have been that the sample was not taken randomly and independently. If this were true the process would not lead to a sampling distribution equivalent to that based on all of the unique samples of that size. Or it might have been that the value used for $\sigma_{\bar{x}}$ was inappropriate or that $\bar{X}$ was not normally distributed in which case inappropriate probabilities were used to determine the likelihood of the sample result by chance under the hypotheses. As a result, if the experimenter is interested in testing the specific hypothesis $\mu = a$, he must make sure that the other conditions in the model have been met so that an unlikely result can be attributed to a mistranslation of the particular hypothesis in which he is interested.

Random and independent sampling can be obtained by assigning to each individual in the population a number and then using a random number table to make the selections for the sample. The conditions under which $\bar{X}$ will be normally distributed have also been discussed. The remaining condition, $\sigma_{\bar{x}} = \sigma_X/\sqrt{n}$, requires that the actual population standard deviation be known. This is not usually the case, although in certain situations it is known.

When these three conditions have been met, and assuming a correct application of logic has been used, samples inconsistent with the model must be attributed to the falsity of the hypothesis that $\mu = a$.

The Decision Model

The Need for a Decision

Under what circumstances should a model be rejected? That is, when is a sample result inconsistent with the model? Since inconsistency is defined in terms of probabilities, the answer becomes one in terms of how infrequently samples like the observed one must occur before the observation is considered inconsistent with the model.

If just by chance samples at least as deviant from the expected as the observed one occur 20 times out of 100 under the hypotheses, should this result be considered inconsistent with the model? Or should unlikely results under the hypotheses be considered those that occur by chance only five times out of 100 or one time out of 100?

There is no absolute criterion for a decision. The stronger the reasons are for believing that the model is an accurate translation of the actual state of affairs, the less likely the class of events defined by the observed result should be before a decision is reached that the model is false in some respect. However, there must, under any circumstances, be some point at which the investigator is willing to say that the model, in some respect, is false. This results from the fact that the true state of affairs about the entire population can never be known from a sample of observations. The hypotheses in the model are not the only ones that might have been made. If no observation, no matter how unlikely it is, leads to a rejection of the model, then errors in judgment will be made because false models will not be rejected.

The Decision

As has been indicated, all of the conditions in the model must be met except for one if the investigator is to be able to make a specific interpretation of that aspect of the model which is a false translation of the real world. This aspect of the model is called the null hypothesis, symbolized H_0, and is usually that hypothesis that deals with the value of a measure of central tendency in the population. Most frequently this is a mean. In the model being examined in this chapter, the null hypothesis would be represented as $H_0 : \mu = a$. This is read: The null hypothesis is that the population mean has the value a. If a rare sample occurs (one that is unlikely under this hypothesis) the hypothesis will be rejected in favor of an alternative hypothesis which will be accepted. The alternative hypothesis is simply a statement that the true value of the parameter is a value other than a. Symbolically, this statement is $H_A : \mu \neq a$.

Thus, rejecting the hypothesis that $\mu = a$ would result in accepting the alternative hypothesis that $\mu \neq a$. This seems quite logical since either $\mu = a$ or $\mu \neq a$ and if $\mu = a$ is determined to be false then $\mu \neq a$ must be accepted as true.

The Decision Model

The probability that defines how unlikely sample results must be before they are considered inconsistent with the model is symbolized by α (the Greek letter alpha). *The decision model will be considered to consist of both α and H_A,* that is, both the basis for the decision as well as the conclusion that is actually made. Frequently, the research that is being conducted is an attempt to prove the null hypothesis false in order to accept the alternative hypothesis. The alternative hypothesis, therefore, is frequently the *research hypothesis,* or the conclusion that the investigator is trying to reach.

SUMMARY

The application of statistics involves real world problems from which abstract models are developed. Since these models are about populations which cannot be measured in their entirety, a sample of observations must be made. These observations most frequently give results, as measured by the value of the statistic, that differ from the expected value, just due to chance. Therefore, within this abstract system logical deductions are made about the expected value of the statistic and its sampling distribution. On this basis, a determination is made of the values of the statistic for samples of a particular size that are consistent with the model. An actual sample is then drawn. The probability is computed for drawing, just by chance under the hypotheses, samples that are at least as deviant from the expected as the observed one is. If this probability is high, then, given the model, the observed result is likely and, therefore, cannot be considered inconsistent with the model. If the probability is low, then the result is considered inconsistent with the model and the conclusion that at least one hypothesis in the model is a false translation of the state of affairs in the real world is made.

Because no sample result is impossible on the basis of a statistical model, some probability value must be defined by which a sample result will be thought rare enough under the model to be considered inconsistent with it. This value is called the α level and is most often set at either .05 or .01.

Those results that are so deviant in either direction from the expected that they would occur by chance as often or less often than α are said to be statistically significant. If the observed result is one of these cases, it is said to be statistically significant, or inconsistent with the model.

In addition, the investigator is usually interested in testing a specific hypothesis in the model. Therefore, all of the conditions except this one, called the null hypothesis, must be met so that rejection of the model can be attributed to the falsity of that particular hypothesis. An alternative hypothesis, which most frequently is the research hypothesis, is stated and, if the null hypothesis is rejected, this alternative is accepted. Of course, the null hypothesis can never be accepted, because no matter how consistent the sample result is with the expected result, there are other models of the population for which it is also consistent. The α level and the alternative hypothesis constitute the decision model.

A schematic representation of the relationship between the real world and statistical models is presented in Figure 4.3.

INTERPRETATION OF FIGURE 4.3

Basically, Figure 4.3 is an expansion of the diagram presented in Chapter 1. This expansion represents, in a detailed way, the relationship between abstract statistical models and the real world.

The arrows in the diagram indicate the steps that are taken in the process of coming to a conclusion about a population based on the evidence in the sample. The verbal descriptions underneath or by the side of the arrows give some indication of the process that is used to proceed from one step to the next.

For most investigators, the process starts in the real world at the *situation* stage. This usually includes a population and a problem about that population that the investigator is interested in. He then tries to abstract from this situation an appropriate *model* that translates the situation from the real world to the abstract world. The model contains hypotheses about the population of elements that the experimenter is dealing with in the real world. These hypotheses consist of a set of *theorems* that have been deduced within the mathematical system of probability which itself is based on general experience that people (mostly mathematical types) have had with uncertain events. In addition, the problem leads to the abstraction of a decision model that includes an alternative hypothesis and an α level.

Once the model has been developed, deductions from it can be made. These deductions are within the abstract system but have counterparts within the real world. The first deduction concerns the *probability distribution* of the outcomes of the conceptual experiment that consists of drawing samples of a particular size from a specified population. This abstract distribution has a counterpart in the distribution of real samples that would be obtained by repeated random and independent sampling from the population. The deduction of the sampling distribution and its relationship to the outcomes of real samples allows a prediction to be made about the actual sample result that should occur if the hypotheses in the model are correct translations of the situation that exists in the real world. Because of sampling variability, this prediction is about the type of sample that will frequently occur under the hypotheses, not about those that will always occur.

The prediction is then tested by doing an experiment. The consequence of the experiment is a sample that gives a particular result to the statistic. This value is related to the sampling distribution that was deduced and its probability of occurring is calculated. Through use of the decision model,

REAL WORLD		ABSTRACT (STATISTICAL) WORLD

REAL WORLD   Abstraction   ABSTRACT (STATISTICAL) WORLD

Experience in a world of ——————▶ *Abstract Model:* Elements and axioms
uncertainty.   that constitute the theory of proba-
                                             bility.

                                                     Deductions based on rules
                                             ┆- - of logic and the theory of
                                                     probability.
                                             ▼
                                             Theorems which are incorporated
                                             into—
                                             ▼

A *situation* involving   A *model* consisting of elements and
populations of elements ——————▶ their outcomes and hypotheses about
and the scores they re-   Abstraction   them.
ceive on a particular   (translation)
attribute.   ┆- - Further deductions
                                             ▼
Observed sample will   *Sampling Distributions:* Expected
give a value to the   ◀——————   value and the probability distribution
statistic that is within an Prediction,   of the statistic.
indicated range of   using α level
values about the ex-   for determining   Determination of proba-
pected value.   consistency with ┆- - bility for continuous
                            the model.   distributions.
┆- - Experiment   ▼
▼
Observed sample and   ——————▶ Probability evaluation for a particular
value it gives to the   Relation of   value in the distribution and com-
statistic.   observed value   parison with values that are defined
                            to sampling   as rare.
                            distribution.
                                             ┆- - Decision model
                                             ▼
Research Conclusion: *Statistical Conclusion:* If a particular
Fail to reject the value   ◀——————   value is not statistically significant
of the parameter or re-   Interpretation   (is consistent with the model), fail
ject the value and accept   of the statistical to reject H_0; or if it is statistically
the conclusion that the   conclusion in   significant (is inconsistent with the
value of the parameter   terms of the   model), reject H_0 and accept H_A.
is different from the one   original prob-
originally supposed.   lem.   ┆- - Nature of statistical models
                                             ▼
Possible Error in   *Possible Statistical Error* (See dis-
Research Conclusion   ◀——————   cussion of Type I and Type II error.)

                            Interpretation

Figure 4.3

a statistical conclusion is reached. Generally, this conclusion concerns the hypothesized value of the parameter as stated in the null hypothesis. This conclusion then has a bearing on the decision about the alternative hypothesis.

The statistical conclusion, which is within the abstract system, is interpreted for the judgment that it implies about the situation or problem that was originally being discussed.

Because of the nature of statistical models which incorporate notions of randomness and probability, any statistical conclusion carries with it the possibility of having made a statistical error. Further, the possible statistical error, when interpreted in terms of the real world, means that there may have been a mistaken judgment about the true nature of the situation that actually exists.

AN EXAMPLE

In order to make the previous discussion more concrete, the situation presented at the beginning of the chapter will be worked through as a problem.

The Situation

In addition to the assumption that the mean travel time in the population is 11.2 minutes, σ_X, the standard deviation of the population, must be known. In this case, suppose the value has been determined to be 9 minutes. The experimenter then takes a random and independent sample of 35 and finds that the mean of the sample, $\bar{X}$, is equal to 15.1. He wishes to determine if the assumed time of 11.2 is reasonable in light of the evidence from the sample, that is, whether the sample is consistent with the hypothesis.

Defining the Real World Population

This step requires an explicit statement of the population and attribute from which the sample was randomly and independently taken. In the stated case it is the collection of all students at the particular university with respect to the amount of time it takes them to get to campus.

The Research Question

What is it that the experimenter is trying to prove? In this case, he is trying to show that a population mean of 11.2 minutes is a reasonable hypothesis. The experimenter is hoping to draw a sample whose result is consistent with the hypothesis.

Translation into the Model

The Model of the Population

Using the values of the problem, the model becomes:

1) $H_0 : \mu = 11.2$ minutes
2) $\sigma_{\bar{x}} = 9/\sqrt{35} = 9/5.9 = 1.5$
3) Random and independent sampling
4) $\bar{X}$ normal

Because the experimenter is interested in testing H_0 specifically, the other conditions in the model must actually be met. Since $\sigma_{\bar{x}} = \sigma_X/\sqrt{n}$ and both σ_X and n are known, the value of $\sigma_{\bar{x}}$ has been precisely determined. The random and independent assumption has been met by the process used for drawing the sample. The normality of $\bar{X}$ is reasonable since the sample size is 35.

The Decision Model

For this problem the investigator set $\alpha = .05$ and the alternative hypothesis $H_A : \mu \neq 11.2$.

Deductions from the Population Model

The sampling distribution of the statistic is deduced as normal with $\sigma_{\bar{x}} = 1.5$. The expected value of the statistic is given by $\mu = E(\bar{X}) = 11.2$. The sampling distribution of the statistic and the transformed statistic are diagrammed in Figures 4.4 and 4.5. (Included in the diagrams are the observed results for which the computations are given in the next step.)

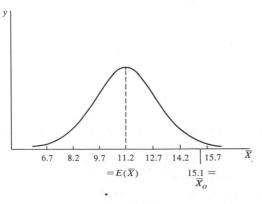

Figure 4.4

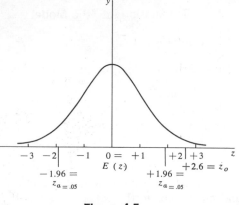

Figure 4.5

Predictions from the Population Model

The observed value of $\bar{X}$ was 15.1. Transforming this value to a z score gives $z_{\bar{x}_o} = (15.1 - 11.2)/1.5 = 3.9/1.5 = +2.6$. The prediction of the investigator using $\alpha = .05$ is that the observed result will be consistent with the model, specifically with $H_0 : \mu = 11.2$. By using $\alpha = .05$, consistency has been defined to be a result with a z score between -1.96 and $+1.96$. That is, the prediction is that $-1.96 \leq z \leq +1.96$. Using the absolute value symbol this can be stated as $|z| \leq 1.96$. The symbol z_α represents that value of z such that $p(|z| \geq z_\alpha) = \alpha$. Thus, if $\alpha = .05$, then $z_{\alpha = .05} = 1.96$ because $p(|z| \geq 1.96) = .05$. The notation $+z_\alpha$ then is that value of z such that $p(z \geq +z_\alpha) = \frac{1}{2}\alpha$ and $-z_\alpha$ is that value of z such that $p(z \leq -z_\alpha) = \frac{1}{2}\,\alpha$. Thus, for $\alpha = .05$, $+z_\alpha = +1.96$ and $-z_\alpha = -1.96$.

The Decision Process

Probability of the Observed Result and Comparison with the Prediction

From the unit normal curve table, the probability of results like the observed result occurring if the model is correct is given as:

$$p(|z| \geq 2.6) = 2(.0047) = .0094$$

where z is the value of the z score for the observed result and $z = z_{\bar{x}_o}$ in the above case.

Note that this probability is based on twice the probability for $z \geq +2.6$, that is, $2p(z \geq +2.6)$. As discussed previously, the observed value of z is known to be positive only after the sample has been taken. The probability question was "what is the probability of obtaining, just by chance if the model is true, results that are at least as deviant from the expected as the observed one is?" Since $p(z \geq +2.6) = .0047$, events are as deviant in the opposite direction which also occur only .0047 of the time. Since events with z scores $\geq +2.6$ and those with z scores ≤ -2.6 are mutually exclusive, the two probabilities must be added together. Therefore, the computed probability is $2(.0047) = .0094$.

Comparison with the prediction yields the following:

$$p(|z| \geq 2.6) < p(|z| \geq 1.96) = .05 = \alpha$$

Conclusions

Statistical Conclusion.   The abstract conclusion is one that states that the value of $z_o = +2.6$ is statistically significant, therefore reject $H_0 : \mu = a$ and accept $H_A : \mu \neq a$.

Research Conclusion.   In terms of the real world problem, the investigator must conclude that the true mean time that it takes the students to get to campus is some value other than 11.2 minutes. His observations were inconsistent with his model and he concludes that his hypothesis, $H_0 : \mu = 11.2$, is a false translation of the real value of the parameter.

Possibility of Error

Possible Statistical Error

Since no result, no matter how unlikely, is impossible under a statistical model, the experimenter knows that he may be rejecting a hypothesis that is in fact true. Occasionally he will observe samples that rarely occur by chance under the model (H_0) and interpret them as inconsistent with the model. It is necessary that this error sometimes be made to avoid making the error of failing to reject the model (or H_0) when it is really false and some other model (or H_A) is true. In the above example, the first type of error may have been made but there is no possibility that the second type of error was made.

Possible Error in Research Conclusion

Each possible statistical error has a concomitant research error. If the null hypothesis is rejected, as it was in the above example, then the conclusion is reached that the true value of the population mean is a value other than supposed. In the above case the conclusion would be that the mean time that it takes students to get to campus was not 11.2 minutes. However, the true mean might really be 11.2 minutes and, therefore, the experimenter could be making a research error in concluding that the true mean in the population is some value other than 11.2 minutes. A schematization of the above problem is given in Figure 4.6.

Probability Theory

- - - Deductions

Theorems: $\mu = E(\bar{X})$, $\sigma_{\bar{X}} = \sigma_{\bar{X}}/\sqrt{n}$, Central Limit Theorem

- - - Incorporation

Situation. A population of all students at a particular university with respect to the amount of time it takes to get to campus: Mean value indicated: 11.2 min. Sample of 35 is to be taken.

Translation ⟶

z Model for the True Mean
1) $\mu = 11.2$
2) $\sigma_{\bar{X}} = 1.5$
3) Sampling random and independent
4) $\bar{X}$ normal

- - - Deduction

Observed sample will have $-1.96(1.5) \leq \bar{X} \leq +1.96(1.5)$ (or $|z_{\bar{X}}| \geq 1.96$).

⟵ Prediction $\alpha = .05$

Sampling Distribution (transformed distribution)
(*See Figure 4.5.*)

Probability for continuous
- - - distributions

- - - Experiment

Sample of 35 yields $X_o = 15.1$ ($z_{\bar{X}o} = +2.6$). ⟶

Probability Evaluation and Comparison
$p(|z| \geq 2.6) < p(|z| \geq 1.96) = .05$
$= \alpha$

Relationship of observed value to sampling distribution.

- - - Decision Model

The value of 11.2 min/ student as a mean for the population is false. The true value is other than 11.2.

⟵ Interpretation

Statistical Conclusion. Result is statistically significant; therefore, reject $H_0: \mu = 11.2$, and accept H_A: $\mu \neq 11.2$.

- - - Nature of statistical models

Possible Error in Research Conclusion. The true value of the mean may be 11.2 min. The sample mean of 15.1 min. may be merely a rare occurrence from the population.

⟵ Interpretation

Possible Statistical Error: May have rejected a true H_0. Sample may have actually come from hypothesized population and have been merely a rare occurrence.

Figure 4.6

Note on Translation to a Model

A particular statistical model is appropriate for one type of real world situation. Various real world situations require other models, some of which will be presented later, for adequate translation. Further, it should be noted that the model only deals with a particular summary characteristic of the population. It may have been that the experimenter was interested in the median of the population. In this case $(H_0 : Md = a)$ would have been appropriate and this would have been tested by comparing it to an observed value of the median (Md_o). It is also entirely possible that the investigator will want to study a real world situation for which no adequate statistical translation exists. This naturally does not mean that the real world problem should not be investigated. It does mean that judgments about the problem may have to be made on other than a formal statistical basis.

ERROR

Types of Error

It is unfortunate that no matter what decision the experimenter makes, he runs the risk of deciding the wrong thing. For example, if the probability of the value of the observed statistic or one more extreme occurring by chance is very small, the experimenter will reject the model. However, it is possible that this rare sample did come from the assumed population. The experimenter would then be *rejecting a hypothesis which is really true*. This kind of error is called Type I error.

The other type of error occurs when the experimenter fails to reject a hypothesis that is really false. This type of error may occur when the probability of the value of the statistic or one more extreme is quite likely under the model that describes the population. In this situation the experimenter would conclude that the evidence was insufficient to reject the null hypothesis about the population. However, in failing to reject this hypothesis about the population, the experimenter may in fact be failing to reject a hypothesis that is really false. Although the evidence is insufficient to reject a hypothesis, the population from which the sample came may still be different from the assumed one. This type of error has been cleverly labeled Type II error.

The probability of Type I error is called α (alpha) and the probability of Type II error is called β (beta). Since Type I error is the probability of rejecting a hypothesis when it is true, the value of α can be set by the experimenter. Usually α is set at either .01 or .05, although these are not the only values for α that may be used, of course. If $\alpha = .01$, for example, the experimenter is saying that if a value at least as deviant as the obtained one could only occur one or fewer times out of a hundred, he is willing to reject the hypothesis and conclude that the sample really came from some other population. At the same time he is saying that he is willing to take a chance on being wrong for he knows that one out of 100 times, when the hypothesis is true, he will reject it. To state this more concisely, p(Type I error) $= \alpha$, where Type I error is rejecting a hypothesis that is really true.

It follows that p(Type II error) $= \beta$, where Type II error is the failure to reject a hypothesis that is really false. Unfortunately, there is no specific value that can be given to β unless there are only two possible values to the population parameter. This circumstance is rather unusual.

Factors that Affect β

Sample Size

If the sample size is increased, then β *will be decreased*. Since $\sigma_{\bar{x}} = \sigma_x/\sqrt{n}$, then as n increases $\sigma_{\bar{x}}$ decreases. Consequently, large sized samples will have a distribution of the sample mean that is quite a bit closer, on the average, to the true parameter since $\sigma_{\bar{x}}$ will be made small. Thus, if the true state of affairs is really different from the assumed state, it should be less likely that a false hypothesis will not be rejected.

Using pictures, the situation can be conceived as represented in Figure 4.7. Imagine that the hypothesized value of the parameter is at μ_{H_0} but that the true value is at μ_T.

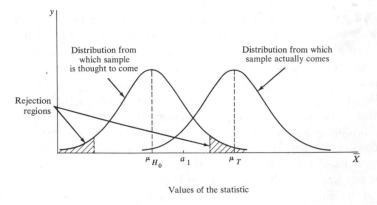

Figure 4.7

If a small sample is selected $\sigma_{\bar{x}}$ will be a fairly large value and samples may be expected to vary quite a bit from the true value. Since the expected value based on the model is at μ_{H_0}, it is quite likely that a sample will be drawn from the true population but still not deviate much from the hypothesized value. An example of this is given by a_1, in Figure 4.7. When this happens, the experimenter will fail to reject the null hypothesis. But the null hypothesis was false, hence a Type II error would have been made with β having a fairly large value.

Suppose, however, that the sample size is fairly large. Then $\sigma_{\bar{x}}$ should be relatively small. Now, even though the hypothesized value of the parameter is the same number of units from the true value as it was before, the sampling distribution of the mean is much closer around the true value of the parameter, as indicated in Figure 4.8.

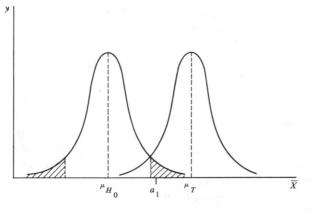

Values of the statistic

Figure 4.8

In this case the sampling distribution generated under the null hypothesis does not greatly overlap the sampling distribution that really exists. Thus, a sample selected is very likely to differ from the hypothesized value of the parameter. When this happens, the null hypothesis is rejected and no Type II error has been made. (Obviously, any time the null hypothesis is rejected, there is no chance of having failed to reject a false null hypothesis.)

To Summarize

The sample selected is one of the unique samples that it is possible to select from the true population. However, since the true population is not known, a hypothesis about the population is made. This hypothesis has a sampling distribution associated with it. The sample is then assumed to come from this distribution. If the true sampling distribution has quite different values from the hypothesized one, the obtained sample is likely to be a rare one *in terms of the hypothesized distribution.* This would result in the rejection of the null hypothesis. As the sample size increases, the values in the true sampling distribution congregate more closely around the true value of the parameter. As a result *a smaller proportion of this sampling distribution overlaps the nonrejection region of the hypothetical distribution.* Thus the probability of rejecting the null hypothesis increases.

Distance between μ_{H_0} and μ_T

It would appear to follow that the further away the true value of the parameter is from the hypothesized value, the less likely is it that one would fail to reject the null hypothesis. Hence, β is reduced in this case also. However, the experimenter has little control over the true value. He cannot manipulate this as he can the sample size.

Changes in α

It should also be apparent, or at least will be shortly, that the larger the value of α, the smaller β is. What does a large α mean? It means that even if an event is fairly likely under the null hypothesis, the hypothesis will be rejected. For example, if $\alpha = .20$, then any observed sample value which could occur 20 or fewer times out of 100, would result in the rejection of the null hypothesis. With $\alpha = .20$, the probability of Type I error must equal .20. That is, if the hypothesis is really true, 20 times out of 100 it will still be rejected. However, since the null hypothesis is more likely to be rejected with $\alpha = .20$ than with $\alpha = .05$, it must be true that it is less likely that one will *fail* to reject a hypothesis if $\alpha = .20$, than if $\alpha = .05$.

The two cases are illustrated in Figures 4.9 and 4.10. The shaded portion of the curve represents the portion of the sampling distribution from which the sample is actually drawn that overlaps the nonrejection region of the sampling distribution that is deduced from the model.

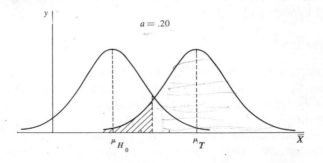

Figure 4.9

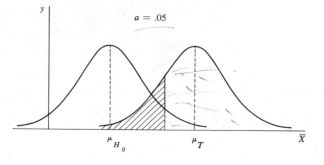

Figure 4.10

Power

A test is considered powerful if it leads to the correct decision. If H_0 is really false then the probability of making a correct decision, that is, of rejecting the false H_0, is $(1 - \beta)$. This represents the proportion of the true sampling distribution that does not overlap the nonrejection region of the hypothesized one. The smaller that β is, the larger is $(1 - \beta)$, and the more powerful is the test, where *power* is defined as $(1 - \beta)$.

SUMMARY

In the following chapters, various measures on samples will be examined. Each of these statistics will have a sampling distribution associated with it. In order to know what the function for that distribution is, restrictions on the population will have to be placed. *It must be understood that the inferences about the parameter can only be legitimately made when all the conditions of the model, except for the assumed value of the parameter, have been met. The assumptions or conditions in the model determine the function for the sampling distribution. It is only when this function is known that the probabilities of obtaining results by chance can be calculated.*

5

SOME OTHER STATISTICAL MODELS

INTRODUCTION

In this chapter, additional statistical models will be examined in which one part of the model will be the assumption that the statistic is normally distributed.

t TEST FOR THE TRUE MEAN

The z test for the true mean will not usually be a possible test. This results from the fact that either the true population variance or the true standard error of the mean must be known. Since populations are not usually measured, this value will not be available.

The best that one could hope for under these circumstances is that an estimate of the standard error might be made. Since the standard error of the mean depends on the population standard deviation, if an estimate of σ_X could be made then the estimation problem for $\sigma_{\bar{x}}$ would be solved.

A moment's reflection (and the reading of this paragraph) will indicate that the sample SD should reflect the population σ_X. If the elements in the population differ greatly from each other, then those selected in the sample should not be greatly alike. On the other hand, if there is little variance in the population, there should be relatively little in the sample. Since the population's value is unknown, the information from the sample should allow an inference about the population to be made.

The formula that is appropriate for this is: $est\ \sigma^2_X = SD^2_X[n/(n-1)]$. This is the best guess that can be made of the population variance from the information in the sample. Then $est\ \sigma_X$ is taken to be $\sqrt{SD^2_X[n/(n-1)]}$ $= SD_X\sqrt{n/(n-1)}$. Because $\sigma_{\bar{x}} = \sigma_X/\sqrt{n}$, it follows that $est\ \sigma_{\bar{x}} = est$ $\sigma_X/\sqrt{n} = [SD_X\sqrt{n/(n-1)}]/\sqrt{n} = SD_X/\sqrt{n-1}$. Thus the standard error is estimated from the standard deviation of the sample. This does not seem unreasonable either. The further apart the individuals in the population are from each other, the more would sample means of a particular size be expected to differ from each other. But this variability in the population has been shown to be reflected in the *SD* of the sample. Hence, a guess about how much sample means would be expected to differ from each other should be possible knowing *SD*. Of course, the variability is also dependent on *n*, the size of the sample, since large samples would be expected to differ less from each other than would small samples.

All of this is fine for the problem of estimating the standard error. However, the problem of standardizing the scores is more difficult than previously. In order to understand why the problem arises it will be necessary to examine the mathematical concept of *transformations*.

Linear Transformations

Previously, $y = f(x)$ has been explained as meaning that y is a function of x. This means that for each value of x there is a value of y that is determined. $f(x)$ turned out to represent a rule that was to be used to compute or determine the value of y. For example, $f(x)$ might be equal to x^2. Then if x were 5, the rule would say that 25 was to be the value of y.

With this background the idea of a linear transformation is not very difficult. A linear transformation is merely a particular type of rule. Anytime $y = f(x)$ is of the form $y = ax + b$, *then y is said to be a linear transformation of x.* x of course is a variable, and a and b are constants.

Some examples of linear transformations are: (1) $y = 5x + 3$, (2) $y = 5x$ (in this case $b = 0$), (3) $y = 6$ (in this case $a = 0$ so that every value of x determines the same value of y).

Besides the two constants a and b, the most obvious characteristic of the linear transformation equation is that x is raised to the first power

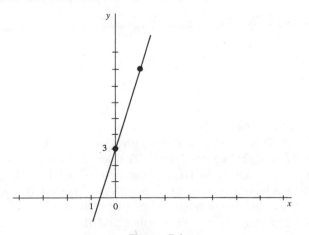

Figure 5.1

and only the first power. This, in fact, is where the name "linear" comes from. If one were to plot $y = f(x)$ and $f(x)$ were of the form $ax + b$, then the graph would always be a straight line. Suppose $y = 5x + 3$. Then the graph would look as it does in Figure 5.1.

If $y = 6$, then the graph would look like the one in Figure 5.2.

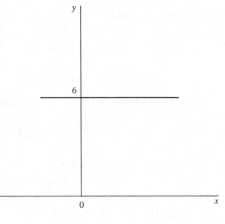

Figure 5.2

In both cases the result is a straight line, as one would expect if the transformation were really a linear one.

By definition, no transformation of $y = f(x)$ is linear if x is raised to some power other than 1. For example, $f(x) = x^2$ and $f(x) = ax^3 + b$ are not linear transformations.

z is a linear transformation of the x axis. Originally, the x axis scores were given in terms of $\bar{X}$. The $\bar{X}$ scores are now transformed to z scores, that is, $z_{\bar{x}} = f(\bar{X})$. However, $f(\bar{X})$ is a linear function as will be apparent from the discussion that follows.

z is of the form $[\bar{X} - E(\bar{X})]/\sigma_{\bar{x}}$. This can be rewritten as,

$$z = \frac{1(\bar{X})}{\sigma\bar{x}} - \frac{E(\bar{X})}{\sigma\bar{x}}$$

This does not change anything, it is just another way of writing z. (For example, $(5 + 7)/6 = 12/6 = 2$. This can also be obtained by writing $5/6 + 7/6 = 12/6 = 2$. However, $5/(6 + 7)$ does not equal $5/6 + 5/7$, since $5/(6 + 7) = 5/13$ which is equal to 0.38 but $5/6 + 5/7 = 0.83 + 0.71 = 1.54$). This appears to be of the form $a\bar{X} + b$ with $a = 1/\sigma_{\bar{x}}$ and $b = E(\bar{X})/\sigma_{\bar{x}}$. Both a and b would have to be constants since the standard deviation of a distribution can only be a single number and therefore a constant. The expected value is a single number and, hence, also a constant.

As a result, it is the x axis that undergoes the transformation. Transforming the scores in this way uniformly changes the units of the x axis. Symbolically, this can be represented as $z = a\bar{X} + b$. The $\bar{X}$ scores have been converted to z scores. The original distribution, $y = f(x) =$ the normal curve, does not have its shape altered when the scores in which it is plotted are altered by a linear transformation. This is true of curves of all shapes. Therefore, transforming any distribution of scores from the original scores to z scores does not affect the shape of the distribution. The scores themselves are altered so that the units along the x axis are also changed. Nonlinear transformations of the scores do alter the shape of the distribution. Cases where this occurs will be examined next.

t—A Nonlinear Transformation

In the z test for a true mean the original sampling distribution of the mean was normal. The transformation that was effected on the scores was a linear transformation of the form $y = ax + b$, and did not affect the shape of the distribution.

In the case that is now being considered, the sampling distribution of the mean is still normal. However the transformation is no longer linear. To see this point consider what would be done to standardize the original scores in the sampling distribution.

As before, the mean of the distribution would be subtracted from each of the scores. Now, however, it is no longer possible to divide by the standard error since that is not known. The best that can be done is to divide by the estimate of the standard error. But this estimate is based on the standard deviation of the sample. Hence, it will vary from sample to sample. Then the denominator will be a variable, dependent on the sample, rather than a constant. Thus, although $z_X = (X - \mu)/\sigma_X$ or $z_{\bar{X}} = [\bar{X} - E(\bar{X})]/\sigma_{\bar{X}}$ were linear transformations on X or $\bar{X}$, $(X - \mu)/est\ \sigma_X$ or $[\bar{X} - E(\bar{X})]/est\ \sigma_{\bar{X}}$ are not linear transformations on X or $\bar{X}$ because the estimate differs from sample to sample. If an attempt is made to put the above ratio into the form of a linear transformation the following is obtained:

$$\frac{1\,(\bar{X})}{est\ \sigma_{\bar{X}}} - \frac{E(\bar{X})}{est\ \sigma_{\bar{X}}}$$

Now, neither $a = 1/est\ \sigma_{\bar{X}}$ or $b = -E(\bar{X})/est\ \sigma_{\bar{X}}$ is a constant.

Note that this transformed distribution could be obtained experimentally by selecting a sample, subtracting from its mean the mean of the sampling distribution, and then dividing by the estimate of the standard error based on this sample. Obviously, upon repeating this procedure over and over again the SD's of the samples would vary and hence so would the estimates.

Fortunately, if the original distribution of scores is normal the distribution of the transformed scores can be obtained, even though this transformed distribution is not normal.

t Distributions

The distribution that describes the transformed statistic when the denominator is an estimate of the standard error is the *t* distribution. Unlike the *z* transformation of a normal curve, there is more than one *t* distribution. This is due to the fact that the variability of the estimates depends on the sample size. Thus, the shape of the *t* distribution also depends on the sample size.

To understand this argument consider that the estimate of the standard error is based on the *SD* of the sample. For small samples, the *SD*'s would differ more from each other than for large samples. Hence the variability of the estimates of the standard error should be greater if the samples are small than if they are large.

But $t = [\bar{X} - E(\bar{X})]/ \; est \; \sigma_{\bar{x}}$. Since the distribution of the sample means must be normal, and since $E(\bar{X})$ is a constant whose value is determined by the hypothesis about the population parameter, it seems reasonable that the shape of the *t* distribution will be dependent on the variability of the denominator.

There are, in fact, a whole family of *t* curves. Each curve is determined by the *degrees of freedom* upon which the estimate of the standard error is based. The degrees of freedom are closely related to the sample size but do not equal it.

Degrees of Freedom

The idea of the degrees of freedom is related to the number of scores that are free to vary. The mean of a group of scores uses up one degree of freedom. To see this consider a group of five scores for which $\bar{X} = 12$. Four of these scores can be any numbers (within limits), for example, 8, 14, 4 and 9. But if the mean of the group is really 12 then the last score is determined. It must be 25 because if $\bar{X} = 12$ and $n = 5$, then $n\bar{X}$ must $= 60$. (Remember that $\bar{X} = \Sigma X/n$.)

Using this idea it becomes easier to understand why the shape of the *t* distribution is dependent on the degrees of freedom upon which the estimate is based rather than the number of scores. Obviously, the degrees of freedom will depend on the sample size. In fact, for the case of the *t* distribution that is being discussed, the degrees of freedom are one less than the sample size. Perhaps the best way to see why this is so is by considering that the estimate of the standard error is dependent on the *SD* of the sample. But the *SD* of the sample is based on the deviations of the scores from their mean. It has already been indicated in Chapter 2 that the mean of the algebraic deviations from the mean equals 0. Therefore, all the deviations are free to vary but the last one. This last deviation must be a value such that the mean deviation equals 0. Since *est* $\sigma_{\bar{x}}$ is dependent on *SD* and the *SD* is based on deviations from the sample mean, the degrees of freedom for $t = [\bar{X} - E(\bar{X})]/est\ \sigma_{\bar{x}}$ is $n - 1$ where n is the sample size.

It is always necessary to know the degrees of freedom in evaluating a t value, because the shape of the t curve depends on the degrees of freedom used in estimating $\sigma_{\bar{x}}$.

In more precise language, the rule which relates the y axis to the x axis in the case of t is $y = f(t) = G(\nu)\,[1 + t^2/\nu]^{-(\nu+1)/2}$ where ν is the degrees of freedom. Obviously, changes in ν will change the rule and therefore change the shape of the distribution.

Computing Probabilities on the *t* curve

Fortunately, the proportion of the total area beyond particular points on the t curves have been tabled. Because there is a different curve for each value of the degrees of freedom, not as many points on each curve are given as with the normal curve of z scores. Generally, those values which are common α levels are given in the tables.

No matter what the value of the degrees of freedom (*df*) is, the t distribution, like the normal, is symmetric. The mean, median, and mode are all at 0. The main difference is that the t curve comes to a sharper peak than the normal. This means that a greater proportion of the total area of the t distribution is beyond a particular t value than is beyond a z score on a normal curve with the same value. That is, $p(|t_{n-1}| \geq a) > p(|z| \geq a)$, where t_{n-1} represents t with $n - 1$ degrees of freedom.

As the *df* increase in value, the t curve approaches a normal curve. It may help to understand this by remembering that increasing *df* means larger sized samples. But the larger the sample size, the less variable would the *SD*'s be, and the less variable the *SD*'s the less variable would be *est* $\sigma_{\bar{x}}$. To state it another way, *est* $\sigma_{\bar{x}}$ tends toward a constant as the sample size increases. (Mathematically, this might be written *est* $\sigma_{\bar{x}} \to c$ as $n \to \infty$.) However, if the denominator of the t ratio were a constant and the sampling distribution of $\bar{X}$ were normal, $[\bar{X} - E(\bar{X})]/est\ \sigma_{\bar{x}}$ would be a linear transformation on $\bar{X}$ and therefore a z transformation of a normal distribution. Thus, as *est* $\sigma_{\bar{x}} \to c$, the t distribution tends toward the normal distribution. For infinite degrees of freedom the t distribution is equal to the normal distribution.

Figure 5.3 illustrates the relationships among the t curves and the unit normal curve. Also shown are the number of transformed units

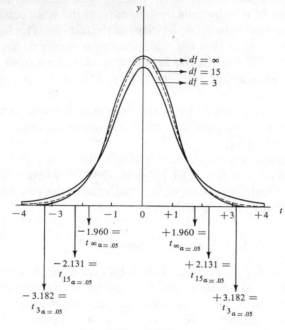

Figure 5.3

away from the mean a score must fall before the probability of obtaining scores at least that deviant is equal to .05.

The Model for the t Test for the True Mean

The following set of conditions determine the function for the t transformation of the sampling distribution of means. In other words, given the following model, a theorem that has been proven within the abstract system is that the distribution of the sample means based on samples of size n is described by the rule, $f(t)$, which has been called the t distribution with $n - 1$ degrees of freedom.

1) $\mu = a$
2) $est\ \sigma_{\bar{x}} = SD/\sqrt{n - 1} = b$
3) Sampling random and independent
4) Sampling distribution of X is normal
5) $df = n - 1 = c$

When the above conditions have been fulfilled, the expected value of the statistic and the values of the statistic and their associated probabilities are determined.

In the above model, condition 4 is stricter than the analogous condition in the *z* test for the true mean. Condition 4 states that the scores in the population must be normally distributed. This, of course, will result in the values of $\bar{X}$ being normally distributed. In the *z* test, the requirement that $\bar{X}$ be distributed normally could be met under certain conditions even though the underlying population of scores was not normally distributed.

The reason for the requirement in the *t* test that X be normally distributed is based on the fact that the same sample is being used to make two estimates. The mean of the sample, $\bar{X}$, is used to estimate one parameter, namely, the mean of the population, and the *SD* of the sample is being used to estimate another parameter, the population standard deviation. In order for the ratio $[\bar{X} - E(\bar{X})]/est \; \sigma_{\bar{x}}$ to be distributed as *t*, it is necessary for the two estimates to be independent of each other. An important theorem in statistics states that these two estimates will be independent of each other if and only if the samples are drawn from a population in which the underlying scores are normally distributed.

As before, the condition that the population be normally distributed is difficult to obtain in many experimental situations. As a practical matter, the condition that the statistic be normally distributed may be substituted for the requirement of a normal population. If samples are small, this can only occur when the underlying population is normal, but if samples are large, then the statistic, which in this case is $\bar{X}$, will be normally distributed. As before, $n \geq 30$ will be the rule for deciding that the distribution of the statistic has met the requirement that it be normally distributed. Of course, if this requirement is substituted for the normality of the population, the independence of the sample means from the sample standard deviations is not assured. However, the larger samples that are required to obtain the normality of the statistic when the underlying distribution is not itself normal partly compensates for the lack of independence between sample means and sample standard deviations. As a result, under the condition of larger samples, the sampling distribution is still very nearly equal to that of *t* with $n - 1$ degrees of freedom. The revised form of the model that may be used is:

1) $\mu = a$
2) $est \; \sigma_{\bar{x}} = b$
3) Sampling random and independent
4) $\bar{X}$ normal
5) $df = n - 1 = c$

In any particular research problem the experimenter is generally interested in testing the hypothesis about the value of the parameter. Therefore, it is again necessary to make sure that all of the conditions of the model except this one have been met. If these conditions have not been met, then a rare or unexpected outcome to the experiment can result only in rejection of the whole model and not necessarily in one particular aspect of it.

An Example

Consider the problem examined earlier. The experimental hypothesis was that the average time it took students to walk to campus was 11.2 minutes, $\mu = 11.2$ minutes. Suppose that the true population standard deviation, σ_X, was not known and that $\sigma_{\bar{x}}$ had to be estimated. The first problem would be to compute the standard deviation of the sample of 35 cases. For simplicity, suppose the computation resulted in $SD = 3$ minutes. Then $est\ \sigma_{\bar{x}} = SD/\sqrt{n-1} = 3/\sqrt{35-1} = 3/\sqrt{34} = 3/5.9 = 0.51$ minutes. The sampling distribution of the means can be considered normal since the sample size is 35. The degrees of freedom are $35 - 1 = 34$. Therefore, if the sampling were conducted randomly and independently the sampling distribution of the means would be normally distributed about an expected value of 11.2, with an estimated standard error of .51. This distribution would be as pictured in Figure 5.4. The

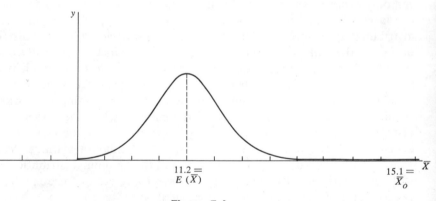

$11.2 =$
$E\ (\bar{X})$

$15.1 =$
$\bar{X}_o$

Figure 5.4

transformed statistic would be t with 34 degrees of freedom (see Figure 5.5). The obtained value of t_{34} would be:

$$t_{34_o} = \frac{15.1 - 11.2}{.51} = \frac{+3.9}{.51} = +7.6$$

From this the evaluation of the probability is:

$$p(|t_{34}| \geq 7.6) < p(|t_{34}| \geq 2.03) = .05 = \alpha$$

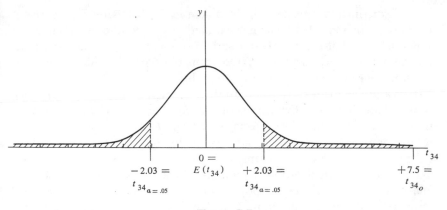

Figure 5.5

Since the decision model is (1) $H_A: \mu \neq 11.2$ minutes, and (2) $\alpha = .05$, it is readily seen that the observed value of the statistic is so deviant that it, or ones more deviant than it was from the expected value, are unlikely to occur by chance if the hypotheses of the model are true. It is therefore the experimenter's conclusion to accept the alternative hypothesis that $\mu \neq 11.2$.

This decision of course means that the experimenter has concluded that the sample he selected really came from a population other than the one he hypothesized. In fact, since the other conditions of the model were met, the population from which the sample came differs specifically from the hypothesized one with regard to the value of the parameter.

By this decision the experimenter cannot possibly have made Type II error. That is, there is no chance that he failed to reject a hypothesis that really was false. There is, however, a possibility that Type I error was made and a true hypothesis was really rejected, since the observed sample could have been a rare one from the assumed population. The probability of Type I error for the above problem is .05 which is the α level.

z TEST FOR THE DIFFERENCE BETWEEN MEANS

It frequently happens that the investigator does not have a hypothesis about a single population that he wishes to test. Instead, he is interested in determining whether two experimental treatments (or two conditions) differ in their effectiveness. The situation that is designed to attack this problem is one in which there are two groups, one under each condition. In experimental situations these groups are frequently a control group and an experimental group.

The experimenter translates his problem in the following way: If there is really a difference between the two methods or conditions, then were I able to test all of the population under one condition, I would find that on the average these scores differed from the scores of the population when it was subjected to the second condition.

This argument can be translated into a null hypothesis of $H_0: \mu_1 - \mu_2 = 0$ and an alternative hypothesis of $H_A: \mu_1 - \mu_2 \neq 0$. The two populations are the collection of objects with respect to the scores that they receive on treatment A and the same collection of objects with respect to the scores they receive on treatment B.

However, the usual problem remains. If the investigator is generally unable to measure the entire population, he certainly cannot expect to measure two entire populations. To solve this problem it is necessary to define a new statistic. This new statistic is $(\bar{X}_1 - \bar{X}_2)$, that is, the difference between sample means where the difference is taken in the same order as is given in the null hypothesis. The argument is completely analogous to that already given. Its form is: If two populations have means that differ from each other then the difference between the means of samples where one is selected from each population should reflect this difference. More specifically, their difference should certainly be greater on the average than that which would be obtained from samples selected from populations with the same mean.

The mathematical problem is again to set up a model, or set of hypotheses, about the population from which both the expected value of the statistic and its sampling distribution are determined. The experimenter then observes one particular value of the statistic. If values like this one are unlikely given the hypotheses, then he concludes that the population is other than he hypothesized. If the probability of the observed value of the statistic or one more deviant from the expected is large, then he would again conclude that the evidence is not against the hypothesis.

The major difference is that the observed statistic in this case is a difference between sample means and that the conclusion about the null hypothesis deals with whether the assumed *difference* between the two population means is false or cannot be said to be false. In fact, the critical determination in this statistical test is not about the possible falsity of an assumption about the population. Instead it is an attempt to determine the possible falsity of the assumed *relation* between two population means.

It is not necessary that the assumed relation be one of equality. In some cases a particular difference may be postulated and the investigator is interested in determining if that specified difference is false. Thus the general form of the null hypothesis is $H_0: \mu_1 - \mu_2 = a$.

The Sampling Distribution of the Differences
Between Sample Means

The problem of evaluating probabilities for the observed values of the statistic $(\bar{X}_1 - \bar{X}_2)$ would not be particularly difficult if the statistic were normally distributed. Then if the expected value of the statistic as well as the standard error of the sampling distribution could be determined from the model, the evaluation would be the same as that used in the z test for the mean. Of course, the samples will have to be selected by a process that is random and independent.

Before examining some of these aspects in more detail, consider how the sampling distribution of the statistic $(\bar{X}_1 - \bar{X}_2)$ is obtained. Since two populations are involved, two sampling distributions of sample means could also be obtained. There is no requirement that the two samples be of the same size, so suppose they are not. Let n_1 be the size of the sample taken from the first population and n_2 be the size of the sample taken from the second.

The two population distributions could be represented as shown in Figures 5.6 and 5.7. The sampling distribution could be represented as drawn in Figures 5.8 and 5.9.

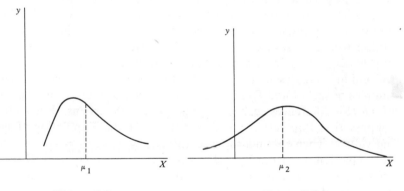

| Figure 5.6 | Figure 5.7 |

The next task is to obtain the sampling distribution of $(\bar{X}_1 - \bar{X}_2)$. This distribution consists of all of the differences between pairs of sample means where one sample from each pair is a unique sample from each of the above distributions. Another way to describe this distribution is: *The sampling distribution is the probability distribution of all possible differences between the means of all the pairs of unique samples of size n_1 and n_2 respectively where one sample is drawn from each of the populations.* Equivalently, the sampling distribution is the probability distribution of the differences between the means of pairs of samples of size n_1 and n_2

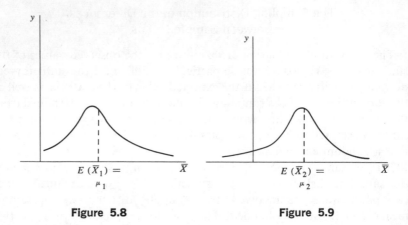

Figure 5.8   **Figure 5.9**

respectively obtained by repeated random and independent sampling of samples of size n_1 from Population I and of size n_2 from Population II.

Conceptually, the sampling distribution can be considered to be obtained by taking the mean of a unique sample from the first sampling distribution. Then, from this mean would be subtracted, one at a time, the means of each of the unique samples in the second distribution. Then a second unique sample would be selected from the first distribution and from its mean each of the means of the samples in the second distribution would be subtracted. This process would be continued until all of the unique samples in the first distribution had been paired with all of the unique samples in the second. Obviously, if there were R unique samples of size n_1 and S unique samples of size n_2 there would be a total of $(R)(S)$ differences between pairs of sample means. For example, suppose that Population I had 6 individuals and Population II had 5 individuals. Then consider the case where $n_1 = 5$ and $n_2 = 2$. The number of unique samples from Population I, if $n_1 = 5$, would be 6. If $n_2 = 2$, the number of unique samples from the second population would be 10. Therefore, the number of differences, $(\bar{X}_1 - \bar{X}_2)$, between the means of pairs of unique samples where one member of the pair comes from each population is $(6)(10) = 60$.

Experimentally, the sampling distribution of the differences between sample means would be obtained by randomly and independently selecting a sample of size n_1 from the first population and then subtracting from this sample mean the mean of a sample of size n_2 randomly and independently selected from Population II. Repetition of this process would, after a long, long time (forever is considered a long time), yield a sampling distribution equivalent to that obtained by the conceptual process.

Expected Value of $(\bar{X}_1 - \bar{X}_2)$

The expected value of the above sampling distribution is quite readily obtained. Since $\mu_1 = a_1$, then $E(\bar{X}_1) = a_1$. If $\mu_2 = a_2$ then $E(\bar{X}_2) = a_2$. Fortunately, since $E(\bar{X}_1) - E(\bar{X}_2) = E(\bar{X}_1 - \bar{X}_2)$, the difference that is assumed to exist between the two populations determines the difference that is expected between the sample means.

Standard Error of the Distribution

Previously it was stated that $\sigma_{\bar{x}}$ is dependent on the population standard deviation, σ_X, and the sample size n. It seems reasonable to expect that $\sigma_{(\bar{X}_1 - \bar{X}_2)}$, which is the standard error of $(\bar{X}_1 - \bar{X}_2)$, would be dependent on both the variability of the distribution of X_1 and that of X_2 as well as n_1 and n_2. The relationship between $\sigma_{(\bar{X}_1 - \bar{X}_2)}$ and the population variances and samples sizes is given precisely by

$$\sigma_{(\bar{X}_1 - \bar{X}_2)} = \sqrt{\frac{\sigma^2_{X_1}}{n_1} + \frac{\sigma^2_{X_2}}{n_2}}$$

This can also be written as

$$\sigma_{(\bar{X}_1 - \bar{X}_2)} = \sqrt{\sigma^2_{\bar{x}_1} + \sigma^2_{\bar{x}_2}}$$

since

$$\frac{\sigma^2_{X_1}}{n_1} = \sigma^2_{\bar{x}_1} \quad \text{and} \quad \frac{\sigma^2_{X_2}}{n_2} = \sigma^2_{\bar{x}_2}$$

Normality of the Distribution

In order that the z transformation of the statistic be normally distributed the distribution of the statistic itself must also be. It has already been pointed out that if the underlying populations are normally distributed then the distributions of the means will be normally distributed no matter what the sample size is. Further, for samples of sufficiently large size, the means will be normally distributed no matter what the shape of the underlying population distribution happens to be.

One important fact concerning the distribution of $(\bar{X}_1 - \bar{X}_2)$ is: *If two distributions are each normally distributed, then the distribution of their differences is also normal.* Hence, if $\bar{X}_1$ and $\bar{X}_2$ are both normally distributed then the distribution of $(\bar{X}_1 - \bar{X}_2)$ is also normal.

However, in order to obtain a normal distribution for $(\bar{X}_1 - \bar{X}_2)$ it is not necessary that $\bar{X}_1$ and $\bar{X}_2$ each be normally distributed. It is generally sufficient if $(n_1 + n_2)$ are ≥ 30. This requirement may sound similar to the requirement that n be ≥ 30 to insure that the distribution of sample means be approximately normal.

The question that the more inquisitive may pose is this: If the requirement is merely that n_1 and n_2 together be greater than 30 then both n_1 and n_2 could each be < 30 (say 15 and 16). This could mean that neither the sampling distribution of $\bar{X}_1$ or of $\bar{X}_2$ is normally distributed. But then, how is it possible to obtain a normal distribution of the differences when these differences are between two distributions neither one of which may be normally distributed?

Part of the answer to this question depends on the observation that the number of differences is far greater than the number of means in either one of the sampling distributions alone. Remember that the number of differences is the product of the two numbers of sample means in the separate distributions. If there were 1000 unique samples in each of the two distributions of means, there would be 1000×1000 or 1 million differences based on the unique samples. The fact that an increase in the number of points in the distribution results in a distribution that is close to the normal is quite consistent with the earlier discussion about sample means. As was pointed out early in Chapter 2, the number of unique samples is far greater than the number of individuals in the population. Thus, for samples of size 30 (the minimum size that was needed for an approximately normal distribution of means), there would be a far greater number of unique samples than of individuals in the population. This increase in the number of points in the distribution was one reason that an underlying non-normal population could yield a normal distribution of sample means. Similarly, although each of the underlying sampling distributions of means might not be normal, the increase in the number of points for the sampling distribution of differences is one factor that allows it to be normal, provided $(n_1 + n_2) \geq 30$.

It should also be clear that in either case the size of the samples that is needed to approach a normal sampling distribution depends on how deviant the original distribution is from normal. If the population distribution is very close to a normal one, then the sample size would not have to be as large as 30 before the sampling distribution of means would be normal. Similarly, if the distribution of $\bar{X}_1$ and $\bar{X}_2$ are each very close to a normal distribution, then $(n_1 + n_2)$ might not have to be as large as 30 to insure that the distribution of $(\bar{X}_1 - \bar{X}_2)$ is normal. In the absence of specific information, it is best to use 30 as the division point. One can almost always be sure then that no matter how deviant the underlying distribution is from the normal, the distribution of the means, or the differences between means, will be normally, or very close to normally, distributed.

The Transformed Distribution

As is true for the linear transformation of any normal distribution, the resulting transformed distribution is also normal. In the z test for the differences between means the transformation is given by $z = [(\bar{X}_1 - \bar{X}_2) - E(\bar{X}_1 - \bar{X}_2)]/\sigma_{(\bar{X}_1 - \bar{X}_2)}$. The only change from the diagrams for the z test for a true mean is in the labeling of the x axis for the distribution of the actual statistic. The two distributions are illustrated in Figure 5.10.

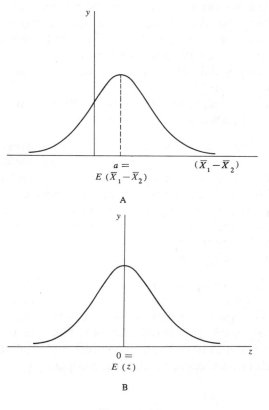

$$a = E(\bar{X}_1 - \bar{X}_2)$$

$$(\bar{X}_1 - \bar{X}_2)$$

A

$$0 = E(z)$$

B

Figure 5.10

An Example

The Situation

Suppose that a market researcher is interested in determining if color has anything to do with the amount of a particular laundry soap consumers use. In order to investigate this possibility, he arranges to have the same product put into two types of boxes. The boxes are identical in size, shape, and format except that the major color of one is red and of the other green.

As customers come through the stores in a particular city, each is asked if they have a home laundry machine. From among those that say yes, two random samples of size 150 are selected. Each person in one sample is given a red box and each person in the other sample a green one.

The researcher then follows each subject home (with their permission of course). He notes the amount of soap each subject uses from the box to do an eight-pound load of laundry. The sample that uses the red box averages 4.25 ounces of soap and those that use the green box average 3.86 ounces. For illustrative purposes it will be supposed that the variances of the two populations are known with $\sigma^2_{X_1} = 3.2$ and $\sigma^2_{X_2} = 3.0$. The α level was set at .01.

As with the previous problem that involved the z test for the true mean, this problem will be worked completely.

Defining the Real World Population.   In this case two populations are being investigated. One sample has been drawn from the population that consists of all of the people who own home laundry machines, who enter the store within a particular time span, and who use the red-boxed laundry soap. The other sample has been drawn from the population that consists of a similar group of elements but who use the green-boxed laundry soap. Both groups are scored with respect to the amount of soap that is used for an eight-pound load of wash.

The Research Question.   The researcher is trying to determine if there is a differential effect on the amount of soap that is used as a result of the different colors of the boxes. In this case he can be concerned specifically only about the possible differential effect of red and green. A large difference between the means of the two samples will tend to support the notion of a differential effect for the entire population.

Translation into the Model

The Model of the Population.   The model that appears appropriate for translating the real situation is:

1) $H_0 : \mu_1 - \mu_2 = 0$

2) $\sigma_{(\bar{X}_1 - \bar{X}_2)} = \sqrt{\dfrac{\sigma^2_{X_1}}{n_1} + \dfrac{\sigma^2_{X_2}}{n_2}} = \sqrt{\dfrac{3.2}{150} + \dfrac{3.0}{150}} = \sqrt{\dfrac{6.2}{150}} = \sqrt{.0413} = .203$

3) Each sample randomly and independently selected

4) $(\bar{X}_1 - \bar{X}_2)$ normal

Again, the test concerns the null hypothesis so that the other conditions must be shown to have been met. $\sigma_{(\bar{X}_1 - \bar{X}_2)}$ is known precisely because

$\sigma^2_{X_1}$ and $\sigma^2_{X_2}$ were given. The R and I sampling condition was met because that is the way it was done. Finally, $(\bar{X}_1 - \bar{X}_2)$ is normal because $(n_1 + n_2) = 300$ (and 300 is larger than 30).

The Decision Model. $H_A : \mu_1 - \mu_2 \neq 0$, and $\alpha = .01$.

Deductions from the Population Model

The sampling distribution of the statistic is deduced as normal with $\sigma_{(\bar{X}_1 - \bar{X}_2)} = .203$. The expected value of the statistic is determined from the null hypothesis to be $\mu_1 - \mu_2 = E(\bar{X}_1 - \bar{X}_2) = 0$. The diagrams of the actual statistic (the differences between pairs of sample means) and the transformed statistic (the normal distribution of z, the unit normal curve) are given in Figure 5.11.

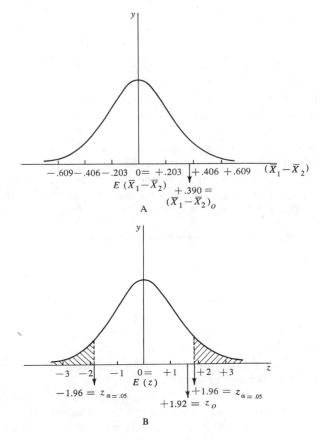

Figure 5.11

Predictions from the Population Model

Since the observed value of $(\bar{X}_1 - \bar{X}_2)$ is given by $(\bar{X}_1 - \bar{X}_2)_o = (4.25 - 3.86) = .39$, then

$$z_{(\bar{X}_1 - \bar{X}_2)_o = .39} = \frac{(\bar{X}_1 - \bar{X}_2) - E(\bar{X}_1 - \bar{X}_2)}{\sigma_{(\bar{X}_1 - \bar{X}_2)}} = \frac{0.39 - 0}{.203} = +1.92$$

If the model is really an accurate translation of the real situation then the predicted value of z is given by $|z| \leq 2.58$ (since $\alpha = .01$ is used to determine consistency).

The Decision Process

Probability of the Observed Result and Comparison with the Prediction. From the unit normal curve tables,

$$p(|z| \geq 1.92) = 2\,(.027) = .054$$

Comparison with the prediction yields

$$p(|z| \geq 1.92) > p(|z| \geq 2.58) = .01 = \alpha$$

Conclusions. Statistical Conclusion. $z_o = +1.92$ is not significant. Therefore, fail to reject H_0. H_A cannot be accepted.

Research Conclusion. The experimenter concludes that a difference in sample means of 0.39 is not unlikely (in terms of the α level) when samples are drawn from populations in which the true difference is 0 and the samples are each of size 150. The observation is consistent with the model. Therefore, he cannot reject the hypothesis that there is no differential effect on the average amount of soap used as a result of the colors red vs. green. Finally, he cannot accept the proposition that these two colors make a difference.

Possibility of Error

Possible Statistical Error. It is possible that Type II error may have been made and a false hypothesis may not have been rejected. This is possible because although the sample result is consistent with the model in which $H_0 : \mu_1 - \mu_2 = 0$, it is also consistent with many other models, for example, one in which $H_0 : \mu_1 - \mu_2 = +0.39$. $H_0 : \mu_1 - \mu_2 = 0$ may be false. The probability of Type II error cannot be ascertained. There is no possibility of having made Type I error, (rejecting a hypothesis that is really true), since H_0 was not rejected.

Possible Error in Research Conclusion. The colors may actually make a difference, even though the sample result is not inconsistent with the hypothesis that they do not. A schematic representation of this problem is given in Figure 5.12.

Note on Experimental Design

The above investigation does not really tell which color is preferred. Had the researcher allowed people to choose the box they preferred from the shelves, he would have been unable to investigate his problem, which concerned the amount of soap actually used to do a wash. This is so because it is possible that twice as many customers would have chosen one, say red, over the other. Then, even if the *average* had been less for the red group, the *amount* used might have been greater. If the investigator felt that brand loyalty was not affected by the color, that is, that just as many people would prefer the brand if red were used than if green were used, then the study was an appropriate one to determine if the *amount* used was affected by the color.

Further, had the customers been allowed to choose the color preferred from the shelves, a problem involving frequencies of choice would have arisen. The investigator would probably have been unable to translate this problem to a statistical model since the models presented thus far have only dealt with measures on the sample (statistics) that involve means. Later in the text some models appropriate for frequencies will be presented. In fact, the question about which color is preferred will become an answerable research question.

t TEST FOR THE DIFFERENCE BETWEEN MEANS

Theoretical Basis

The problem that arises when the variances of the population are not known is similar to that discussed under the *t* test for a true mean. In this case, the standard error of the statistic must be estimated. This estimate will be based on the standard deviations of the two samples. Again, in order for this estimate to be independent of the value of the sample mean in the numerator, one requirement of the model is that the populations from which the samples are selected be normally distributed. As in the *t* test for a true mean, the degrees of freedom must be specified. For the *t* test for the difference between means, the degrees of freedom are $n_1 + n_2 - 2$ since one degree of freedom is lost for each sample. That is, the estimate of the standard error is based on the number of observations in each sample but one observation in each sample is not independent of the other observations in the sample.

Essentially, the major difference between the models of the *t* test for the true mean and the *t* test for the difference between means is the requirement of the latter that the variances of the populations from which

REAL WORLD		ABSTRACT WORLD

Probability Theory

$\mid$ - - Deductions

Theorems — Example: $E(\bar{X}_1 - \bar{X}_2)$
$= \mu_1 - \mu_2$

$\mid$ - - Incorporation

Situation. Home laundry machine users in a particular city who use red box or who use green box with respect to amount of soap used for an 8-pound load: Two samples (each of 150) taken to determine if two populations differ on the average.	Translation $\longrightarrow$	*z Model for Differences Between Means* 1) H_0: $\mu_1 - \mu_2 = 0$ 2) $\sigma_{(\bar{X}_1 - \bar{X}_2)} =$ $\sqrt{\sigma_{\bar{X}_1}^2 / n_1 + \sigma_{\bar{X}_2}^2 / n_2} = .203$ 3) Sampling random and independent 4) $(\bar{X}_1 - \bar{X}_2)$ normal

$\mid$ - - Deductions

Observed value of $\bar{X}_1 - \bar{X}_2$ will be $= -2.58$ (.203) $\leq \bar{X}_1 - \bar{X}_2 \leq$ $+2.58(.203)$ or $\|z_{(\bar{X}_1 - \bar{X}_2)}\| \leq 2.58$	Prediction $\alpha = .01$ $\longleftarrow$	*Sampling Distribution (transformed statistic)* (See Figure 5.11B.)

Probability for continuous
$\mid$ - - distributions

$\mid$ - - Experiment

$n_1 = n_2 = 150$ $(\bar{X}_1 - \bar{X}_2)_o = +0.39$ $z_{(\bar{X}_1 - \bar{X}_2)o} =$ $+1.92$	Relationship of observed value to sampling distribution. $\longrightarrow$	*Probability Evaluation and Comparison* $p(\|z\| \geq 1.92) > p(\|z\| \geq 2.58) =$ $.01 = \alpha$

$\mid$ - - Decision Model

The value of 0 as the difference between the means of the two populations cannot be said to be false; thus research hypothesis that color makes a difference cannot be accepted.	Interpretation $\longleftarrow$	*Statistical Conclusion.* Result is not statistically significant; therefore fail to reject H_0: $\mu_1 - \mu_2 = 0$ and do not accept H_A: $\mu_1 - \mu_2 \neq 0$.

$\mid$ - - Nature of statistical models

Possible Error in Research Conclusion. Color may actually make a difference, even though the sample result is not inconsistent with the hypothesis that it does not.	Interpretation $\longleftarrow$	*Possible Statistical Error.* May have failed to reject a false H_0 (Type II error). Statistic, although not inconsistent with Null hypothesis, H_0: $\mu_1 - \mu_2 = 0$, is also not inconsistent with other hypotheses, for example, H_0: $\mu_1 - \mu_2 = +.39$.

Figure 5.12

the samples were drawn be equal. The full model includes the following conditions:

1) $\mu_1 - \mu_2 = a$
2) *est* $\sigma_{(\bar{X}_1 - \bar{X}_2)} = b$
3) Sampling random and independent
4) X_1 and X_2 normal
5) $df = n_1 + n_2 - 2$
6) $\sigma^2 x_1 = \sigma^2 x_2$

As before, the condition that the population be normally distributed is difficult to obtain in many experimental situations. Again, as a practical matter, the condition that the statistic be normally distributed may be substituted for the requirement of normal populations. If samples are small, this can only occur if the underlying populations are normal, but if samples are large, then the statistic, which in this case is $(\bar{X}_1 - \bar{X}_2)$, will be normally distributed. As before, $(n_1 + n_2) \geq 30$ will be the rule for guaranteeing the approximate normality of the distribution of the statistic. Of course, if this requirement is substituted for the normality of the population, the independence of the sample means from the sample standard deviations is not assured. However, the larger samples that are required to obtain the normality of the statistic when the underlying distribution is not itself normal partly compensates for the lack of independence between sample means and sample standard deviations. The revised form of the model that may be used is:

1) $\mu_1 - \mu_2 = a$
2) *est* $\sigma_{(\bar{X}_1 - \bar{X}_2)} = b$
3) Sampling random and independent
4) $(\bar{X}_1 - \bar{X}_2)$ normal
5) $df = n_1 + n_2 - 2 = c$
6) $\sigma^2 x_1 = \sigma^2 x_2$

It should also be apparent that the requirement that $\sigma^2 x_1 = \sigma^2 x_2$ frequently cannot be met. Fortunately, deviations from the equality of the population variances do not seem to be critical (especially if the samples are of equal size). This means that if all the conditions of the model have been met except for $\sigma^2 x_1 = \sigma^2 x_2$, the distribution of the transformed statistic will still be close to that of *t* with $n_1 + n_2 - 2$ degrees of freedom, especially if $n_1 = n_2$.

In order to estimate the standard error of the distribution of $(\bar{X}_1 - \bar{X}_2)$ both sample standard deviations must be used. Since the samples do not necessarily have to be of the same size, the *SD*'s must be weighted by the size of the sample. That is, if one sample is of size 15 and another of size

30, the standard deviation of the second sample should count more in the estimate than that of the first.

The precise formula for estimating $\sigma_{(\bar{X}_1 - \bar{X}_2)}$ is given by

$$est\ \sigma_{(\bar{X}_1 - \bar{X}_2)} = \sqrt{\frac{n_1 SD_1^2 + n_2 SD_2^2}{n_1 + n_2 - 2}\left(\frac{n_1 + n_2}{n_1 n_2}\right)}$$

where n_1 and n_2 are the sizes of the two samples.

If the two samples are of equal size then $n_1 = n_2 = n$ and the formula becomes

$$est\ \sigma_{(\bar{X}_1 - \bar{X}_2)} = \sqrt{\frac{nSD_1^2 + nSD_2^2}{n + n - 2}\left(\frac{n + n}{nn}\right)}$$

$$= \sqrt{\frac{n(SD_1^2 + SD_2^2)}{2n - 2}\left(\frac{2n}{n^2}\right)}$$

$$= \sqrt{\frac{n(SD_1^2 + SD_2^2)}{2(n - 1)}\frac{2n}{n^2}}$$

$$= \sqrt{\frac{SD_1^2 + SD_2^2}{n - 1}}$$

An Example

An experimenter knows that two strains of rats have different learning abilities on a certain task. Strain A learns the task in 7.8 trials and strain B learns the task in 12.3 trials. However, he feels that the difference is due, at least in part, to the task. So he randomly and independently selects two samples, one of size five from strain A and one of size four from strain B, and runs them on a second task. The results, in number of trials needed to learn the task are:

Strain A	Strain B
9	9
8	15
10	10
7	10
6	

What did the experimenter conclude?

The experimental problem is translated in the following way. If there is no difference between the two tasks, the difference in the two strains should remain the same. That is, $H_0: \mu_1 - \mu_2 = -4.5$ where μ_1 is the mean number of trials it takes strain A to learn the second task and μ_2 is the mean number of trials it takes strain B to learn the second task. The experimenter is trying to prove the H_A: that the difference between the two strains on the second task is not the same as it was on the first task.

This becomes $H_A: \mu_1 - \mu_2 \neq -4.5$. Note that this is a problem in which the assumed difference between the means of the populations is not zero.

Examination of the revised model indicates that some conditions cannot be definitely said to have been met. Because the sample sizes are small ($n_1 + n_2 < 30$), ($\bar{X}_1 - \bar{X}_2$) is not guaranteed normal. However, since the measure is of the number of trials needed to learn a task, there may be reason to believe that the underlying distribution of scores in the population is approximately normal and, therefore, the distribution of ($\bar{X}_1 - \bar{X}_2$) is also. An additional problem is the requirement that $\sigma^2_{X_1} = \sigma^2_{X_2}$ is not known to have been met.

The other conditions of the model are met in the problem. Sampling is random and independent, the $df = 5 + 4 - 2 = 7$, and

$$est\ \sigma_{(\bar{X}_1 - \bar{X}_2)} = \sqrt{\frac{n_1 SD_1^2 + n_2 SD_2^2}{n_1 + n_2 - 2} \frac{(n_1 + n_2)}{(n_1 n_2)}}$$

Using the above data, the following is obtained: $\bar{X}_1 = 8$, $\bar{X}_2 = 11$, $SD_1^2 = 2$ and $SD_2^2 = 22/4$.
Thus

$$est\ \sigma_{(\bar{X}_1 - \bar{X}_2)} = \sqrt{\frac{5 \times 2 + 4 \times 22/4}{7} \left(\frac{9}{20}\right)} = \sqrt{2.06} = 1.44$$

The value of the observed statistic is ($\bar{X}_1 - \bar{X}_2$)$_o = (8 - 11) = -3$. This is diagrammed in Figure 5.13.

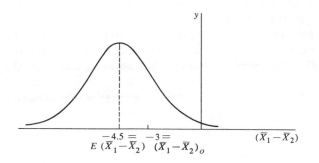

Figure 5.13

The value of the transformed statistic is the value of

$$t_{7_o} = \frac{-3 - (-4.5)}{1.44} = \frac{1.5}{1.44} = +1.04$$

This is diagrammed in Figure 5.14.
The evaluation, using $\alpha = .05$ is:

$$p(|t_7| \geq + 1.05) > p(|t_7| \geq 2.36) = .05 = \alpha$$

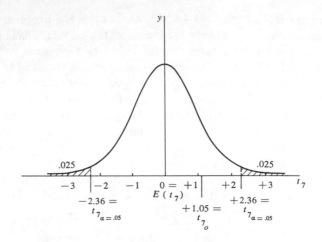

Figure 5.14

Thus, the probability of observing, just by chance when the model is true, values of the statistic at least as deviant from the expected value as the observed value was, is greater than α. The conclusion is, therefore, that values at least as deviant as the observed one are not rare, and hence, not significant. The model cannot be rejected. Retranslating this conclusion in terms of the experiment, the experimenter must decide that the evidence is insufficient to reject the alternative hypothesis that the strains of rats have a different difference in learning times on the new task compared to the old.

Of course, there is the possibility that the experimenter, by this conclusion, made a Type II error and failed to reject a hypothesis that was really false. He could have done this because, although the observed value of the statistic was not unlikely if the model were true, it was also not unlikely if other models were true (that is, the observed result is consistent with populations other than the hypothesized one). A schematic representation of this problem is given in Figure 5.15.

Note on Experimentation and Statistics

As indicated in the problem, the sample sizes were too small to guarantee that the statistic, $(\bar{X}_1 - \bar{X}_2)$, was approximately normally distributed. Of course, if the underlying scores in the population were normally distributed, then $(\bar{X}_1 - \bar{X}_2)$ would also be for samples of any size. In this instance, the scores were the number of trials and it was supposed that their distribution was normal. This may have been a questionable assumption. For relatively easy tasks, the number of trials needed to learn may well be non-normal, with most of the scores clustering about

Probability Theory

$\vdash$ - - Deductions

Theorems

$\vdash$ - - Incorporation

Situation. Two strains of rats known to differ by -4.5 trials in learning of a particular task: Samples of 5 and 4 taken to determine if they differ by a different amount when some other task is used.

$\xrightarrow{\text{Translation}}$

t model for Differences Between Means

1) $H_0: \mu_1 - \mu_2 = -4.5$
2) $est \; \sigma_{\bar{x}_1 - \bar{x}_2} =$
$$\sqrt{\left(\frac{n_1 SD_1^2 + n_2 SD_2^2}{n_1 + n_2 - 2}\right)\left(\frac{n_1 + n_2}{n_1 n_2}\right)}$$
$= 1.44$
3) Sampling random and independent
4) X_1, X_2 normal
   or $(\bar{X}_1 - \bar{X}_2)$ normal
5) $df = n_1 + n_2 - 2 = 7$
6) $\sigma^2_1 = \sigma^2_2$

$\vdash$ - - Deduction

Observed value of $(\bar{X}_1 - \bar{X}_2)$ will equal $-4.5 + 2.36 \,(1.44)$ (or $|t_7| \leq 2.36$).

$\xleftarrow{\text{Prediction}}$
$\alpha = .05$

Sampling Distribution (transformed statistic)
(See Figure 5.14)

$\vdash$ - - Experiment

$n_1 = 5, n_2 = 4$
$(X_1 - X_2)_o = -3$
$t_{7(\bar{x}_1 - \bar{x}_2)} = +1.05$

- - Probability for Continuous distributions

$\xrightarrow{\quad}$
Relationship of observed value to sampling distribution.

Probability Evaluation and Comparison
$p(|t_7| \geq 1.05) \geq p(|t_7| \geq 2.36) = .05$
$= \alpha$

$\vdash$ - - Decision Model

The value of -4.5 trials as the difference between the means of the two populations cannot be said to be false, therefore, the research hypothesis that the new task makes a difference which is different from that which the old one makes cannot be accepted.

$\xleftarrow{\text{Interpretation}}$

Statistical Conclusion. Result is not statistically signficant, therefore, fail to reject $H_0: \mu_1 - \mu_2 = -4.5$ and do not accept $H_A: \mu_1 - \mu_2 \neq -4.5$.

$\vdash$ - - Nature of statistical models

Possible Error in Research Conclusion. The new task may actually make a different difference, even though the sample result is not inconsistent with the hypothesis that it had the same effect on learning as the old task did.

$\xleftarrow{\text{Interpretation}}$

Possible Statistical Error: May have failed to reject a false H_0 (Type II error). The statistic, although not inconsistent with $H_0: \mu_1 - \mu_2 = -4.5$ is also not inconsistent with other hypotheses, for example, $H_0: \mu_1 - \mu_2 = -3$.

Figure 5.15

numbers like 3, 4, and 5 but with stupid rats giving scores of 15 or 20 trials. Thus, since scores could not go below 1 trial, the distribution of trials needed to learn easy tasks might be sharply skewed to the right.

Perhaps a more severe criticism could be made of the experiment itself. The experimenter was interested in determining if the difference in learning ability changed depending on the learning task. However, there could be at least two possible reasons for a change in the difference when the tasks are changed. One is that the tasks might differ with respect to the abilities they require and one task would be easier for one strain to learn than would be the other task. Another reason for a change in the difference, however, could merely be a consequence of one task being easier for both strains to learn than another. For example, bright rats may learn 25 percent faster then dull rats so that more difficult tasks would result in a larger absolute difference between the two strains. The experiment described above was not really designed to differentiate between the two possibilities.

Thus, this example illustrates two difficulties in the use of statistical models for answering research questions. One is that the required assumptions may not have been met and, therefore, a specific decision cannot legitimately be made. In the stated case, increasing the sample sizes would have overcome questions about the distribution of $(\bar{X}_1 - \bar{X}_2)$ and would have lessened the problem of not knowing that $\sigma_{X_1}^2 = \sigma_{X_2}^2$. The second difficulty is that the experiment may be poorly designed in terms of trying to answer the research problem that was originally posed. The appropriate design of the experiment is not determined by the abstract statistical model that represents the translation of aspects of the real world to the abstract world. Ultimately, the intelligence of the experimenter must be utilized. Statistics is an aid, not a substitute, for thought.

6

ESTIMATION

INTRODUCTION

It frequently is the case that the experimenter does not have a specific value of the parameter that he wishes to test. In this case a sample is selected and on the basis of the evidence from the sample, inferences are made about the values of the population parameter for which the observations are consistent.

POINT ESTIMATES

The single best guess from the evidence in the sample that the experimenter can make about the population parameter, when that parameter is either the mean or the difference between means, is the value of the analogous statistic in the sample. This estimate is called a *point estimate*. Obviously, the point estimate will most often not be precisely correct because most often the sample value is not precisely the same as the population value. However, it is still true that the point estimate made in this way is the best that can be made.

This follows because the most likely value for a sample statistic is the most frequently occurring value, or the mode. Therefore, the best single guess that can be made about the value of the statistic that one has observed is to guess it is the mode of the sampling distribution. However, the distributions of the statistic that have been dealt with thus far have all been normal. In the case of a normal distribution (as well as some others), the mode, mean, and median are all equal. Thus, guessing the modal value also results in guessing the mean value, or the expected value. But the expected value of the sampling distribution equals the value of the population parameter. Thus, estimating the value of the parameter to be the same as the observed value of the statistic results in estimating that value of the parameter that makes the observed sample result more likely than any other sample result. There is no other value of the parameter that could result in as high a likelihood for the observed sample.

CONFIDENCE INTERVALS

Because the point estimate, although it is the best specific guess, has such a low probability of equaling the value of the parameter, the estimation of the parameter that is frequently made is imprecise. In this case, the investigator is not interested in the single best guess for the parameter but rather in the values of the parameter which are reasonable in light of the evidence from the sample. An equivalent way to state this is to say that the attempt is to find those values of the parameter for which the observed value of the statistic is consistent.

To phrase the problem more specifically, this chapter will be concerned with determining *all of the values of the null hypothesis* which could not have been rejected on the basis of the evidence from the sample. These values will constitute a range or interval of nonrejectable null hypotheses. Since the range of values will differ depending on the α level, this value must be specified. If $\alpha = .01$, the interval will then be called the 99 percent confidence interval. If $\alpha = .05$, the interval will be the 95 percent confidence interval.

The procedure for computing the confidence interval consists of finding only two values. The first value is the lowest possible value for H_0 that could not have been rejected on the basis of the sample and the second is the highest possible value for H_0. Once the procedure is understood for one of the cases, the other uses of the confidence interval follow easily.

As in the inferential tests discussed previously, models of the population must be used. Fortunately, these models are precisely the ones that have already been used. As before, all of the conditions of the model must be met except for the value of the parameter. In the case of confidence intervals, however, the value of the parameter is not assumed and then tested. Instead, the highest and lowest values of the parameter with which the data are consistent are determined.

Part of the simplicity of the confidence interval computation derives from the fact that the distributions of the statistic that have been dealt with are of sample means. The standard error and shape of the sampling distribution of means (or differences between means) is not affected by the value of the parameter, the population mean. Thus, for computations of the confidence interval in the cases to be examined, the fact that this parameter's value is not specified does not affect either $\sigma_{\bar{X}}$ (or $\sigma_{(\bar{X}_1 - \bar{X}_2)}$) or the shape of the distribution.

Confidence Interval for the True Mean—Population Variance Known

This situation is similar to the z test for the true mean except that no value has been hypothesized for the population mean. The problem is to determine, using the information from the sample, values of the population mean that could not have been rejected on the basis of the sample.

An Example

Reconsider the problem presented in Chapter 4. Suppose that the experimenter had no reason for testing the specific value of 11.2 minutes. Instead, he wished to select a sample of students and, from the sample, estimate the true value of the population mean. Obviously, there are many values of the population mean with which a particular sample mean is consistent. The problem is to find the interval that contains all such values of the population mean when a given α level is specified.

The conditions of the model that must be met, except for the value of the parameter, are:

1) $\sigma_{\bar{x}} = b$
2) Sampling random and independent
3) $\bar{X}$ normal

From the information given in the problem, all of these conditions were met, and it was determined that $\sigma_{\bar{x}} = 1.5$. Further, $\bar{X} = 15.1$ based on a sample of size 35.

The above conditions determine the standard error and the shape of the sampling distribution of the statistic, $\bar{X}$, around *any* value for the population parameter. As stated before, for the sampling distribution of means the particular value of the population mean does not affect $\sigma_{\bar{x}}$ or the shape of the distribution.

In order to compute the confidence interval an α level must be stated. Let $\alpha = .05$, then the computation will be the 95 percent confidence interval for the true mean.

Since the sample yielded an observed mean of 15.1, the computation can be started by drawing an x axis (really an $\bar{X}$ axis) and placing the observed value of the mean on it.

$$15.1 = \bar{X}_o \qquad\qquad \bar{X}$$

Obviously, some population exists from which this sample came. And this sample is only one of a great number of unique samples that might have been selected. Thus, 15.1 is one value of the statistic in the sampling distribution that is appropriate for the population. Unfortunately, the population from which the sample came is not known. But sufficient conditions have been met so that the shape of the sampling distribution is known, no matter what the value of the population mean is.

The search for all of the values of the population mean that could have reasonably yielded this sample is the same as the problem of determining all of the sampling distributions of means in which the observed sample mean of 15.1 is not a rare one. Since α has been given as .05, it follows that the experimenter is searching for *all the values of the population parameter that yield sampling distributions in which the class of events defined by the observed value of the statistic has a probability of at least $\frac{1}{2}\alpha$.*

As a trivial instance, if $\mu = 15.1$, then $\bar{X}_o$ is not rare. Mathematically, $p(|\bar{X} - \mu| \geq 0) = 1.00$. The problem is to find all of the values of μ such that $p(|\bar{X} - \mu_i| \geq d_i) \geq .05$. This is a precise way of saying that the problem is to find all μ such that the probability of obtaining a value of $\bar{X}$ that is as extreme or more so from μ as 15.1, is greater than or equal to .05.

As values of μ are taken further and further away from 15.1, the probability of the observed $\bar{X}$ of 15.1 and values more deviant than it, decreases. Consider a whole set of values of the population parameter and their sampling distributions, as diagrammed in Figure 6.1.

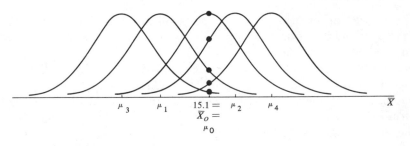

Figure 6.1

For values of the parameter that are close to the observed sample mean, such as μ_0, μ_1, and μ_2 it is apparent that values as deviant or more so from the expected value as the sample mean is, have a high probability of occurring. (Note that μ_0 is not the observed value of the parameter but merely that value of the parameter that is taken equal to $\bar{X}_o$.) As the value of the population mean (μ_3 and μ_4) gets further from the sample mean, the sample mean becomes more deviant from the expected value. Hence, the probability of values as extreme or more so than it is, decreases. Finally, it would be expected that a point would be reached such that if μ were taken to be this value, the sample result would deviate so far from it that the probability of values like it (as extreme or more so) would be less than or equal to .05. This value for μ would then have had to have been rejected on the basis of the evidence from the sample. Therefore, this value would lie outside of the confidence interval.

In order to compute the interval, consider that value of μ, labeled μ_L, such that the $p(|\bar{X} - \mu_L| \geq d_L) = .05$. That is, consider that value of $\mu = \mu_L$ such that $\bar{X}_o$ is so rare that it, and values more extreme than it is from μ_L, would occur exactly 5 percent of the time. This is diagrammed in Figure 6.2.

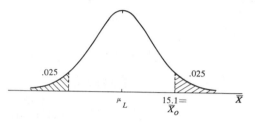

Figure 6.2

Since the statistic is normally distributed, it follows that $\bar{X}_o$ must be exactly 1.96 standard deviations from μ_L. But $\sigma_{\bar{x}}$ is given in the problem as equal to 1.5. Therefore,

$$z = \frac{\bar{X}_o - \mu_L}{\sigma_{\bar{x}}} = +1.96 \quad \text{or} \quad \frac{15.1 - \mu_L}{1.5} = +1.96$$

Then

$$-\mu_L = 1.96\,(1.5) - 15.1$$

and

$$\mu_L = 15.1 - 1.96\,(1.5) = 12.2$$

It is obvious that if μ_L is such that $p(|\bar{X} - \mu_L| \geq d_L) = .05$, then any value selected for μ, say μ_{L_1}, that makes $\bar{X}_o$ more deviant from it than $\bar{X}_o$ is from μ_L must result in $p(|\bar{X} - \mu_{L_1}| \geq d_{L_1}) < .05$. That is, the probability of values as extreme or more so from μ_{L_1} as $\bar{X}_o$ is must be less than .05. As a result, μ_{L_1}, or any value below μ_L, would have had to have been rejected on the basis of the evidence from the sample. Thus any value below μ_L cannot be in the 95 percent confidence interval. Similarly, any value of μ above μ_L (say μ_{L_2}) is such that $\bar{X}_o$ is not as deviant from it as it was from μ_L. The probability of obtaining values as extreme or more so from this expected value as $\bar{X}_o$ is, must be greater than .05. Therefore, values of the population parameter between μ_L and $\bar{X}_o$ are such that they could not have been rejected on the basis of the evidence from the sample.

Thus, μ_L represents *the lowest possible value for the null hypothesis that could not have been rejected on the basis of the evidence from the sample.* This situation is diagrammed in Figure 6.3.

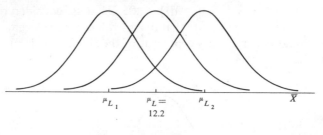

Figure 6.3

Summary. The logic of the described procedure is apparent. First the value of the sample statistic is obtained. Then the value of the parameter, μ_L, is found for which the probability of the sample statistic, or values more extreme than it is from the expected value, is exactly equal to the α level. It then follows that any value of the parameter below this value is such that the observed value of the statistic is even more deviant than it was from μ_L. It further follows that the probability associated with the value of the statistic in this sampling distribution must be less than α. Therefore, any value of the parameter below the first selected value, μ_L, must be a rejectable value on the basis of the sample. Similarly, any value of the parameter selected between μ_L and $\bar{X}_o$ is such that the deviation of $\bar{X}_o$ from the value is less than from μ_L. Hence the probability associated with the value of the statistic in this sampling distribution must be greater than α. Therefore, these values of the parameter could not have been rejected on the basis of the evidence from the sample. Fortunately, the argument is as simple as it is because in these cases the value of the parameter does not affect the function that determines the sampling distribution.

This discussion can be formalized as follows. If d_L is such that $p(|\bar{X} - \mu_L| \geq d_L) = .05$, then if $d_{L'} > d_L$, $p(|\bar{X} - \mu_{L'}| \geq d_{L'}) < .05$, and if $d_{L'} < d_L$ then $p(|\bar{X} - \mu_{L'}| \geq d_{L'}) > .05$. Obviously, $d_{L'} > d_L$ only when $\mu_{L'} < \mu_L$ and $d_{L'} < d_L$ only when $\mu_{L'} > \mu_L$.

Similarly, the highest value for the parameter, μ_U, which could not be rejected on the basis of the sample, is found. Let $\alpha = .05$. This value must be such that $\bar{X}_o$ is exactly 1.96 standard deviations below it. This is diagrammed in Figure 6.4.

To find μ_U, it is known that the z score of $\bar{X}_o$ must be -1.96. Thus

$$z = \frac{\bar{X}_o - \mu_U}{\sigma_{\bar{X}}} = -1.96 \quad \text{or} \quad \frac{15.1 - \mu_U}{1.5} = -1.96$$

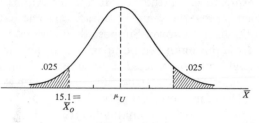

Figure 6.4

Therefore,

$$-\mu_U = -1.96 \, (1.5) - 15.1$$

or

$$\mu_U = 15.1 + 1.96 \, (1.5) = 18.0$$

If any value of μ above μ_U, such as μ_{U_1}, is considered, the conclusion must be that it would have had to have been rejected on the basis of the evidence from the sample. Similarly, any value of the parameter between μ_U and $\bar{X}_o$, for example, μ_{U_2}, is such that $\bar{X}_o$ is not a rare observation. Hence these values would not have been rejected on the basis of the evidence from the sample. The complete diagram illustrating this is given in Figure 6.5.

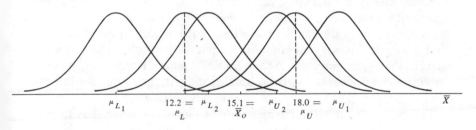

Figure 6.5

Obviously, in any computation only μ_L and μ_U need be drawn.

Interpretation of the Confidence Interval

The confidence interval represents an interval of nonrejectable null hypotheses at some specified α level based on the evidence from the sample. In the above example, the 95 percent confidence interval went from 12.2 to 18.0. Any value of the parameter within this interval could not have been rejected at $\alpha = .05$ on the basis of the sample that was observed. Similarly, every value for α that falls outside of this interval would have had to have been rejected on the basis of the sample.

Another interpretation of the confidence interval is based on the following. Remember that the sample comes from some actual population but this population is not known. Suppose that samples were taken over and over again from this unknown population and each time a 95 percent confidence interval was constructed as discussed. Then it is true that 95 percent of the intervals so constructed would contain the true value of the parameter. Therefore, one can say that the probability that the constructed interval is one that contains the true value of the parameter is .95. However, it is false to say that the probability that the parameter is in a specific interval is .95. It is not possible to attribute a probability to the parameter. There is only one true value for the population parameter and it is either in the interval or it is not. Thus the probability that the parameter is in the interval is 1.00 if it is and 0.00 if it is not. In interpreting the confidence interval in the above way *it is important to attribute the probability to the interval and not to the parameter.*

Confidence Intervals with Other α Levels

It is not necessary that α be .05. In fact, any α can be chosen. It should be apparent that the smaller the α level, the wider the range will be. That is, if α is very small, then the probability that the intervals will contain the true value of the parameter is larger but the interval itself is wider. Similarly, if α is a large value then the probability that the intervals will contain the true parameter is smaller but the interval is smaller. Roughly speaking, the smaller the α level, the more confident one can be that the interval is one that contains the parameter but the interval is less precise, that is, its range of values is wider. And the larger the α, the less confident one is that the interval contains the parameter but the interval is more precise, that is, its range of values is narrower.

The reason for this should be apparent. Small α's mean that the observed result can deviate further (a greater number of standard deviations) from the expected value. Therefore, the distance between the lowest and highest possible values of the parameter should be greater. Large α's mean that the sample statistic cannot deviate greatly from the expected value. Consequently, the distance between the lowest and highest possible values of the parameter is smaller.

An Example

Using the data in the previous example, the 99 percent confidence interval will be computed. Obviously, $\bar{X}_o = 15.1$ must fall 2.58 standard errors above μ_L and 2.58 standard errors below μ_U. (See Figure 6.6.)

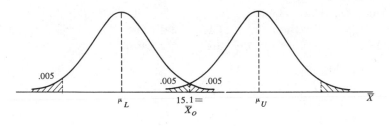

Figure 6.6

Computationally,

$$z = \frac{\bar{X}_o - \mu_L}{\sigma \bar{X}} = +2.58$$

therefore,

$$\mu_L = 15.1 - 2.58(1.5) = 11.2$$

and

$$z = \frac{\bar{X}_o - \mu_U}{\sigma \bar{X}} = -2.58$$

so that

$$\mu_U = 15.1 + 2.58 \, (1.5) = 19.0$$

The range of null hypotheses that could not have been rejected on the basis of the sample at $\alpha = .01$ goes from 11.2 minutes to 19.0 minutes. To restate the above discussion: As the probability of Type I error decreases for the nonrejectable null hypotheses in the confidence interval, the range of the interval increases, that is, its precision decreases.

Confidence Interval for the True Mean—Population Variance Unknown

This section and the succeeding ones on confidence intervals should cause no problems, since the argument is basically the same. The primary difference will be the manner in which the computations are carried out.

An Example

Suppose an investigator were interested in determining, for a particular city, about how much money people on the average spend for automobiles. A random and independent sample of 50 sales slips representing sales during the current model run, obtained from the dealers in the city, resulted in $\bar{X}_o = \$2750$ and $SD = \$200$. The problem is to determine a confidence interval for the true mean.

Since the true population variance is not known, the appropriate statistic to use is the t statistic. The conditions of this model, again excluding the hypothesis of the value of the parameter are:

1) $est\ \sigma_{\bar{x}} = b$
2) Sampling random and independent
3) X normal
4) $df = n - 1 = c$

While there is some doubt about condition 3, since it is not known for sure that the distribution of purchase prices is normal, all of the conditions in the modified model have been met (that is, $\bar{X}$ may be taken as approximately normal in the above case).

The actual value for $est\ \sigma_{\bar{x}}$ is $SD/\sqrt{n-1} = 200/\sqrt{49} = 200/7 = 28.6$, and the df are equal to $50 - 1$ or 49.

To compute a confidence interval, say the 95 percent confidence interval, it is necessary to determine the lowest value for μ (μ_L) and the highest value for μ (μ_U) that could not have been rejected on the basis of the evidence from the sample. The tables for the t distribution indicate that $p(|t_{49}| \geq 2.01) = .05$. That is, t values whose absolute value is equal to or exceeds 2.01 would be expected to occur .05 of the time. Thus, the value of μ_L must be such that the observed sample mean of \$2750 and ones more deviant from μ_L would occur exactly .05 of the time. That is, μ_L is the border value. This is the same as saying that $\bar{X}_o$ must fall exactly 2.01 t scores above μ_L when there are 49 degrees of freedom. Since

$$t_{49} = (\bar{X}_o - \mu_L)/28.6 = +2.01$$

then

$$\mu_L = 2750 - 2.01(28.6) = \$2693$$

Similarly, μ_U must be a value such that \$2750, or values more deviant than it is from μ_U would occur only .05 of the time. Therefore, $\bar{X}_o$ must fall at exactly a t score of -2.01.

The computation for μ_U is

$$t_{49} = (\bar{X}_o - \mu_U)/est\ \sigma_{\bar{x}} = -2.01$$

and

$$\mu_U = 2750 + 2.01(28.6) = \$2807$$

The 95 percent confidence interval, therefore, runs from \$2693 to \$2807. At $\alpha = .05$, this interval contains all of the null hypotheses which could not have been rejected on the basis of the evidence from the sample. Diagrammatically, the representation is given in Figure 6.7.

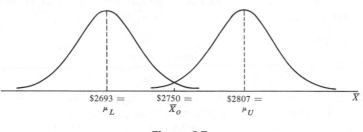

$2693 = \mu_L$ \qquad $2750 = \bar{X}_o$ \qquad $2807 = \mu_U$ \qquad $\bar{X}$

Figure 6.7

The usefulness of confidence intervals is apparent especially when there is no specific value for the parameter that is to be tested.

Confidence Intervals for the Differences between Means

Rather than test the hypothesis that two treatments do not differ, or differ by a particular amount, the experimenter may instead be interested in determining the range of possible differences between the two treatments that appears reasonable in light of the evidence from the sample. The computation involves, as before, either a z or a t score depending on whether the standard error of the statistic is known or must be estimated.

Population Variances Known

If the standard error is known and the other conditions of the model, excluding the value of the parameter, have been met, the lowest difference between the population means that is consistent with the difference in the sample means is obtained by solving for $(\mu_1 - \mu_2)_L$ in the equation

$$z = [(\bar{X}_1 - \bar{X}_2)_o - (\mu_1 - \mu_2)_L]/\sigma_{(\bar{X}_1 - \bar{X}_2)} = z_\alpha$$

where z_α is determined by the α level. If the 99 percent confidence interval is to be constructed, then $\alpha = .01$ and $z_{.01} = 2.58$ and if the 95 percent confidence interval is desired then $z_{.05} = 1.96$. (What is the value of $z_{.10}$?)

An Example. Through a particular quaint little town a set of railroad tracks runs dividing the town into two portions. A social science type lives on one side of the tracks. One day (no doubt after the academic year had ended) he thought it would be interesting to try to get some idea about the difference in the amount of money that was spent on clothes between college girls that lived on his side of the tracks and that spent by girls on the other side of the tracks. He selected random and independent samples of 20 each and conducted interviews to determine the amount of money each had spent on clothes during the past year. The conditions of the modified model are (excluding the hypothesis about the parameter),

1) $\sigma_{(\bar{X}_1 - \bar{X}_2)} = b$
2) Sampling random and independent
3) $(\bar{X}_1 - \bar{X}_2)$ normal

Condition 3 may be taken as having been met since $n_1 + n_2 \geq 30$. Suppose also that the information about the population standard deviations is available and that $\sigma_{X_1} = \$55$ and $\sigma_{X_2} = \$42$. The interviews conducted indicated $\bar{X}_1 = \$475$ and $\bar{X}_2 = \$348$. The experimenter wishes to compute the 99 percent confidence interval.
First

$$\sigma_{(\bar{X}_1 - \bar{X}_2)} = \sqrt{\sigma^2 x_1 / n_1 + \sigma^2 x_2 / n_2} = \sqrt{4789/20} = \sqrt{239.45} = 15.5$$

Then

$$z = [(\bar{X}_1 - \bar{X}_2) - (\mu_1 - \mu_2)_L] / \sigma_{(\bar{X}_1 - \bar{X}_2)} = +2.58$$

and

$$(\mu_1 - \mu_2)_L = (\bar{X}_1 - \bar{X}_2)_o - 2.58 \, \sigma_{(\bar{X}_1 - \bar{X}_2)} = \$127 - \$40 = \$87$$

Analogous computations yield a value for $(\mu_1 - \mu_2)_U$ of \$167. (Work this out.) Diagrammatically, the confidence interval is represented in Figure 6.8.

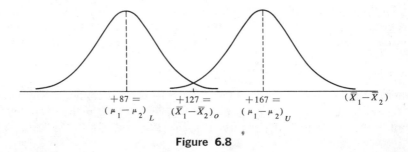

Figure 6.8

The interpretation of this interval is similar to the interpretations given previously for the confidence interval. For any hypothesis about the difference between the population means between + \$87 and + \$167, the sample would have resulted in a failure to reject H_0 at $\alpha = .01$. In terms of the original problem, the experimenter has found a reasonable range for the difference between the population means. Since the range only includes positive values, he can be reasonably confident that the samples came from populations in which μ_1 is greater than μ_2, that is, all of the hypotheses which could not have been rejected are of the form

$\mu_1 > \mu_2$ (which is equivalent to $\mu_1 - \mu_2 > 0$). Similarly, any hypothesis that the girls on the other side of the tracks spent an amount on clothes equal to that of the girls on his side ($\mu_1 - \mu_2 = 0$) or any hypothesis that would have indicated that they spent more ($\mu_1 - \mu_2 < 0$) would have had to have been rejected on the basis of the evidence from the sample.

Note that the data was collected from interviews. Hence, the confidence interval dealt only with the amount of money that the girls *said* they spent on clothes and this is not necessarily the same as that which was actually spent.

Population Variances Unknown

In the case of two samples drawn from populations with unknown variances, the *t* ratio must be used rather than *z* to compute the confidence interval. Otherwise, this situation causes no additional problems. Of course, all of the conditions of the model must be met except for the value of the parameter.

An Example.   A highway commissioner was interested in getting some idea about the effect on the number of traffic accidents that variable highway speeds had. The following experiment was devised. Across the country, all of the federal highways of the United States, including expressways, were examined. From this system, two random and independent samples, each of size 12, were taken. The elements in the samples were continuous 100 mile stretches of highway. In one sample of 12, no changes were made. This was the control group. However, in the second sample, each 100 mile stretch of highway was divided into four 25 mile sections. Within each 25 mile section there was a three-mile speed control zone. The first half mile was a slowing down zone and the next two and a half miles had a speed limit that was 10 miles slower than under normal conditions. Normal law enforcement was maintained in both samples of highway. At the end of one year, the number of accidents that had occurred in each of the 100 mile stretches was observed. The results are given in Table 6.1.

The commissioner wanted to determine the 90 percent confidence interval for the difference between the two conditions.

Note that the populations are all of the 100 mile stretches of highway on the United States highway system with respect to the number of accidents in a year. One population consists of the above units when variable speeds are introduced and the other population consists of these units when there is only the regular speed limit. The samples consist of the 100 mile sections and have been scored in terms of the number of accidents under each condition.

Table 6.1

Number of Accidents in 100 Mile Sections of Highway Under Two Different Conditions

| Number of Accidents | |
Speed Control	No Speed Control
10	8
9	8
7	9
12	10
14	15
7	14
9	14
12	11
11	14
11	10
10	8
9	9
$\bar{X}_1 = 10.1$	$\bar{X}_2 = 10.8$

In terms of the model, the following are the conditions that must be met:

1) $est\ \sigma_{(\bar{X}_1 - \bar{X}_2)} = b$
2) Sampling random and independent
3) X_1 and X_2 normal
4) $\sigma^2{}_{X_1} = \sigma^2{}_{X_2}$
5) $df = n_1 + n_2 - 2 = c$

Working this example has two problems. Condition 4 is not known to be met. However, since the samples are of equal size this requirement is probably not critical. Secondly, condition 3 has not been met. The scores are probably not normally distributed. Further, the samples are too small to guarantee that the modified model has been met. That is, since $n_1 + n_2 < 30$, $(\bar{X}_1 - \bar{X}_2)$ is not guaranteed approximately normal. Of course the unanswered question is how far from normal the sampling distribution of $(\bar{X}_1 - \bar{X}_2)$ is. It would seem safe to say that the approximation to the normal distribution is not as close as one would prefer. Consequently, the legitimacy of the interval to be constructed is more questionable than it would have been had the sample size been larger.

First, $est\ \sigma_{(\bar{X}_1 - \bar{X}_2)}$ must be computed. From the above data $SD_1{}^2 = 46.9/12$ and $SD_2{}^2 = 79.7/12$. Therefore

$$est\ \sigma_{(\bar{X}_1 - \bar{X}_2)} = \sqrt{\frac{SD_1{}^2 + SD_2{}^2}{n - 1}} = \sqrt{\frac{46.9 + 79.7}{12 \cdot 11}} = \sqrt{\frac{46.9 + 79.7}{132}}$$

$$= \sqrt{\frac{126.6}{132}} = \sqrt{.96} = .98$$

The degrees of freedom are $n_1 + n_2 - 2$ or 22. At an α of .10 with 22 *df* the observed difference in sample means must fall at a *t* score of $+$ 1.72. Therefore, solving for $(\mu_1 - \mu_2)_L$

$$t_{22} = \frac{(\bar{X}_1 - \bar{X}_2)_o - (\mu_1 - \mu_2)_L}{est\ \sigma_{(\bar{X}_1 - \bar{X}_2)}} = +\ 1.72$$

$$(\mu_1 - \mu_2)_L = -0.7 - 1.72(.98) = -2.4$$

and

$$(\mu_1 - \mu_2)_U = -0.7 + 1.72(.98) = +\ 1$$

The diagram of this is given in Figure 6.9.

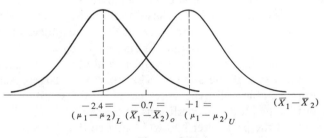

$$\begin{array}{cccc} -2.4 = & -0.7 = & +1 = & (\bar{X}_1 - \bar{X}_2) \\ (\mu_1 - \mu_2)_L & (\bar{X}_1 - \bar{X}_2)_o & (\mu_1 - \mu_2)_U & \end{array}$$

Figure 6.9

The interpretation of this confidence interval is that for any hypothesis in which the difference for the population means is between -2.4 and $+1$ (that is, for $-2.4 \leq (\mu_1 - \mu_2) \leq +1$) the evidence from the sample is insufficient to reject it. Note that this interval runs from minus values to plus values. In terms of the original problem this means that some hypotheses that state that the number of accidents is less under the speed control method $[(\mu_1 - \mu_2) = D_i$ where $D_i < 0]$, as well as some hypotheses that state that the number of accidents is greater under the speed control method $[(\mu_1 - \mu_2) = D_i$ where $D_i > 0]$ could not have been rejected on the basis of this sample. Also included among the nonrejectable null hypotheses is $H_0: \mu_1 - \mu_2 = 0$, that is, the two conditions do not differ at all in terms of their effect on the number of traffic accidents.

It should again be pointed out that the described interval construction is questionable because several conditions in the model had not been met. In fact, the question about the effect of variable speed controls on the accident rate is a good illustration of the difficulty that frequently exists in trying to design a study in such a way that an important real world problem can be translated into an appropriate statistical format. In the above case, if a judgment were made that some condition(s) in the model deviated greatly from that which is required, the construction of the interval would have been inappropriate.

Summary of Confidence Intervals

The last part of this chapter has been concerned with determining a range of nonrejectable values for the parameter on the basis of evidence from a sample or pair of samples. This approach is especially useful when there is no specific hypothesis which it seems critical to test. Instead, the investigator is interested in getting some idea about the values of the parameter with which the data are consistent.

The procedure involved determining the lowest value of the parameter and the highest value of the parameter that could not have been rejected on the basis of the sample, for some given α level. It was then seen that any value of the parameter within the limits determined by these two values was such that the sample or ones more deviant than it was from the expected value had a probability greater than α. Hence, values of the parameter in this interval could not have been rejected on the basis of the sample. For any value of the parameter outside of the interval, the sample deviated so much that ones like it could only occur by chance less than α percent of the time. Therefore, these values would have had to have been rejected on the basis of the sample. The interval thus represented the range of nonrejectable null hypotheses based on the sample.

Computationally, all of the conditions of the model except that dealing with the value of the parameter had to be met so that the standard error and the shape of the sampling distribution would be known. The problem of computing the limits on the interval was simplified by the fact that various values hypothesized for the parameter did not have any effect on the standard error or the shape of the distribution. Hence, only one unknown, that of the value of the parameter, was involved.

7

ONE-TAILED HYPOTHESIS TESTS

INTRODUCTION

The presentation of one-tailed hypothesis tests will be divided into two parts. The first part will be consistent with the traditional approach to this topic. The student, however, is warned that this author considers one-tailed hypothesis tests inappropriate because of problems in logic. These problems will be discussed in the second part.

ONE-TAILED vs. TWO-TAILED HYPOTHESIS TESTS

Nature of One-Tailed Hypotheses

Whether a test is one-tailed or two-tailed depends on the nature of the alternative hypothesis. To this point the alternative hypothesis has been of the form $H_A: \mu \neq a$. That is, if the null hypothesis were rejected it resulted in the acceptance of an alternative that simply stated that the value of the parameter was other than that assumed in the model. This seems sensible enough. If the sample is so deviant from the expected value that ones like it are unlikely to have occurred by chance from that population, the decision is to reject the null. The conclusion that the true value is some value other than the null is straightforward and in fact follows logically from the conclusion to reject the null. Under these circumstances the alternative hypothesis is called a two-tailed hypothesis.

In many instances, however, the experimenter is not interested in merely concluding that the true value is some value other than the null. Instead he wishes to conclude that, if the null hypothesis is false, the true value must be on one side of the null value, that is, the true value is greater than the null or the true value is less than the null. Which direction is chosen depends on the problem. This choice must be made *before the data is gathered.* The alternative hypothesis then takes the form of one of the following:

1) $H_A : \mu < a$
2) $H_A : \mu > a$
3) $H_A : \mu_1 - \mu_2 < a$
4) $H_A : \mu_1 - \mu_2 > a$

One of the first two forms would be appropriate for the z or t tests for the true mean and one of the second for the z or t test for the difference between means.

In the case of one-tailed hypotheses, as in the case of two-tailed hypotheses, the rejection of the null hypothesis carries with it the acceptance of the alternative. However, the alternative has a directional value rather than only being a statement that the true value is different from the null.

Why One-Tailed Tests Are Used

Sometimes it does not make sense to do a test, the conclusion of which will be an alternative that says the true value is some value other than the hypothesized value. For example, suppose a theory has been formulated that specifies that under certain classroom conditions learning will increase over what takes place in the standard classroom situation. In this case the research hypothesis is not merely that learning will be different under the new conditions but that it will improve. The experimenter is not interested in rejecting $H_0 : \mu_1 - \mu_2 = 0$ in favor of $H_A : \mu_1 - \mu_2 \neq 0$. Instead he explicitly hopes to reject $H_0 : \mu_1 - \mu_2 = 0$ and accept $H_A : \mu_1 - \mu_2 > 0$. (μ_1 is the mean learning rate for the population receiving instruction under the conditions specified by the theory.) Obviously, if a two-tailed alternative were accepted, the conclusion could not be that the theory's prediction was substantiated. If $\mu_1 - \mu_2 \neq 0$, it could either mean that learning improved under the new conditions or that it decreased under the new conditions. Only one of these conclusions is consistent with the theory. Obviously, it is much more reasonable to formulate a test in which the rejection of the null hypothesis will result in the acceptance of an alternative that is consistent with the theory.

A second case in which a one-tailed test is more appropriate than a two-tailed test is one in which the decision will be different only if the conclusion is directional. For example, suppose that a manufacturer is interested in marketing a new type of spark plug. He knows that, on the average, spark plugs on the market that cost as much as he plans to sell his new one for last 20,000 miles. It is apparent that if $H_0 : \mu = 20,000$ is rejected and if $H_A : \mu \neq 20,000$ is accepted (where μ is the mean lifetime for the new spark plugs) the manufacturer will not have a basis for a decision. Only if he can demonstrate that $\mu > 20,000$, does he have hopes of capturing enough of the market to make the venture profitable. (This problem is of course an idealized one and ignores the role of advertising.) Clearly, if the true value is judged to be 20,000 (or less) one decision will be made. If the value of the parameter is judged to be greater than 20,000 the decision will be something else. This problem is then translated into a null and alternative hypothesis of $H_0 : \mu = 20,000$ and $H_A : \mu > 20,000$.

ARGUMENT FOR THE ONE-TAILED TESTS

As in the two-tailed tests discussed previously, two models are needed, the one that determines or generates the sampling distribution, and the decision model which consists of the α level and the alternative hypothesis.

In order to demonstrate the differences between one-tailed and two-tailed tests, an example will be worked.

Consider the problem of the spark plug manufacturer discussed previously. Suppose the manufacturer actually wanted to carry out an experiment to determine the feasibility of producing his spark plug. Naturally, he would not want to test all of the population. As a matter of fact this would be impossible since the population consists of all of the new type spark plugs that he might manufacture. This is obviously a theoretical population. The reasonable strategy would be to take a sample of spark plugs and test them to see how long they will last. The null hypothesis is $H_0 : \mu = 20,000$ miles and the alternative is $H_A : \mu > 20,000$ miles. Suppose a sample of 12 were taken with the following results (rounded off to the nearest hundred):

Number of Miles New Type
Spark Plugs Lasted

22,300
24,700
26,200
19,400
18,700
20,600
21,400
23,400
20,100
27,800
27,000
19,900

$$\bar{X}_o = 271,500/12 = 22,600 \quad SD_X = 10^2\sqrt{10,894/12} = 10^2\sqrt{908} = 3000$$

Since the population variance is not known but must be estimated, the problem is a t test for a true mean provided that certain conditions have been met. It will be recalled that the model for the t test is:

1) $H_0 : \mu = a$
2) $est\ \sigma_{\bar{x}} = b$
3) Sampling random and independent
4) X normal ($\bar{X}$ normal in modified model)
5) $df = n - 1 = c$

The only condition that is suspect is the requirement that the scores (miles which the new type spark plugs last) are normally distributed. Further, the sample size of 12 is too small to guarantee that the condition of the modified model that requires the sample means be normally distributed is met. However, the length of time that the units last is a physical characteristic and this particular type of score is probably one that can be assumed to be approximately normally distributed. It therefore would appear reasonable to do the test.

From $\bar{X}_o = 22,600$, SD_X is determined to be 3000. Therefore, $est\ \sigma_{\bar{x}}$ $= SD_X/\sqrt{n-1} = 3000/\sqrt{11} = 3000/3.3 = 909 = 900$ (rounded to the nearest hundred).

The $df = n - 1 = 11$. For this problem let $\alpha = .01$.

The expected value of the distribution is determined by the value of μ which is 20,000. Hence the sampling distribution of the mean can be diagrammed as in Figure 7.1.

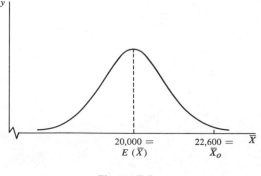

Figure 7.1

Now the critical problem of evaluating the probability of the class of events defined by the observed value arises. If events are considered deviant when they deviate from the expected in either direction, rejection of the null hypothesis would be equivalent to accepting the alternative that $\mu \neq 20,000$. Clearly, this is not the alternative that the manufacturer desires to accept because he will only make a decision to manufacture the spark plugs if he decides that the spark plugs will last, on the average, more than 20,000 miles. Therefore, only results that deviate from the expected *in the predicted direction* can be taken as evidence *against the null and in favor of the alternative*. The above sample mean is in the predicted direction. The only question that remains is whether or not it is so deviant from the expected result that the null hypothesis must be rejected in favor of the alternative. It should be emphasized that with $\alpha = .01$, events are still considered rare if they are unlikely to have occurred by chance more than one percent of the time under the assumptions of the model. The difference is that for one-tailed tests the observed value of the statistic or ones more deviant *in the predicted direction* must have a probability of less than or equal to .01 to be considered evidence against the null hypothesis.

Observe that no matter how deviant an observed result is from the expected in the direction opposite to the predicted, it could not be used as evidence against the null and in favor of the alternative. In the above example, even if the mean lifetime of the sampled spark plugs had been one mile, this could not be taken as evidence against the null and in favor of the alternative. Certainly, if the observation of one mile is unlikely to have occurred when the true value of the population is 20,000, this could not be used as evidence that the true value was even greater than 20,000. To put it another way, an event that is unlikely to have occurred if the true value is 20,000 because it deviated greatly in a minus direction (as 1 does from 20,000) is certainly even less likely to have occurred if the true value is any value greater than 20,000 because it deviates even more from this value.

The probability of Type I error is of course still .01 if $\alpha = .01$. One percent of the time, when the model is correct, it will be rejected. The only difference is that the most extreme one percent are from a *particular* direction rather than from the most extreme one half percent of both directions.

The computation of the transformed statistic in the above problem is:

$$t_{(n-1)_o} = (\bar{X}_o - \mu)/est\ \sigma_{\bar{x}} = (22{,}600 - 20{,}000)/900$$
$$= 2{,}600/900 = +2.89$$

The probability is given by $p(t_{11} \geq +2.89) < p(t_{11} \geq +2.72) = .01$. This is diagrammed in Figure 7.2. The symbol $t_{11\alpha_1=.01}$ represents the value of t_{11} such that the *one-tailed* probability for the extreme values of t_{11} is equal to .01.

The conclusion is, therefore, to reject the null hypothesis in favor of the alternative and conclude that the lifetime of the new spark plugs is greater than that of the old.

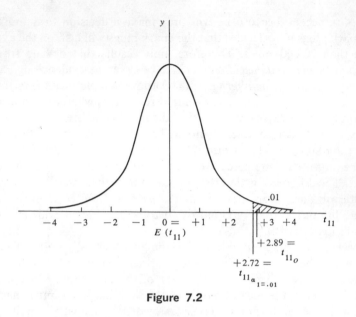

Figure 7.2

Notice some changes in the computation.

First, the probability that was evaluated was without the absolute value signs. That is, it was not $p(|t_{11}| \geq 2.89)$ but $p(t_{11} \geq +2.89)$. The absolute value sign must be omitted and the sign of the transformed statistic kept because the probability of interest is for *deviations in a particular direction*.

Also note that all of the .01 is in the tail predicted by the alternative. The value 2.72 is equivalent to the .02 probability for a two-tailed test. That is, $p(|t_{11}| \geq 2.72) = .02$ which means, if only one direction is considered, that $p(t_{11} \geq +2.72) = .01$.

Obviously, the direction of the alternative must be specified *before the data is observed*. Otherwise, the probability of the observed result occurring just by chance in the predicted direction cannot be computed. If the direction is not specified until after the data is examined, one is no longer talking about the result occurring *by chance* in that direction. Furthermore, the theory or decision process must be decided upon before the data is examined since the reason for drawing a sample in the first place when one is doing a hypothesis test is to see if the results are consistent with the predictions of a theory.

Some brief examples will be given to demonstrate more fully the use of one-tailed tests. As with two-tailed tests, the similarities among the various tests are great. The differences are primarily concerned with the type of research problem and its translation into mathematical form, and with slight computational differences.

ONE-TAILED z TEST FOR THE TRUE MEAN

As in the two-tailed z test for the true mean, either the true population variance or the true standard error of the mean must be known.

An Example

An agriculturist who had been working with a type of corn that took 90 days to mature believed that he had discovered conditions under which the growing season could be shortened. Five hundred seeds were selected. Under the new conditions which involved changes in fertilizer treatment and watering, the average time for maturation was 88.9 days. The experimenter knew that the standard deviation of the old population was nine days and assumed that the same standard deviation held for the new conditions. Did the new conditions shorten the growing time?

The above problem can be translated into the following model.

1) $H_0 : \mu = 90$
2) $\sigma_{\bar{x}} = \sigma_x/\sqrt{n} = 9/\sqrt{500} = 9/22.4 = .40$
3) Random and independent selection of seeds
4) $\bar{X}$ normal

The experimenter decided to do the test with $\alpha = .01$. Since the new conditions would only be used if it could be shown that they shortened the growing season, $H_A : \mu < 90$.

$$z_o = (88.9 - 90)/.40 = -1.1/.40 = -2.8$$

$$p(\bar{X} \le 88.9) = p(z \le -2.8) = .003 < .01 = \alpha$$

The conclusion would be to reject the null hypothesis that the new conditions did not affect the growing season in favor of the alternative

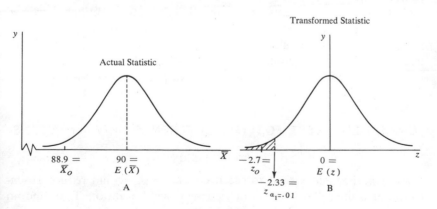

Figure 7.3

that they shortened it. However, it is possible that the null hypothesis was rejected because $\sigma_X \neq 9$. This value was derived from the knowledge about the previous conditions but it is not necessarily true that the standard deviation of the growing time is the same under the new conditions as under the old. Subjectively, it seems very likely that the standard deviation is about the same, but this is not guaranteed. Technically, then, the model was rejected but the part of the model that is false cannot with certainty be attributed to the assumed value of the population mean. It could be due to the assumption about the population standard deviation. The above results are digrammed in Figure 7.3.

For this problem it is possible to determine the value of σ_X that would have to exist if this hypothesis were to have contributed primarily to the rejection. Obviously, if $\sigma_X < 9$, z would have been an even larger negative value than it was and the model still could have been rejected. How much larger than 9 could σ_X be and the model still be rejected at $\alpha = .01$? The solution is as follows:

$$z = (88.9 - 90)/\sigma_{\bar{x}} = -2.33$$

Then

$$\sigma_{\bar{x}} = (88.9 - 90)/-2.33 = -1.1/-2.33 = 0.47$$

But $\sigma_{\bar{x}} = \sigma_X/\sqrt{n}$; therefore, $0.47 = \sigma_X/22.4$, and $\sigma_X = 22.4(.47) = 10.5$.

Thus, even if σ_X were as large as 10.5, the observed sample mean of 88.9 would have deviated by enough in the predicted direction from the expected value of 90 so that its z score would have been -2.33. Since $p(z \leq -2.33) = .01$, the hypothesis about the population mean would have been rejected.

On the basis of this it is reasonable to conclude that whatever the true standard deviation of the new population is, it is probably less than 10.5. Therefore, the conclusion remains that the new conditions shortened the growing time. (Of course, if the data for each of the 500 seeds is available, then SD_X could be used to obtain $est\ \sigma_{\bar{x}}$ and a one-tailed t test for the true mean could have been performed.)

A schematic representation of the above problem is drawn in Figure 7.4.

ONE-TAILED z TEST FOR THE DIFFERENCE BETWEEN MEANS

An Example

An experimenter wished to see if coffee breaks would reduce absenteeism of white collar workers in a particular organization. Two random samples, one of 25 and the other of 20, were selected. One group was

Probability Theory

⊦ - - Deductions

Theorems

⊦ - - Incorporation

Situation. Corn seeds under new fertilizer and watering conditions with respect to time they take to achieve maturation: Sample of 500 seeds taken to determine if the conditions shorten the growing time.

Translation ⟶

z Model for the True Mean
1) H_0: $\mu = 90$
2) $\sigma_{\bar{X}} = \sigma_X/\sqrt{n} = .40$
3) Sampling random and independent
4) $\bar{X}$ normal

⊦ - - Deduction

Observed value $\bar{X}$ will be between 90 and $90 - 2.33(.40)$ or ($z_{\bar{x}} \le -2.33$)

⟵ Prediction
$\alpha = .05$

Sampling Distribution (transformed statistic)
(See Figure 7.3B)

⊦ - - Experiment

$n = 500$
$\bar{X}_o = 88.9$
$z_{\bar{x}_o} = -2.8$

Probability for continuous
⊦ - - distributions

Relationship of observed value to sampling distribution.

Probability Evaluation and Comparison
$p(z \le -2.8) < p(z \le -2.33) = .01 = \alpha$

⊦ - - Decision Model

The researcher concludes that the hypothesis that average growing time is 90 days is false and accepts the alternative hypothesis that the average time is less than 90 days.

Interpretation ⟵

Statistical Conclusion. Result is statistically significant; therefore, reject H_0: $\mu = 90$ and accept H_A: $\mu < 90$.

⊦ - - Nature of statistical models

Possible Error in Research Conclusion. May be that growing time is not really shorter but still is 90 days. Rejection of this H_0 may have been a mistake since:
a) Sample result may have been a rare observation from the assumed population and/or
b) True σ_X of population may be > 10.5 days. Thus the wrong variance might have been assumed for the computations.

Interpretation ⟵

Possible Statistical Error. Possible that H_0: $\mu = 90$ is true and that Type I error has been made by rejecting it and accepting H_A. $\mu = 88.9$ is unlikely under H_0, but not impossible. Further, it is possible to have made Type I error because $\sigma_X = 9$ is inappropriate but $H_0 : \mu = 90$ is really true; that is, it is possible that the problem is with the use of an inappropriate value of σ_X and consequently of $\sigma_{\bar{X}}$ rather than with a wrong assumption about μ.

Figure 7.4

allowed a 15 minute coffee break each morning of the work week. The other group was not. At the end of one year, the number of days each worker had been absent was noted. $\bar{X}_1 = 6.4$ and $\bar{X}_2 = 6.6$. Suppose the variances of the populations are known and $\sigma^2_{X_1} = 9$ and $\sigma^2_{X_2} = 9$. Then the model is as follows:

1) $H_0 : \mu_1 - \mu_2 = 0$
2) $\sigma_{(\bar{X}_1 - \bar{X}_2)} = \sqrt{\sigma^2_{X_1}/n_1 + \sigma^2_{X_2}/n_2} = \sqrt{9/25 + 9/20} = \sqrt{.36 + .45}$
   $= \sqrt{.81} = .9$
3) Sampling random and independent
4) $(\bar{X}_1 - \bar{X}_2)$ normal

For $\alpha = .05$ and $H_A : \mu_1 - \mu_2 < 0$,

$$z_0 = [(\bar{X}_1 - \bar{X}_2)_o - (\mu_1 - \mu_2)]/\sigma_{(\bar{X}_1 - \bar{X}_2)} = (-0.2 - 0)/.9 = -.22$$

$$p(z \leq -.22) > .05 = \alpha$$

Therefore, the null hypothesis cannot be rejected and it cannot be concluded that coffee breaks reduce the amount of absenteeism. The diagrams for this problem are given in Figure 7.5.

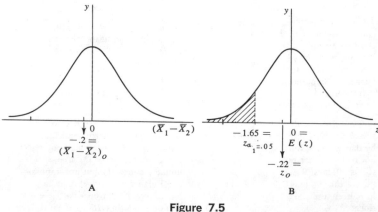

Figure 7.5

Note that in the given problem the populations are theoretical. The judgment that is to be made is about future white collar workers as well as those currently employed. Of course, the experimenter can only use workers for the experiment who are presently employed. As a result, even the measurement of everyone in the organization would have been an inferential problem because this is not really the whole population to which inferences are to be made. Legitimately then, the random and independent assumption could be questioned since the sampling obviously was not from the whole population. Whether this is a critical problem depends on several factors. For example, what is the turnover rate? If it is small then most of the same people will be around for a while. Other questions involve future changes. Will the organization change much in the future? Will the type of person hired for these jobs (in terms of personality, education, and so forth) change much in the future? How far into the future are the results to be applied?

Again this is an illustration of the difficulty of translating a real problem into a statistical model. The problem could be dealt with by taking measurements on the workers periodically so that there would be stronger grounds for decisions.

ONE-TAILED t TEST FOR THE DIFFERENCE BETWEEN MEANS

An Example

Two random and independent samples, each of size 20, were drawn to study the effects of alcohol on reaction time. One group was given two shots (3 ounces) of whiskey one hour before the reaction times were taken. The other group was tested without any alcohol. The results were:

$$\bar{X}_1 = .171 \text{ sec} \qquad \bar{X}_2 = .099 \text{ sec}$$

$$SD_1{}^2 = .006 \text{ sec}^2 \qquad SD_2{}^2 = .004 \text{ sec}^2$$

Did the alcohol increase reaction time?
The model for this problem is:

1) $H_0 : \mu_1 - \mu_2 = 0$
2) $est\ \sigma_{(\bar{X}_1 - \bar{X}_2)} = \sqrt{(SD_1{}^2 + SD_2{}^2)/(n - 1)} = \sqrt{.010/19}$
   $= \sqrt{.00053} = 10^{-2} \sqrt{5.3} = .023$
3) $\sigma^2{}_{X_1} = \sigma^2{}_{X_2}$
4) Sampling random and independent
5) $df = n_1 + n_2 - 2 = 38$
6) X_1 and X_2 normal [or $(\bar{X}_1 - \bar{X}_2)$ normal]

The decision model is:

1) $H_A : \mu_1 - \mu_2 > 0$
2) $\alpha = .05$

In terms of the model, it is not definitely known that $\sigma^2{}_{X_1} = \sigma^2{}_{X_2}$ or that X_1 and X_2 are normal. However, the sample sizes are large enough that the alternative model requirement that $(\bar{X}_1 - \bar{X}_2)$ be normal is met. This leaves only $\sigma^2{}_{X_1} = \sigma^2{}_{X_2}$ as a possible assumption of the model that has not been met outside of the null hypothesis.

The evaluation of the probability is as follows:

$$t_{38_o} = [(\bar{X}_1 - \bar{X}_2)_o - (\mu_1 - \mu_2)]/est\ \sigma_{(\bar{X}_1 - \bar{X}_2)}$$
$$= (.072 - 0)/.023 = +3.1$$

This is diagrammed in Figure 7.6.

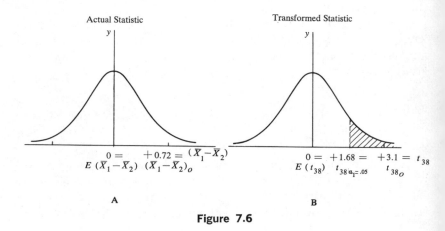

Figure 7.6

The evaluation of the probability is

$$p(t_{38} \geq +3.1) < p(t_{38} \geq +1.68) = .05 = \alpha$$

Therefore, the null hypothesis is rejected in favor of the alternative that says that the alcohol did increase reaction time. There are two reasons why Type I error may have been made. First, there is a possibility that $\sigma^2_{X_1} \neq \sigma^2_{X_2}$ so that the model may have been rejected even though H_0 is true. Secondly, the sample may not have come from a population other than the hypothesized one. Instead it may have, just by chance, been a rare sample from the hypothesized population.

A CRITICAL LOOK AT ONE-TAILED LOGIC

The material presented up to this point on one-tailed tests is consistent with the traditional presentation. However, severe questions might be raised about one-tailed tests. The main point to be contended is whether they are, in fact, hypothesis tests.

The logic of two-tailed tests was essentially the following. Because a population could not usually be measured in its entirety, it was necessary to make assumptions or hypotheses about the population. These hypotheses formed the model. A sample was then drawn and the value of the statistic examined. If the probability was low that, just by chance, values of the statistic would be drawn as extreme or more so from the expected value of the statistic as the observed one was, the decision was to reject the model. Rejecting the model meant concluding that at least one of the assumptions was false. Generally, however, one was interested in coming to a conclusion about the value of the population parameter. This hypothesis then became the null hypothesis and all of the other assumptions of the model had to actually be met so that the conclusion would be precisely about the null hypothesis.

If the null hypothesis were rejected, this was due to the fact that the probability of values of the statistic like the observed one was very low. So low, in fact, that it was necessary to conclude that the sample did not come from a population with a value of the parameter equal to that which had been assumed. In other words, $H_0 : \mu = a$ was determined to be false. Since either $\mu = a$ or $\mu \neq a$, if $\mu = a$ is false then $\mu \neq a$. (Of course, falseness here is in a statistical sense. It is possible that Type I error has been made, and the conclusion that $\mu = a$ is false may be an incorrect conclusion.) Thus, in a two-tailed test, the acceptance of H_A is logically forced by the rejection of H_0.

Consider one-tailed tests. The form of the null hypothesis remains the same. That is, it is of the form $H_0 : \mu = a$ or $H_0 : \mu_1 - \mu_2 = a$. However, the alternative is changed. Now H_A only deals with values in a particular direction from the value given in the null hypothesis, for example, $H_A : \mu < a$, or $H_A : \mu_1 - \mu_2 > a$.

The logical problem is this. Rejection of H_0 does not compel the the acceptance of H_A. Take a particular case where $H_0 : \mu = a$ and $H_A : \mu > a$. If the null hypothesis is rejected then the alternative hypothesis is accepted. This means that the conclusion is made in this case that the true value of the parameter is greater than a. But if the true value of the parameter is greater than a, it must be false that the parameter has a value less than or equal to a. Again resorting to simple logic, either $\mu > a$ or $\mu \leq a$. $\mu > a$. Therefore, $\mu \leq a$ is false.

The problem is that the null hypothesis that was rejected was $H_0 : \mu = a$, but the acceptance of the single direction alternative $H_A : \mu > a$ implies that $H_0 : \mu \leq a$ was rejected. But since $H_0 : \mu \leq a$ was not tested it could not have been rejected.

Well then, why not test $H_0 : \mu \leq a$? That is, why not have a hypothesis in the model that the value of the parameter is less than or equal to some value? The reason is this. The assumptions in the model determine the expected value of the sampling distribution of the statistic. In addition, they determine the function for the sampling distribution, that is the values of the statistic and the probabilities associated with them for the unique samples of a particular size from the population. If one of the hypotheses is $H_0 : \mu \leq a$, how could the expected value of the sampling distribution be determined? It is apparent that the null hypothesis must give a specific value to the parameter in order to obtain an expected value of the sampling distribution. Further, the values of the statistic and the probabilities associated with them could not be determined for a null hypothesis that did not have a specific value for the parameter, and without an expected value it is not even possible to say how far a particular result deviates from the expected in terms of either units or probabilities. As a result, it is not possible to test $H_0 : \mu \leq a$.

Further, the one-tailed test goes against the intuitive argument that has been presented as a partial basis for rejecting a model. Previously, it was agreed that the further away an observed result was from the expected, the less probable should results like it be and the more evidence it should be against the model. However, in the one-tailed argument above, sample results that deviate in the wrong direction were not considered evidence against the model no matter what the extent of the deviation and no matter how small the probability was.

It is apparent that one-tailed tests test the specific value $\mu = a$ since a is always taken, even in one-tailed tests, as the expected value of the statistic. The argument generally offered to justify the actual rejection of $H_0 : \mu \leq a$ is as follows: If $\mu = a$ is rejected in favor of $\mu > a$ certainly any value $< a$ would have also had to have been rejected. When $H_A : \mu > a$ is accepted the sample result must be such that it deviates from the hypothesized value by a large amount and in the positive direction. If this sample result is unlikely to have come from a population whose value of the mean is a, then certainly it is even less likely to have come from any population whose value of the mean is less than a.

The student may recall that this type of argument was actually offered before but not in the discussion of hypothesis testing. It is the same argument that was offered in the determination of confidence intervals.

This is the major point of this section. One-tailed tests are not really hypothesis tests since they do not test the hypothesis that they reject. Instead, they are estimation tests. They do, however, differ from the two-tailed confidence intervals in the following way: The experimenter is not merely interested in determining the range of two-tailed hypotheses that could not have been rejected on the basis of the evidence obtained from the sample. He is interested in finding a range that will only include hypotheses that fall to one side of some given value (the value that is usually stated in the null hypothesis).

For example, if $H_0 : \mu = a$ and $H_A : \mu < a$ is the form that one arrives at for the null and alternative hypotheses, the problem may be translated into a confidence interval problem with the experimenter wishing to find an interval such that both μ_L and μ_U are less than a. He would then be able to conclude that any null hypothesis that was equal to or greater than *a* would have had to have been rejected on the basis of the evidence from the sample.

In order to illustrate these points again consider the case of the spark plug manufacturer (who is probably out of business by now).

The observed result was $\bar{X}_o = 22,600$ and the attempt is to determine whether the two-tailed confidence interval (with $\alpha = .01$) is such that both μ_L and μ_U are greater than 20,000.

The computation of the interval results in $t_{11} = (\bar{X}_o - \mu_L)/est\ \sigma_{\bar{x}} = +3.11$.

Therefore,

$$(22,600 - \mu_L)/900 = +3.11$$

$$\mu_L = 22,600 - 3.11(900) = 22,600 - 2799 = 19,801$$

Computation of μ_U yields $\mu_U = 25,399$.

The 99 percent confidence interval, therefore, goes from 19,801 miles to 25,399 miles. Unfortunately, for the spark plug manufacturer, one of the null hypotheses that cannot be rejected on the basis of the sample result is $H_0 : \mu = 20,000$ (or $H_0 : \mu = 19,801$ for that matter). Thus, in terms of the specified α level, the sample is consistent with hypotheses that say the new manufacturing process is no better or even slightly worse than the old. On the basis of this information the manufacturer would not go ahead with the manufacture of the new plugs.

COMPUTATIONAL NOTE

If $H_0 : \mu = a$ and $H_A : \mu > a$ then if $\mu_L > a$, μ_U must be greater than a also. Similarly, if $H_0 : \mu = a$ and $H_A : \mu < a$ then if $\mu_U < a$, μ_L must also be $< a$. Thus, it is only really necessary to compute one of the limits in the translation of the one-tailed situation to a confidence interval problem.

WHAT TO DO

Two approaches to the one-tailed problem have been given. Most investigators use the first.

As a point of research pragmatism, the use of one-tailed tests has led to correct conclusions about the real world over a long period of time. Since for most people success conquers logic and mathematical habit is as resistant to change as is social custom, the student should be capable of doing one-tailed tests according to the procedure given in the first part of this chapter. Even this text will present additional examples of the traditional use of one-tailed tests.

8

SCALING AND ASSOCIATION

SCALING

Inferential statistics deals with populations of elements that receive scores on a common attribute. To this point only one type of score has been dealt with. Actually there are several different types of scores that elements may receive. The following discussion will examine these types and some of their differentiating characteristics.

The common attribute is generally referred to as a variable. Elements may vary on the variable in different ways. These different ways define *levels of scaling*. The four levels that will be discussed are *Nominal*, *Ordinal*, *Interval*, and *Ratio* scaling.

Nominal Scaling

The essential feature of nominal scaling is that elements can only be classified into categories on a variable. For example, the variable *sex* has two categories, male and female. Elements can only be classified as to whether they are male or female. The only judgment that can be made about two elements is whether they are the same or are different. Another example of a nominal variable would be hair color. There are any number of categories that might be formed, for example, blonde, brunette, redhead, other. These four categories represent the scores that elements can receive. Again, two elements can only be compared in terms of whether they are the same or different. The only measure of central tendency that is appropriate is the mode. That is, the categories can be quantitatively described in terms of the frequency with which elements occur in them. It then becomes possible to note which category is the most frequently occurring, that is, which is the modal category.

Ordinal Scaling

There are many variables in which the scores are ordered. For example, the positions in a race are ordered; the runner who finishes first runs faster than the one who finishes second and the second runs faster than the one who finishes third, and so on. There can also be ties in ordered data so that more than one element can be at a particular rank in the order.

Attitude scales frequently consist of ordered categories. For example, people might be asked about foreign aid in terms of three categories, whether they favor more foreign aid, about the same amount of foreign aid, or less foreign aid. These three categories are ordered. Individuals who prefer category one are in favor of more foreign aid than those in category two, and those in category two favor more than those in category three.

The essential added characteristic of ordered data is that two elements can be compared not only in terms of same or different, but also in terms of greater than and less than. Further, one element can be between two other elements. Of course, the mode is still a legitimate measure of central tendency, since some one of the ordered classes is a most frequently occurring one. In addition, the median is a measure of central tendency that can be computed on ordered data. Since elements are ordered it is possible to determine a point such that 50 percent of the cases fall at or below that point.

Interval Scaling

All of the inferential tests presented thus far in this text have required data to be at least at the level of interval scaling. The essential feature of interval scaling is that the variables have a unit of measurement. The unit of measurement allows distances between scores to be computed. An example of an interval scale is the centigrade scale of temperature. An object with a temperature of 30°C is 10°C less than an object with a temperature of 40°C, and this object is 10°C less than one of 50°C. Consider how this situation differs from the one in which runners are recorded in terms of the position that they finish in a race. It is not reasonable to consider the distance between the first place runner and the second place runner to necessarily be equal to the distance between the second and the third. Since only the order is known, no unit of measurement was used to measure the racers. Similarly, grades in school are not on an interval scale. All one can say is that an A is better than a B which is better than a C and so on. The distance between an A and a B is not necessarily the same as between a B and a C.

In addition to a fixed unit of measurement, an interval scale has an arbitrary zero point. In the case of centigrade temperature, the 0 point is the freezing point of water. This is quite arbitrary. There is no necessary reason why the freezing point of ethyl alcohol could not have just as well been used. Of course the Fahrenheit scale is also an example of an interval scale.

The interval scale allows the computation of a mean as a measure of central tendency. Scores can be added together since this involves addition of amounts of a particular unit or numbers of a unit. Further, measures of variability, like the standard deviation, the variance, and the average absolute deviation can also be computed. All of these measures of variability require the computation of distances; this is not possible unless the level of interval scaling has been reached. Obviously, the average rank for ordinal data cannot be computed. For example, if a person finishes a race in first place and the next race in third place, is his average finish equal to second place? If it is, then a person who finishes second both times would have averaged the same. There is no way, knowing just the above ordinal properties, to determine that this is so.

With grades, a similar problem exists. An A and a C do not necessarily equal two B's. Although assigning a 1 to an A, 2 to a B, and 3 to a C does result in a grade point average of 2 in each case, it is the assignment of the numbers in the first place *as interval scores* that is not justified. This is because the letters are not based on a common unit of measurement. Just as in the case of the runners, the distances between the letters are not determined.

Strictly speaking, most psychological tests or scales are not really intervally scaled. The most common one used as an interval scale is IQ. If IQ were intervally scaled then the distance between an intelligence quotient of 80 and 100 would be the same as that between 140 and 160, or 40 and 60. This conclusion is not really warranted. All that can be said, strictly speaking, is that an IQ of 140 is better than one of 139, which is better than one of 125.

z scores are on an interval scale. There is a specific unit of measurement which is the standard deviation of the distribution. The zero point, however, is arbitrary. There is no necessary reason why the number of standard deviations could not be taken from the median or the mode as opposed to the mean.

It should be made clear that numbers can always be assigned to objects and these numbers can be added, subtracted, divided, or multiplied. It is possible to assign to the letter grade A the number 4, to a B the number 3, to a C a 2, to a D a 1 and to an E a 0. These numbers can be averaged. Thus, a person with two B's and an A can be said to have a grade point average of 1%. Further, a person with two A's and a C could have his grade point average computed and it would also be 1%. The problem occurs when these numbers are interpreted. Although each person may be said to have the same grade point average, there is no way to legitimately state that their grades are equal on the basis of the grade point average. Similarly, although two A's and a D would result in an average of $\frac{9}{3}$ and this number is smaller than $\frac{10}{3}$, one cannot say, on this basis, that the grades in this last instance are poorer than those in the first instance. (Based on just the ordinal information it is possible to say that two A's and a C are better than two A's and a D.)

Another example of an assignment of numbers might be to give a score of 1 to a female and a 0 to a male. A group of three males and one female would have a mean of $\frac{3}{4}$. A group of 2 males and 6 females would have a mean of $\frac{2}{8}$. Obviously, $\frac{2}{8} < \frac{3}{4}$. But there is no way of interpreting this result in terms of a concept like the "average sex" of the group.

These considerations lead to two points. One is that within the abstract system, numbers can be operated on in any way that is consistent with the logic of the system. However, the numbers that are operated on must be legitimate abstractions of real world objects if they are to lead to meaningful interpretations of those objects and their relationships.

The second point is a matter of practice. Frequently, ordinal data is treated as if it is interval data. Good examples of this are the use of grade point averages and of IQ scores. This is done because there is greater deductive power with interval data than with ordinal data. If the distances between ranks are treated as equal even when it is not known that this is the case, the greater deductive power may enable greater predictive ability. In a practical situation, this consideration may overcome the problem of the distortion of the rank information that may occur when ranks are treated as interval numbers.

Ratio Scaling

The highest form of scaling (the one requiring the most information) is ratio scaling. Here not only is there a unit of measurement, but there is also an absolute zero rather than an arbitrary zero. For example, the Kelvin temperature scale is a ratio scale. There is an absolute zero which represents a point below which measures cannot be made. Weight is also a ratio scale as is height.

In addition to all the measures of central tendency and variability that have been used with other forms of scaling, the absolute zero allows one to make comparisons in terms of the number of times greater one quantity is compared to another. For example, on the Kelvin scale an object that is $100°K$ is twice as hot, or has twice as much heat, as one that is only $50°K$. This is not true on the Centigrade scale. An object that is $10°C$ is not twice as hot as one that is $5°C$ because the zero point is arbitrary. These temperatures can be changed by converting them to Fahrenheit. Ten degrees C is the same as $32° + \frac{9}{5}(10°) = 50°F$, and $5°C$ is $41°F$. This conversion does not of course change the heat of the bodies but only changes their scores by shifting both the zero point and the unit of measurement. Now the objects are rated as 50°F and 41°F respectively, and the temperature of the first is not twice as large as that of the second. It must be apparent that the number of times warmer one object is compared to another depends on how warm the objects are relative to an absolute zero, not on their scores on a scale with an arbitrary zero point.

Other ratio scales also illustrate the idea of "times." A person 60 inches tall is twice as tall as one 30 inches tall. A person of 200 pounds is twice as heavy as one that is only 100 pounds. However, suppose the reference point on weight were taken as 150 pounds. Then a person of 175 pounds would be classified as +25 pounds and one of 100 pounds would be classified as −50 pounds. It is again apparent that a person of 200 pounds (now scored as +50) is not twice as heavy as a person of 175 pounds (now scored as +25).

An important point to be made is that one can go from higher levels of scaling to lower ones but not vice versa. That is, the higher the level of the scale, the more information it requires. If some of this information is thrown away then a lower level can be reached. But if one starts at a lower level it is not possible to add the information necessary to reach a higher level unless one makes additional assumptions about the data.

For example, given a redhead and a blond, it is not possible to say one is greater than the other, (no matter what one's personal experience in the matter would indicate). However, if individuals are measured as to height and the results of two such measurements are 69 inches and 63 inches, it is possible to throw away the information about the absolute 0 point and simply say that the first individual is 6 inches taller than the second. More information, that concerning the unit of measurement, can be thrown out and it could simply be stated that individual one is taller than individual two (ordinal scaling). Finally, the ordered information could be ignored and the statement could merely be that one individual is in the class of things that is 69 inches tall and the other is in the class of things 63 inches tall. The principle illustrated above is probably important enough to be italicized. The principle: *One can go from higher levels of scaling to lower levels of scaling by ignoring some of the information present in the higher level but one cannot go from lower levels to higher levels without making additional assumptions about the data.*

A last comment: Given interval scaling, it is possible to compute the mean. By considering only ordinal properties it is possible to compute the median, and by considering only nominal properties it is possible to compute the mode, that is, the most frequently occurring class. However, given nominal data it is not possible to go to higher levels. For example, it is not possible to add a male to a female and divide by two to get an average sex.

ASSOCIATION

Introduction

To this point the elements have been scored on only a single attribute at a time. The next task is to look at those cases in which there are two variables and the elements are scored on each of them. For example, if the elements are adults in the United States, then they might be scored as to sex and also as to height. Or students in the sixth grade of a school might each be scored as to their grades in history and also their grades in English.

The elements do not need to be single individuals. They can consist of pairs. For example, each pair could consist of a father and his son. One variable could be the height of the father and the other could be the height of the son. If the pair is conceived as an element then these elements are also scored on each of the two variables. First the element is scored in terms of the variable — height of the father, and then it is scored in terms of the variable — height of the son.

Both of these types of elements can be considered to be matched pairs. When individual elements, as in the first example, are scored on two variables, the individual can be considered matched with himself. In the second example, the fathers are matched with the sons. Each matched pair is a compound element each part of which is scored on one of the variables.

Association and Correlation

The question that is of usual interest when elements are scored on both variables is whether or not the variables are associated. Association exists when information about the score an element receives on one variable allows one to better predict the score that the element will receive on the other variable than would have been possible had information from the first variable not been available. For example, suppose one knows the heights of a group of fathers. Does this information help in predicting the heights of their sons? If it does, then the two variables would be considered to be associated. If it does not, then they would not be associated.

The association measures that will be discussed in this text are symmetric. That is, if the heights of the fathers are associated with the heights of their sons, then the heights of the sons are associated with those of their fathers. Consequently, prediction can be from either variable to the other.

Association may be measured in different ways through the use of various mathematical relationships or rules. The correlation between two variables is their association when it is measured in certain ways. The correlation coefficient measures the degree of association between the variables for the particular correlation rule that is used. In the following sections, several correlation coefficients will be examined. These coefficients differ in terms of the data for which they are appropriate. That is, as has now been pointed out, variables can differ in terms of their level of scaling. Some correlation coefficients require one level of scaling and others require other levels (just as the mean requires interval level of scaling and the mode requires scaling to at least be nominal). As with the measures of central tendency, information can be ignored so that a correlation coefficient that only requires a low level of scaling can be computed when information at high levels of scaling is available.

Descriptive Measures of Association

All of the measures of correlation or association are descriptive measures on a group of elements. At this point there is no question about the likelihood that the observed correlation might have occurred by chance from a population with some particular assumed value for the true value of the correlation. Hence, the correlation coefficient, which measures the degree of the association in the observed data, is descriptive of the relationship between the variables, just as the mean of a sample is descriptive of the average score that has been observed in a group of scores.

The Phi-Coefficient

φ is a measure of the degree of association between two nominally scaled variables each of which has two categories. For example, a group of college students could be classified as to their sex and their smoking behavior. The results of measurements on a group of 100 could then be summarized in a table such as the following:

		SEX		
		Male	*Female*	
SMOKING	*Smokers*	25	15	40
		a	*b*	
BEHAVIOR		*d*	*c*	
	Nonsmokers	25	35	60
		50	50	100

Note that the cells have been given letters *a*, *b*, *c*, *d*, so that all 2 x 2 (two by two) tables can be discussed abstractly. The *entries* in each of the cells represent the frequency with which each type of element occurred. Hence there were 25 males who smoked, 35 females who didn't, and so on. The numbers around the edges are called the *marginals*. These indicate that there were 50 males and 50 females in the sample. There were also 40 smokers and 60 nonsmokers. The final entry is *n* or the total number in the group of scores. (This group may or may not have been a sample. Remember that the correlation coefficient is merely descriptive of the association between two variables for a group of scores.)

The formula for the computation of φ is:

$$\varphi = \frac{ac - bd}{\sqrt{(a + b)(c + d)(a + d)(b + c)}}$$

In the above example then,

$$\varphi = \frac{25(35) - (15)(25)}{\sqrt{(40)(60)(50)(50)}} = \frac{875 - 375}{500\sqrt{24}}$$

$$= \frac{500}{500 \times 2\sqrt{6}} = \frac{500}{500 \times 2 \times 2.4} = \frac{1}{4.8} = +.21$$

Since the data is only nominal, the $+$ sign indicates that the association is along the *ac* diagonal rather than the *bd* diagonal. This merely means that if a person is a male he is more likely to be a smoker than a non-smoker *than would be expected just on the basis of the number of smokers and the number of nonsmokers.* Similarly for the females the chances are greater that the female is a nonsmoker than a smoker *than would be expected on the basis of the number of smokers and nonsmokers.*

The conclusion obviously is that there is some association when it is measured in the above way.

To examine the problem a bit more carefully, consider what the situation would have had to have been for φ to be 0, that is, for there to have been no association.

Since 40 percent of the group were smokers then 40 percent of the males and 40 percent of the females should have been smokers if smoking was not related at all to sex. Similarly 60 percent of the males and 60 percent of the females should have been nonsmokers. Under these circumstances the table would have appeared as follows:

		SEX			
		Male		*Female*	
	Smokers	20		20	40
SMOKING			*a*	*b*	
BEHAVIOR			*d*	*c*	
	Nonsmokers	30		30	60
		50		50	100

Then

$$\varphi = \frac{20 \times 30 - 20 \times 30}{\sqrt{(40)(60)(50)(50)}} = 0$$

The discussion could also have been approached from the point of view of sex. That is, since 50 percent of the sample were male and 50 percent were female, then 50 percent of the smokers should have been male and 50 percent female. Similarly, for the nonsmokers. The above table reflects this fact also.

What would have had to exist for the correlation to have been perfect, that is, for φ to be either -1.00 or $+1.00$? The most extreme that the entries could have been is indicated below:

		SEX			
		Male		*Female*	
	Smokers	40		0	40
SMOKING			*a*	*b*	
BEHAVIOR			*d*	*c*	
	Nonsmokers	10		50	60
		50		50	100

This yields

$$\varphi = \frac{40 \times 50 - (0)(10)}{500 \times 2 \times 2.4} = \frac{2000}{2400} = \frac{5}{6} = +.833$$

Of course the table could also have been examined from the point of view of the most extreme association along the *bd* diagonal but the results would have been the same.

It will not always be true that the extremes along the *ac* marginal will give the same results as those along the *bd* marginal. For example consider the following case:

		SEX			
		Male		*Female*	
	Smokers				40
SMOKING			*a*	*b*	
BEHAVIOR			*d*	*c*	
	Nonsmokers				60
		30		70	100

The extreme situation along the *ac* diagonal results in a table as follows:

		SEX			
		Male	*Female*		
	Smokers	30	10	40
SMOKING		*a*	*b*		
BEHAVIOR		*d*	*c*		
	Nonsmokers	0	60	60
		30	70	100

This gives

$$\varphi = \frac{(30)(60) - (10)(0)}{\sqrt{(30)(70)(40)(60)}} = \frac{+1800}{600\sqrt{14}} = \frac{+3}{\sqrt{14}}$$

For the most extreme situation along the *bd* marginal given the same marginals, the results are:

		SEX			
		Male	*Female*		
	Smokers	0	40	40
SMOKING		*a*	*b*		
BEHAVIOR		*d*	*c*		
	Nonsmokers	30	30	60
		30	70	100

This gives

$$\varphi = \frac{(30)(0) - 1200}{600\sqrt{14}} = \frac{-2}{\sqrt{14}}$$

Had the marginals been those indicated below it would have been possible to achieve the maximum correlation of $+ 1.00$ by obtaining the indicated frequencies in the cells (since individuals are only scored in terms of the class in which they fall, the entries obviously represent the frequencies with which certain classes occurred).

		SEX			
		Male	*Female*		
	Smokers	50	0	50
SMOKING		*a*	*b*		
BEHAVIOR		*d*	*c*		
	Nonsmokers	0	50	50
		50	50	100

Now $\qquad \varphi = \dfrac{(50)(50) - (0)(0)}{\sqrt{(50)(50)(50)(50)}} = \dfrac{2500}{2500} = +1.00$

One important conclusion to be gained from this is that the marginals may prevent perfect correlation from occurring. In the first example, where the marginals were 40, 60, 50, and 50, the maximum correlation that could possibly have occurred was 0.833.

This has led to an examination of the phi-coefficient not simply in terms of the actual coefficient that the data yield but in terms of the maximum φ that could have been obtained for the given marginals. The measure then becomes $\varphi' = \varphi_0/|\varphi_{max}|$ where φ_0 is the observed φ and φ_{max} is the maximum coefficient that could have been obtained for the given marginals. Since φ_{max} may differ depending upon the diagonal that is selected, the absolute value of φ_{max} *for the same diagonal as is represented by φ_0 is used as the denominator.*

In the example presented then:

$$\varphi' = \frac{+.21}{|+.83|} = +.25$$

The final question to be posed concerns the following situation. The second φ table gave $\varphi_0 = +.833$. Then the value of $\varphi' = +.83/|+.83|$ $= 1.00$. That is, this table represents the greatest value of φ that could have been obtained for the given marginals. Does this mean that the association was perfect? Hardly. In terms of the discussion at the beginning of this section, perfect association means perfect prediction. An examination of the second φ table indicates that prediction is not perfect. For example, if an element is a male one cannot with certainty predict whether he will be a smoker or a nonsmoker. The chances are, according to this table, that he will be a smoker. But sometimes there are males who are nonsmokers. Thus, prediction is not perfect. Knowing the sex classification of an individual does not allow perfect prediction about his smoking behavior.

As indicated before, the above correlation is symmetric. This is illustrated by the fact that knowing that an element has been classified as a nonsmoker does not allow perfect prediction about its sex. Most often it is female but sometimes nonsmokers are males according to the table.

Thus it is necessary to realize that φ_{max} does not represent the greatest amount of association that is theoretically possible, but the greatest amount of prediction that is possible given the marginals that exist for the data (and given φ as the index of the association). Similarly, a φ' of 1.00 does not mean that association is perfect. It only indicates that the entries in the cells are the greatest that could be achieved given the marginals that exist.

A question that might be asked is why the marginals could not be changed. The answer is: The marginals represent the state of the group that has been selected. If 40 percent smoke and 60 percent do not, then 40 percent smoke and 60 percent do not. If 50 percent are male and 50 percent are female, then that is that. The question is, given these frequencies for the scores of the elements on each of the variables, what is the degree of association that does exist and how does this compare to the greatest degree of association that could exist? If the marginals are of particular values (like 40, 60, 50, 50) then this means that for this group it is not possible for there to be perfect association or predictability. Another way to say this is that, if this is the state of nature for this group, predictability (or association) between smoking and sex classification cannot be perfect.

γ—Association for Ordinal Data

Frequently elements have been measured on scales that are ordinal. For example, a group of adults may have been measured in terms of their level of education and their attitude toward integration. A useful measure for determining the degree of association that exists between the two variables is γ. (Greek lower case gamma). This coefficient is valid when the two variables are measured at the ordinal level. There can be any number of categories and the two variables do not have to contain the same number of them.

An Example.   Suppose that a group of 57 adults have been measured on two ordinal scales. The first is attitude toward integration and the second is level of education. Consider the following hypothetical results:

HIGHEST LEVEL OF EDUCATION

		Grade School	High School	College	Graduate Training	
ATTITUDE TOWARD THE SPEED OF INTEGRA-TION	*Should be slower*	1 /1	6 /2	4 /3	1 /4	12
	Should be same	3 /5	13 /6	5 /7	2 /8	23
	Should be faster	7 /9	11 /10	3 /11	1 /12	22
		11	30	12	4	57

The question is whether or not these two variables are associated and, if they are, in what direction and to what degree.

The computation of the gamma coefficient is based on the following argument: Prediction means being able to determine the direction of change of an element on one variable from its change in position on another. This means that as the scores (ranks) go up on one variable, if there is an association, then there should be a corresponding trend for the scores to go up on the second variable (positive association) or down on the second variable (negative association). If there is no association, then knowing the change on one variable should not at all allow one to predict the direction of change on the second variable. Of course, if the association is perfect, then the direction of change on one variable should enable perfect prediction to be made about the direction of the change of that element's score on the second variable.

Consider cell 1 in the above example. What is the direction of change on the two variables for the elements in cell 2 compared to those in cell 1? The elements go up on the education variable, but they stay the same on the attitude variable. Thus, there is neither a positive nor a negative association between the variables based on the comparison of the elements in the first cell with those in the second cell. However, compare cell 1 with cell 6. The elements in cell 6 are higher on both variables when compared to the elements in cell 1. This would then be indicative of positive association between the variables. An example of negative association would be cell 6 compared to cell 9. Cell 9's elements are in a positive direction from those of cell 6 on the attitude variable but in a negative direction on the education variable. Another way to phrase this is to say that as one goes from the elements in cell 6 to those in cell 9 the scores on one variable are higher and on the other they are lower. Hence the relationship is negative.

The actual computation of γ involves counting all of the + comparisons and all of the − comparisons and noting which type occurs more frequently. The comparisons that indicate no association are not counted. All individuals are compared to all other individuals. Thus, if there are 5 individuals in one cell and 6 in another, there are a total of 30 comparisons; all 6 of the individuals in the second cell are compared to *each* individual in the first cell. The individuals in a particular cell are tied with each other, that is, they have the same rank on both variables.

Cell by cell the comparisons are noted that are + or −. Cell 1 has $1 \times [13 + 5 + 2 + 11 + 3 + 1] = 35$ + comparisons. Cell 2 has $6 [5 + 2 + 3 + 1] = 66$ + comparisons. However cell 2 also has $6(3 + 7) = 60$ negative comparisons.

To summarize the whole table, the results are tabulated as follows: S_+ represents the plus comparisons and S_- the negative comparisons.

Cell		S_+		S_-
1	$1(13 + 5 + 2 + 11 + 3 + 1)$	$= 35$		
2	$6(5 + 2 + 3 + 1)$	$= 66$	$6(3 + 7)$	$= 60$
3	$4(2 + 1)$	$= 12$	$4(3 + 13 + 7 + 11)$	$=136$
4			$1(3 + 13 + 5 + 7 + 11 + 3)$	$= 42$
5	$3(11 + 3 + 1)$	$= 45$		
6	$13(3 + 1)$	$= 52$	$13(7)$	$= 91$
7	$5(1)$	$= 5$	$5(7 + 11)$	$= 90$
8			$2(7 + 11 + 3)$	$= 42$
		$\overline{215}$		$\overline{461}$

Then $|\gamma|$ is the proportion of the total plus and minus comparisons that are an excess of plus over minus or minus over plus:

$$\gamma = \frac{S_+ - S_-}{S_+ + S_-} = \frac{215 - 461}{215 + 461} = \frac{-246}{676} = -.36$$

That is, of the $+$ and $-$ comparisons, which totaled 676, over one third (or 246) represent an excess of minus over plus comparisons. The interpretation of this coefficient is that as the scores increased on education, there was a corresponding tendency to favor slower integration *for this particular group of scores.* For a table in which the γ coefficient is negative the trend is along the upper right to lower left diagonal whereas a positive correlation is along the upper left to lower right diagonal. In order for a negative γ to actually represent a negative correlation and a positive γ to represent a positive correlation it is necessary that the categories on the two variables be ordered in one of the two following ways. Either 1) from lower to higher as one goes from left to right and from top to bottom or, 2) from higher to lower in both of the above directions.

A Possible Defect in γ.   An examination of γ indicates a possible defect. This can be illustrated by the following two tables.

TABLE A

Variable I

Variable II		1	2	3	
	1	3	4	5	12
	2	0	0	7	7
	3	0	0	5	5
		3	4	17	24

TABLE B

Variable I

Variable II		1	2	3	
	1	3	0	0	3
	2	0	3	0	3
	3	0	0	3	3
		3	3	3	9

The computation of γ for Table A gives:

Cell			S_+	S_-
1	$3(7 + 5)$	$=$	36	
2	$4(7 + 5)$	$=$	48	
			84	0

$$\gamma = \frac{S_+ - S_-}{S_+ + S_-} = \frac{84}{84} = +1.00$$

The computation for Table B gives:

Cell			S_+	S_-
1	$3(6)$	$=$	18	
5	$3(3)$	$=$	9	
			27	0

$$\gamma = \frac{S_+ - S_-}{S_+ + S_-} = \frac{(18 + 9) - 0}{27} = +1.00$$

In both cases the result is a γ of $+1.00$ which is the highest coefficient possible, that is, the number of comparisons that represents the excess of plus over minus can never be greater than the total number of comparisons and hence the proportion cannot be greater than 1.00. Similarly, γ can never be less than -1.00, in which case the proportion determined by $|\gamma|$ is still 1.00.

However, in the first case there are many ties and the γ of $+1.00$ does not really indicate perfect prediction. For example, if a person scores in category 3 on the first variable there is no way to predict, even with a γ of $+1.00$, what category he will fall into on the second variable. These 17 cases are almost evenly distributed across the categories of the second variable. Similarly, the 12 people in category one on the second variable are distributed across all three categories on the first variable.

In Table B, this is not the case. Knowledge about the category that a person is in on either variable gives full knowledge about the category in which the person is on the other variable.

γ could be modified by including the nondirectional comparisons as well and then considering the proportion of the total that is represented by the excess of plus over minus or minus over plus.

Then

$$\gamma' = \frac{S_+ - S_-}{S_+ + S_- + S_0}$$

where S_0 represents the comparisons that were neither plus nor minus. For Table A, S_0 is computed as follows:

Cell			S_0
1	3(4 + 5)	=	27
2	4(5)	=	20
3	5(7 + 5)	=	60
6	7(5)	=	35
			142

Then

$$\gamma' = \frac{84}{84 + 142} = \frac{84}{226} = +0.37$$

For Table B, $S_0 = 0$ so γ' remains $+1.00$.
Since

$$S_+ + S_- + S_0 = \sum_{i=1}^{jk-1} n_i \sum_{g=i+1}^{jk} n_g$$

the expression could be rewritten as

$$\gamma' = \frac{S_+ - S_-}{\sum_{i=1}^{jk-1} n_i \sum_{g=i+1}^{jk} n_g}$$

The student is warned that current discussions of γ in the literature are limited to its uses as presented in the first instance, that is

$$\gamma = \frac{S_+ - S_-}{S_+ + S_-}$$

In computing γ, it should be noted that it is not necessary to look back in the table. Examine again the attitude-education example. Consider cell 6. It is true that cells 3 and 4 are in a negative relation to cell 6 and cell 1 is in a plus relation. However, these comparisons are not counted since the comparisons with cell 6 and cells 1, 3 and 4 were made when these lower numbered cells were examined. The effect of looking back in the table would merely be to double the size of both the numerator and denominator and this would not change the size of the proportion (that is, $x/2x = 2x/4x$). It is important in computing γ to examine the cells in order from 1 to 2 to 3 to 4, and so on.

Pearson's r–Interval Data

When both variables are at least intervally scaled, Pearson's r becomes an appropriate measure of association. The full name of this coefficient is the Pearson product-moment correlation coefficient. Pearson's r, or r, will be used for brevity.

Consider two variables scaled at least at the interval level, like height and weight. These are actually on a ratio scale so r, which requires only interval data, is certainly appropriate. Suppose that scores have been collected on a group of 10 adult males and the results are:

Person	Height (in inches)	Weight (in pounds)
1	69.0	160
2	67.0	165
3	74.0	210
4	70.0	200
5	63.0	150
6	67.0	145
7	69.0	180
8	70.0	168
9	65.0	140
10	73.0	200

If height is the X variable and weight is the Y variable, the scores can be represented as in Figure 8.1.

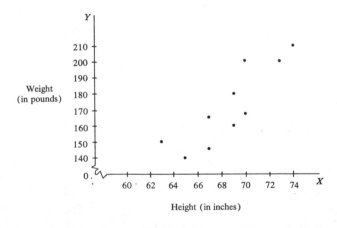

Figure 8.1

It is clear from the diagram that there is a tendency for an increase in the height scores to be associated with an increase in the weight scores. This is not true for all individuals. For some persons an increase on the height variable is accompanied by a decrease on the weight variable. (For example, look at the above table and notice the changes on each variable for persons 5 and 6. Thus, although there is a definite positive association, it is less than perfect.)

The formula for r is given by

$$r = \frac{\sum_{i=1}^{n} z_{X_i} z_{Y_i}}{n}$$

where z_{X_i} is the z score of the ith person on the X variable and z_{Y_i} is the z score of this same person on the Y variable. The verbal definition of r is — the average cross product of the z scores.

In order to compute r, each z score must be computed for each individual on each of the variables. The results of these computations are presented in Table 8.1.

Table 8.1

**Computation of $\Sigma\, z_{X_i} z_{Y_i}$ for 10
Elements on Height and Weight**

i	z_{X_i}	z_{Y_i}	$z_{X_i} z_{Y_i}$	
1	+0.1	−0.5	−0.05	$\bar{X} = 68.7$
2	−0.5	−0.3	+0.15	$SD_X = 3.2$
3	+1.7	+1.6	+2.72	
4	+0.4	+1.2	+0.48	$\bar{Y} = 172$
5	−1.8	−0.9	+1.62	
6	−0.5	−1.1	+0.55	$SD_Y = 23.5$
7	+0.1	+0.3	+0.03	
8	+0.4	−0.2	−0.08	$z_{X_i} = \dfrac{X_i - \bar{X}}{SD_X}$
9	−1.2	−1.4	+1.68	
10	+1.3	+1.2	+1.56	
			$\Sigma\, z_{X_i} z_{Y_i} = 8.92$	$z_{Y_i} = \dfrac{Y_i - \bar{Y}}{SD_Y}$

For each person, the cross-product of his z score on each variable is computed $(z_{X_i} z_{Y_i})$. The correlation obtained is

$$r = \frac{\sum_{i=1}^{n} z_{X_i} z_{Y_i}}{n} = \frac{8.92}{10} = +.89$$

This value for r is not surprising since the *scatter diagram*, or *scatter plot*, of the scores indicated strong but not perfect positive correlation. As with the other measures of correlation, r can range between a $+1.00$ and a -1.00, with $+1.00$ representing a perfect positive correlation and -1.00 representing a perfect negative correlation.

Interpretation of r. r represents the degree to which a straight line can be fitted to the data. It is obvious that no straight line could go through all of the above given points and therefore the correlation could not have been $+1.00$. To understand the idea of a straight line fit to the data it is beneficial to consider the scatter diagram of the z scores and also the formula for predicting scores on one variable from the scores on another. The scatter plot for the z scores is given in Figure 8.2. It is again apparent that the points will not fit on a straight line. But there is a best straight

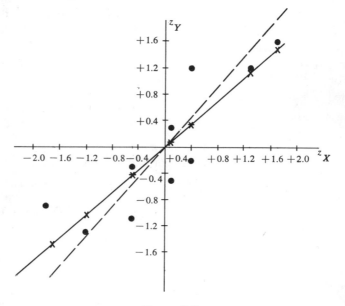

Figure 8.2

line, that is, a line that will come, on the average, closer to the points than any other straight line. The best line is defined as *that line which on the average makes the squared distance of the points from the line a minimum.*

The concept of the best line is analogous to the concept of the best number that was discussed in Chapter 2. That is, a measure is sought that will minimize the errors that will be made when that measure is used to describe a distribution. In this case it is a measure of the association between two variables. The concept of error is again the squared deviations, but in the case of association the measure that minimizes the errors is a line rather than a point.

The correlation coefficient, r, enters into the formula for the best straight line. It may be recalled that in Chapter 3 the concept of functions was discussed. One type of function was a linear function. This function could be represented as $y = f(x)$, where $f(x)$ was a rule of the general form $ax + b$. For each value of x a value was assigned to y in such a way that a straight line resulted.

In the case of correlation, the rule given for $f(x)$ is quite simple. It is rz_X. Hence $z'_Y = rz_X$. This rule is of the form $y = ax + b$ where $b = 0$, and results in a line that fits the points the best in terms of minimizing the squared deviations of the points from the line. However, the points are in a plane, that is, in two dimensions. Hence they can deviate from the line either in terms of their distance from the line along the x axis or their distance along the y axis. The formula $z'_Y = rz_X$ gives the line that *minimizes the squared deviations along the y axis* (the solid line in the diagram). The formula $z'_X = rz_Y$ gives the line that minimizes the squared deviations of the points from the line along the x axis (the dotted line in the diagram).

Undoubtedly, you have perceived that the formula was written $z'_Y = rz_X$ rather than $z_Y = rz_X$. This is because z_X and z_Y represent the actual z scores in the data. It is obvious that the straight line cannot go through all of these points. That is, when there is imperfect correlation the line cannot go through the (z_X, z_Y) coordinate of the original data. Hence z'_Y denotes the z score on the Y variable that is actually on the line for a given z_X score. Sometimes this z'_Y value will also be equal to z_Y and at other times it will not.

The line $z'_Y = rz_X$ is also the prediction line. That is, when there is association between the two variables, a score on one variable can more easily be predicted on the basis of the score on the other variable than would have been possible had the score on this second variable not been known. Then for each z_X in the data, z'_Y is the *predicted z score on the Y variable*, that is, it is the z score on the Y variable that falls on that straight line that best fits the data.

Plotting the Line.   For any line to be plotted only two points need be determined. One point is always readily available. If the scores are in z scores then the line must go through the origin of the axes (the point 0,0). That is, for $z'_Y = rz_X$, if $z_X = 0$, then $rz_X = 0$ no matter what the value of r is, so z'_Y must equal 0. Similarly for $z'_X = rz_Y$, $z'_X = 0$ if $z_Y = 0$. From the problem that was presented one more point will be determined for each line.

Since $r = +0.89$, then when $z_X = 1$, $z'_Y = 0.89(1) = 0.89$. For $z_Y = 1$, $z'_X = +0.89(1) = +0.89$. Note that the z_X and z_Y selected to compute the second point through which the line passes do not have to be actual z scores obtained in the data. $y = f(x)$ in this case is a continuous function. For *every* value on the x axis (that is, every z_X value) a z'_Y value is determined.

A look at the diagram indicates that the solid line ($z'_Y = rz_Y$) minimizes the squared deviations of the points from it along the y axis and the dotted line does the job for the deviations along the x axis. The two lines will become the same for $r = +1.00$. This may be apparent to you. For the case $r = \pm 1.00$ *all* of the data points must fall on the line. Obviously there is only one straight line that will accomplish this.

Regression to the Mean.   The best fitting line is often called the *regression* line. This term arises because the predicted scores are always as close or closer to the mean than the original scores. Consider $z'_Y = rz_X$. Each data value of z_X determines a z'_Y score that falls on the regression line. Since r can never be greater than $+1.00$ or less than -1.00, z'_Y must always be a z score whose absolute value is less than or equal to the absolute value of z_X, that is, $|z'_Y| \leq |z_X|$. If r is not $+1.00$ or -1.00 then $|z'_Y| < |z_X|$. But the absolute value of z represents the number of standard deviations away from the mean a score is. If the number of standard deviations a score is from the mean decreases, then the score lies closer to the mean. Whenever $|r| < 1.00$, each predicted score, whether a z'_X or a z'_Y, will be closer to the mean than the data score from which it was predicted.

Since each predicted score will be closer to the mean, the variance of the predicted scores will be less than those of the original scores, $SD^2_{z'_Y} < SD^2_{z_X}$ for $|r| < 1.00$ and $SD^2_{z'_Y} = SD^2_{z_X}$ for $|r| = 1.00$. However, the variance of any set of data z scores always equals unity. Therefore, for $|r| < 1.00$ the variance of the predicted scores will be less than 1, or, $SD^2_{z'_Y} < 1$ and $SD^2_{z'_X} < 1$.

The exact relationship among the variances is given by $SD^2_{z_Y} = SD^2_{z'_Y} + SD^2_{est\ z_Y \cdot z_X}$ or $1 = SD^2_{z'_Y} + SD^2_{est\ z_Y \cdot z_X}$. This last variance is the variance of the errors made in estimating z_Y from z_X. The meaning of the three variances will be explained before the relationship of r to them is presented.

$SD^2_{z_Y}$ is the easiest symbol. It represents the variance of the z scores that are obtained from the original raw scores on the Y variable. (For the X variable, the analogous measure would be $SD^2_{z_X}$). By definition

$$SD^2_{z_Y} = \frac{\sum_{i=1}^{n} (z_{Y_i} - \bar{z}_Y)^2}{n}$$

As has been repeatedly stated, $SD^2_{z_Y} = 1$ and $SD^2_{z_X} = 1$.

$SD^2_{z'_Y}$ represents the variance among the predicted z scores. The regression line contains these predicted z scores. For any $|r| < 1.00$, z'_Y will sometimes be equal to z_Y and at other times it will not. Of course the values of z'_Y will differ from each other. This is easily seen since $z'_Y = rz_X$. Since r is a constant for a particular set of data, z'_Y varies as the values of z_X do. It is the variance of these z'_Y scores that is symbolized by $SD^2_{z'_Y}$. Thus,

$$SD^2_{z'_Y} = \frac{\sum\limits_{i=1}^{n} (z'_{Y_i} - \overline{z'_{Y_i}})^2}{n}$$

This variance, $SD^2_{z'_Y}$, is called *the variance predicted by the relationship of X to Y.*

The points are marked with an x on Figure 8.2. Since their y axis differences from each other can be accounted for by the differences among the X scores from which they were predicted, their variability is accounted for. Obviously, when $|r| = 1.00$, $z'_{Y_i} = z_{X_i}$ for every i, and this variability equals 1, which is the most it can equal. That is, all of the variability of the z_Y scores can then be predicted by the relationship of X to Y since all of the z_Y scores fall on the regression line and are, hence, predictable.

Since all of the original variability among the z_Y scores is generally not accounted for because $|r|$ is usually < 1.00, some is still left over. This leftover variability is error variance, or technically, the variance of the errors in estimating z_Y from z_X. Errors are reasonably defined as the difference between the z'_Y score and the original z_Y data score, for a given z_X score.

For example, the data given in Table 8.1 indicates that for $i = 2$, $z_{X_i} = -0.5$ and $z_{Y_i} = -0.3$. Since $r = +0.89$, then $z'_{Y_i} = (+0.89)$ $(-0.5) = -0.445$. Hence, the error between the obtained value z_Y, and the predicted value z'_Y, is $(z'_Y - z_Y)$. The squared error would be $(z'_Y - z_Y)^2$, or, in this case, $[-0.445 - (-0.3)]^2 = .021$.

The regression line was the best fitting line in terms of minimizing the *squared* deviations of the points from the line. Hence $SD^2_{est\ zY\cdot zX}$ represents the variance of these errors of estimation. Symbolically, the definition is:

$$SD^2_{est\ zY\cdot zX} = \frac{\sum\limits_{i=1}^{n} (z_{Y_i} - z'_{Y_i})^2}{n}$$

where z_Y is the z score for Y in the original data and z'_Y is the z score for Y that is predicted from the relationship of X to Y. *The average of the squared deviations of predicted from actual scores is the variance of estimation.*

Now that these three terms are understood, the relationship of r to them can be explained. r^2 represents the proportion of the original variance that can be predicted by the relationship of X to Y. That is,

$$r^2 = \frac{SD^2_{z'_Y}}{SD^2_{z_Y}} \quad \text{or} \quad r^2 SD^2_{z_Y} = SD^2_{z'_Y}$$

However $SD^2_{z_Y}$ always equals 1. Thus $r^2 = SD^2_{z'_Y}$. In the above example $r^2 = (.89)^2 = .79$. Hence 79 percent of the original variance of the z_Y scores can be predicted by the relationship of X to Y.

Since $SD^2_{z_Y} = SD^2_{z'_Y} + SD^2_{est\ z_Y \cdot z_X}$, it follows that $SD^2_{est\ z_Y \cdot z_X} = SD^2_{z_Y} - SD^2_{z'_Y}$, but $SD^2_{z_Y} = 1$ and $SD^2_{z'_Y}$ has been computed to be r^2. Therefore, $SD^2_{est\ z_Y \cdot z_X} = 1 - r^2$ which in this case is .21. Therefore, 21 percent of the original variance in the z_Y scores has still not been accounted for by the relationship of X to Y.

To summarize:

$$(1)\ SD^2_{z_Y} = SD^2_{z'_Y} + SD^2_{est\ z_Y \cdot z_X}$$

$$r^2 = SD^2_{z'_Y}/SD^2_{z_Y}$$

Therefore, from (1):

$$SD^2_{est\ z_Y \cdot z_X}/SD^2_{z_Y} = \frac{SD^2_{z_Y}}{SD^2_{z_Y}} - \frac{SD^2_{z'_Y}}{SD^2_{z_Y}}$$

or

$$SD^2_{est\ z_Y \cdot z_X}/SD^2_{z_Y} = 1 - r^2$$

Since $SD^2_{z_Y} = 1$, then $SD^2_{est\ z_Y \cdot z_X} = 1 - r^2$.

The proportion of the original variance that is accounted for by the relationship is r^2 and the proportion that is not accounted for by the relationship is $1 - r^2$.

Since $r^2 + (1 - r^2) = 1$, all of the variance (a proportion of 1) is either accounted for or not accounted for. Isn't statistical logic elegant?

Other Prediction Equations. From $z'_Y = rz_X$, it is possible to obtain an equation that will allow the prediction of the Y score, symbolized Y', directly from the X score. This is accomplished as follows:

$$z'_Y = rz_X$$

But $z'_Y = \dfrac{Y' - \bar{Y}'}{SD_Y}$, by definition.

Since $\bar{Y}' = \bar{Y}$ this can be rewritten as

$$z'_Y = \frac{Y' - \bar{Y}}{SD_Y}$$

Further, $z_X = \dfrac{X - \bar{X}}{SD_X}$, by definition.

Substituting into $z'_Y = rz_X$ the result is,

$$\frac{Y' - \bar{Y}}{SD_Y} = r\frac{X - \bar{X}}{SD_X}$$

Solving for Y' gives:

$$Y' = r\frac{SD_Y}{SD_X}(X - \bar{X}) + \bar{Y}$$

This may also be written:

$$Y' = r\left(\frac{SD_Y}{SD_X}\right)X - r\left(\frac{SD_Y}{SD_X}\right)\bar{X} + \bar{Y}$$

All of the values on the righthand side of the equation are available from the original data. Note that this equation is of the form $Y' = f(X)$. $f(X)$ is still a linear function since all of the values on the righthand side of the equation are constants except for X. Hence, let $r(SD_Y/SD_X) = a$ and $r(SD_Y/SD_X)\bar{X} + \bar{Y} = b$. Then $f(X)$ becomes $aX + b$.

Now all of the predicted scores are labeled Y's and the relationships for the variances given above become: $SD_Y^2 = SD_{Y'}^2 + SD^2_{est\ Y \cdot X}$ where

$$SD_Y^2 = \frac{\sum_{i=1}^{n}(Y_i - \bar{Y})^2}{n}$$

is the variance of the original data scores on the Y variable,

$$SD_{Y'}^2 = \frac{\sum_{i=1}^{n}(Y'_i - \bar{Y})^2}{n}$$

is the variance among the predicted Y scores (and hence is predicted variance), and

$$SD^2_{est\ Y \cdot X} = \frac{\sum_{i=1}^{n}(Y'_i - Y_i)^2}{n}$$

and is the variance of estimating Y from X.

Algebraically, the relationship of r^2 to the variances of the actual scores can be derived. The results yield the following:

$$r^2 = \frac{SD_{Y'}^2}{SD_Y^2}, \qquad \text{and} \qquad 1 - r^2 = \frac{SD^2_{est\ Y \cdot X}}{SD_Y^2},$$

so that r^2 is still the proportion of the original variance accounted for by the predicted scores and $1 - r^2$ is the proportion that is still error.

Since SD_Y^2 does not usually equal 1 (it is the variance of a set of data scores not of a set of z scores), the formulae are not further reducible although the interpretations are the same as before.

Since correlation is symmetric, $r_{XY} = r_{YX}$ for a set of scores, all of the above formulae can just as well be expressed in terms of predictions of X from Y. These formulae are:

1) $z'_X = rz_Y$ and $X' = r\dfrac{SD_X}{SD_Y}(Y - \bar{Y}) + \bar{X}$

2) $r^2 = \dfrac{SD^2_{X'}}{SD^2_X}$ and $1 - r^2 = \dfrac{SD^2_{est\ X\cdot Y}}{SD^2_X}$

3) $r^2 = \dfrac{SD^2_{z'X}}{SD^2_{zX}}$ and $1 - r^2 = \dfrac{SD^2_{est\ zX\cdot zY}}{SD^2_{zX}}$

where

$$SD^2_X = \dfrac{\sum\limits_{i=1}^{n} (X_i - \bar{X})^2}{n}, \quad SD^2_{X'} = \dfrac{\sum\limits_{i=1}^{n} (X'_i - \bar{X}')^2}{n},$$

and

$$SD^2_{est\ X\cdot Y} = \dfrac{\sum\limits_{i=1}^{n} (X'_i - X_i)^2}{n}$$

Since the mean of the predicted scores always equals the mean of the original data scores,

$$SD^2_{X'} = \dfrac{\sum\limits_{i=1}^{n} (X'_i - \bar{X})^2}{n}, \quad \text{and} \quad SD^2_{Y'} = \dfrac{\sum\limits_{i=1}^{n} (Y' - \bar{Y})^2}{n}$$

The degree of association is determined by the absolute value of r and not by the sign. Thus, $r = -0.7$ represents as high a degree of association between the two variables as does $r = +0.7$. Since the proportion of variance accounted for is represented by r^2, and both $(-0.7)^2$ and $(+0.7)^2 = 0.49$, the proportion of variance that is predictable from the relationship is the same in both cases. The negative sign merely indicates that as scores on one variable go up, scores on the other variable tend to go down. (An example of a negative correlation might be the correlation between the height of 11-year-old boys and the time in which they run a race. Generally, the taller boys would run the race in less time.)

Other Ways to Compute r.   Although the definition of r is given by

$$r = \dfrac{\sum\limits_{i=1}^{n} z_{X_i} z_{Y_i}}{n}$$

its computation is simplified by substituting for z_{Y_i}, y_i/SD_Y, and for z_{X_i}, x_i/SD_X, where $y_i = Y_i - \bar{Y}$ and $x_i = X_i - \bar{X}$. The formula then becomes

$$r = \frac{\sum\limits_{i=1}^{n} (y_i/SD_Y)(x_i/SD_X)}{n}$$

and this reduces, since SD_Y and SD_X are constants, to

$$r = \frac{\dfrac{1}{SD_Y \cdot SD_X} \sum\limits_{i=1}^{n} x_i\, y_i}{n} = \frac{\sum\limits_{i=1}^{n} x_i\, y_i}{n\, SD_Y\, SD_X}$$

This form of the equation saves the effort of dividing by the standard deviation for every score to get the z score. The denominator, $nSD_Y \cdot SD_X$, is a constant and need only be computed once. The numerator is obtained by cross multiplying the deviation scores instead of the z scores and then summing these cross products just as was done for z scores. This reduces the operation of dividing every deviation score by the standard deviation to only dividing the sum of the cross products of the deviation scores once by $n(SD_X)(SD_Y)$.

Caution on r.   *r represents the degree to which the best straight line will fit the data.* It is possible for there to be a high degree of association between the two variables yet r will be close or equal to 0. Consider the relationship between IQ and performance of a routine task. Those with extremely low IQ's would probably not have intelligence enough to perform the task and those with high IQ's might not perform the task well because they were bored. The best performers might be those of average intelligence. This situation is summarized in Figure 8.3.

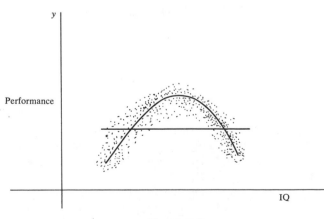

Figure 8.3

No straight line could really fit the data well. This is because the association is really curvilinear rather than linear, as the curved line which fits the data quite well demonstrates. Thus, a low *r* does not necessarily mean low association between the two variables. It does mean that a straight line does not fit the data well, or that the degree of *linear* association between the two variables is low. Other correlation procedures are available for determining the degree of curvilinear relationship between two variables.

Necessity for z Scores in Defining r.   The need to define *r* in terms of *z* scores can be easily indicated. If the cross products of the raw scores were taken as the measure of *r*, the degree of association would always be larger for variables in which there were large numbers of observations than for those which had small numbers. It would further be dependent on the unit in which the measurements were expressed. In the previous example of height vs. time for 11 year old boys running a race, the correlation would be smaller if height were in feet than if it were in inches. This would be an unsatisfactory situation. In order to be satisfied, it is not used. Similarly, with the cross product of deviations from the mean, the correlation would depend on the unit of measurement. It is necessary to standardize each of the variables in terms of both the number of observations and the variability of the scores themselves so that the correlation is not altered by artificial changes in the data. When *z* scores are used it makes no difference whether height is measured in inches, feet, or yards, since the *z* score of an individual in the group remains the same no matter what the unit of measurement is. If height is in feet and this is converted to inches by multiplying every score by 12, then the standard deviation of the scores is also increased by a factor of 12 and the ratio of x/SD_X remains the same. Clearly, dividing by *n* eliminates the dependence of the size of *r* on the number of observations.

An examination of

$$r = \frac{\sum_{i=1}^{n} z_{X_i} z_{Y_i}}{n}$$

will indicate the types of situations that determine positive, negative or zero correlations. A positive correlation means that as scores on one variable increase, scores on the other increase also and as they decrease on one they do on the other. Thus, if a score is above the mean on one variable ($+$ *z* score) it should generally be above the mean on the other ($+$ *z* score) and if below the mean on one ($-z$ score) it should also be below on the other ($-z$ score). The result is that the cross product of the *z* scores is generally plus [either a ($+$) ($+$) or a ($-$) ($-$)] and hence the correlation is positive.

A negative correlation means that if the scores on one variable are above the mean ($+z$ score) they are below on the other ($-z$ score) or vice versa ($-$) ($+$). These cross products yield minus numbers [($+$) ($-$) or ($-$)($+$)] and hence the formula gives a negative correlation. A correlation close to or equal to zero means that scores above the mean on one variable are sometimes associated with scores above the mean on the other variable [($+$) ($+$)] and sometimes with scores below the mean [($+$) ($-$)]. Similarly, scores below the mean are sometimes associated with scores above the mean ($-$) ($+$) and sometimes with those below. The net result is that the cross products are sometimes positive [($+$) ($+$) or ($-$) ($-$)] and sometimes negative [($+$) ($-$) or ($-$)($+$)]. The positive cross products cancel the negative ones and the correlation is close to zero.

Spearman's r_s for Intervally Scaled Ranks

Sometimes data consists of ranks and it seems reasonable to treat the ranks as if they are intervally scaled. In this case Pearson's r may be used as a measure of the association. However, certain mathematical properties of ranks allow a simpler computational formula to be used than

$$r = \frac{\sum_{i=1}^{n} zx_i zy_i}{n}$$

Spearman discovered that if the scores were ranks, and there were no ties in ranks, then

$$r_s = 1 - \frac{6\sum_{i=1}^{n} d_i^2}{n(n^2 - 1)}$$

(where d_i^2 is the squared difference between the ranks for the ith person and n is the number of pairs). The above formula is then equivalent to:

$$\frac{\sum_{i=1}^{n} zx_i zy_i}{n}.$$

One reason that it is possible to obtain this formula is that the mean and standard deviation of a set of ranks is dependent on the number of elements that are ranked.

For example, suppose eight elements are ranked on a particular variable. Then, if there are no ties, the scores will be 1, 2, 3, 4, 5, 6, 7, 8. By pairing the first number with the last (1,8) and the next number with the next to last (2,7), and so on, the sum of the above scores is seen to be $4(9) = 36$. In fact, the sum of n ranks is always $(n/2)$ (n $+$ 1). Since the mean is obtained by dividing by the number of scores the mean of a set of ranks always equals:

$$\frac{\sum_{i=1}^{n} X_i}{n} = \frac{(n/2)(n+1)}{n} = \frac{n+1}{2}$$

Similarly the standard deviation is directly related to the number of scores.

An Example. Suppose that the ten individuals whose height and weight were presented in a previous example had their scores converted to ranks, with the largest height and the largest weight given a rank of 1. The results would then be:

Person	Rank on Height	Rank on Weight	d_i	d_i^2
1	5.5	7.0	−1.5	2.25
2	7.5	6.0	+1.5	2.25
3	1.0	1.0	0.0	0.00
4	3.5	2.5	+1.0	1.00
5	10.0	8.0	+2.0	4.00
6	7.5	9.0	−1.5	2.25
7	5.5	4.0	+1.5	2.25
8	3.5	5.0	−1.5	2.25
9	9.0	10.0	−1.0	1.00
10	2.0	2.5	−0.5	0.25

$$\Sigma\ d_i^2 = 17.50$$

$$r_s = 1 - \frac{6(17.50)}{10(100-1)} = 1 - \frac{105}{990} = 1 - 0.11 = +0.89$$

Note that the computed value of r_s compares very favorably with the value of r for the original scores which was +0.89. This is in spite of the fact that two requirements for the computation of r_s were violated in the above data. First, there were ties in the ranks so that the formula for r_s was not precisely correct. Secondly, there is no particular reason to treat the ranks as intervally scaled. These problems have not seemed to bother too many people. Spearman's r_s is still a frequently computed measure of association, especially where a fairly good measure of the degree of association in the data is desired quickly.

r as a Statistic

Significance Test for Pearson's *r*

It is possible to test for the statistical significance of Pearson's r. The problem is a bit more complicated than were the previous ones concerning the significance of the means or the differences between the means.

(The test for the significance of φ will be examined later and that for γ will not be presented.)

A problem arises with r because the sampling distribution of this statistic is not always normal. Naturally, because of familiarity with the normal sampling distribution, statisticians are eager to deal with statistics that are normally distributed. In these cases the next step is to find the standard error of the distribution. These steps cannot immediately be taken with r as the statistic.

To see why this is so, it is necessary to be cognizant of the fact that r has a minimum value of -1.00 and a maximum value of $+1.00$. If the true value of the correlation in the population is taken to be ρ, then ρ may also have any value between that of -1.00 and $+1.00$. For $\rho = 0$, it is not too difficult to obtain a normal sampling distribution of r. This is because the distribution of the statistic can easily be symmetric. If $\rho = 0$, r can have values up to $+1.00$ and down to -1.00. This allows a sampling distribution, for large enough samples, to be approximately normal as diagrammed in Figure 8.4.

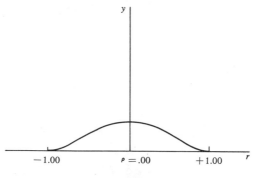

Figure 8.4

However, as the value of the parameter approaches either $+1.00$ or -1.00 the symmetry of the sampling distribution of r is destroyed and becomes more and more skewed. For example, if $\rho = +0.80$, then the values of r could range all the way down to -1.00 but they can only range upward to a value of $+1.00$. It becomes difficult to achieve symmetry in the sampling distribution even if the underlying population of scores is normal, except for extremely large samples. Since symmetry is one of the characteristics of a normal curve no nonsymmetric curve can be normal. The situation for $\rho = +0.80$ is diagrammed in Figure 8.5. As can be seen, the curve is sharply skewed to the left.

Fortunately, R.A. Fisher came to the statisticians' rescue. He showed that it was possible to transform the sampling distribution of r to one that was almost always normally distributed even for large absolute

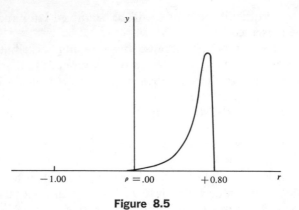

Figure 8.5

values of ρ, and even when the sampling distribution was based on samples of small size.

The transformation is accomplished in the following way. Consider all of the values of r based on all of the unique samples of a particular size for a given ρ (that is, a particular sampling distribution of r). If each and every one of these values of r is given a new value, Z_r, where $Z_r = \frac{1}{2}\log_e (1 + r)/(1 - r)$, then, even for values of ρ that are far from 0 and even for sampling distributions based on samples of relatively small n, the sampling distribution of Z_r will be approximately normal. The statistic for correlation has been transformed so that it is normally distributed. The remaining problem is to determine the standard error of the statistic. (Note that Z_r is not a z score. To avoid confusion it would have been better to label it differently, perhaps Q_r or P_r. Unfortunately, quantitatively oriented persons are frequently confusing.)

First of all it is not necessary to estimate the standard error of Z_r. Secondly, the value of the standard error, σ_{Z_r}, is dependent only on the sample size. The precise value of σ_{Z_r} is given by:

$$\sigma_{Z_r} = \frac{1}{\sqrt{n - 3}}$$

Since the sampling distribution is normal and the true standard error is known, the test for the significance of r reduces to one that is formally almost identical to the z test for the true mean (here ρ is analagous to μ).

The model for the z test for Z_r is as follows:

1) $\rho = a \ (Z_\rho = a')$
2) $\sigma_{Z_r} = b$
3) Observations random and independent
4) Z_r normal
5) Population is bivariate normal

The fifth assumption of the model is the only one that is not a variant of a condition in the model for the z test for the true mean. This requirement is a rather stringent one and is more honored in the breach than in the practice.

The fifth assumption requires that for the population of elements that receive scores on both of the variables, both of the following conditions must hold:

1) For any specified Y score, the distribution of the scores on the X variable must be normal.

2) For any specified X score, the distribution of the scores on the Y variable must be normal.

When it is realized that even if the two distributions of scores are normal, (that is, all of the X scores are normally distributed and all of the Y scores are normally distributed), a bivariate normal distribution is not guaranteed, the strictness of this assumption is readily seen.

To illustrate the above, consider the following example. Suppose the correlation between blood pressure and reaction time is being investigated. Let X be the blood pressure and Y the reaction time. Let the population of elements be all of the licensed automobile drivers in the United States. Then the X variable is normally distributed if the blood pressure scores are normally distributed across all of the drivers in the United States and the Y variable is normally distributed if the reaction time scores across all of the drivers are normally distributed.

This still does not guarantee that the distribution is bivariate normal. In order for this to be the case it would be necessary that for any selected Y score, say a reaction time of $\frac{1}{4}$ second, all of the blood pressure scores for people having this reaction time are normally distributed. Similarly for any X score, say a blood pressure score of $\frac{120}{80}$, all of the people having this blood pressure would have their reaction time scores normally distributed.

The situation is diagrammed in Figure 8.6.

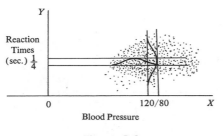

Figure 8.6

Fortunately, the assumption that the scores be distributed as a bivariate normal distribution is not very critical. That is, departures from this assumption do not appreciably alter the sampling distribution of the statistic.

An Example.   Suppose 19 freshmen women are randomly and independently selected from colleges across the United States in order to determine whether or not the number of dates that they had in high school was related to family income. For the purposes of the problem it will be assumed that the population is bivariate normal. Suppose that the computed r is $+0.62$. Is there a significant statistical relationship between the two variables?

The conditions of the model and of the decision model are as follows:

1) $\rho = 0, (Z_\rho = 0)$
2) $\sigma_{Z_r} = 1/\sqrt{19 - 3} = +0.25$
3) R and I sampling
4) Z_r normal
5) Bivariate normal population

The decision model is:

1) $H_A : \rho \neq 0 \ (Z_\rho \neq 0)$
2) $\alpha = .01$

Note that H_A is two-tailed since a direction to the relationship was not specified.

The sampling distribution that is of interest is that of Z_r since this statistic is normally distributed no matter what the original distribution of r is. Since the observed value of r was $+0.62$, a look into Table III in the Appendix indicates that $Z_r = \frac{1}{2} \log_e (1 + 0.62)/(1 - 0.62) = +0.73$. Similarly for $\rho = 0$, $Z_\rho = \frac{1}{2} \log_e (1 + 0)/(1 - 0) = 0$. The diagram of the sampling distribution of the statistic is drawn in Figure 8.7.

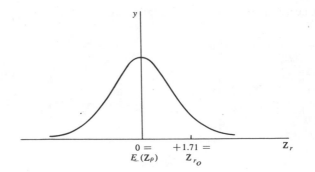

$$\begin{array}{ccc} 0 = & +1.71 = & Z_r \\ E_-(Z_\rho) & Z_{r_o} & \end{array}$$

Figure 8.7

The z score for $Z_r = +.73$ is obtained by $z = (Z_r - Z_p)/\sigma_{Z_r} = (+.73 - 0)/+.25 = +2.92$. The evaluation of this probability is: $p(|z| \geq 2.92) < p(|z| \geq 2.58) = .01 = \alpha$.

The experimenter thus rejects the null hypothesis that there was no association in favor of the alternative hypothesis that the two variables in the population are associated.

The diagram of the z distribution is given in Figure 8.8.

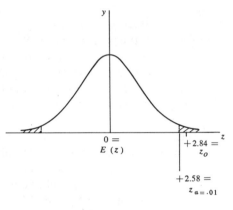

Figure 8.8

Confidence Interval for r

If instead of a test for the significance of the correlation, the problem had been to construct the confidence interval, no special problems would have been raised (especially if you understand this stuff). For example, the above problem gave $r = +0.62$ for which the corresponding $Z_r = +0.73$. Since $\sigma_{Z_r} = +0.25$, the problem would be to find the values of Z_{ρ_L} and Z_{ρ_U}. Diagrammatically, this is represented in Figure 8.9.

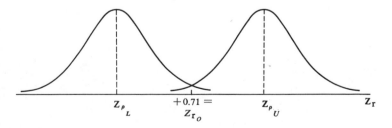

Figure 8.9

The solution to the problem of finding the 99 percent confidence interval is now obvious,

$$z = \frac{Z_r - Z_{\rho L}}{\sigma_{Z_r}} = +2.58$$

Therefore $\qquad Z_{\rho_L} = +.73 - (2.58)\,(.25) = .08$

and $\qquad Z_{\rho_U} = +.73 + 2.58\,(.25) = 1.38$

However, the problem is not quite completely solved. The actual interest is not in the range of values of the nonrejectable hypotheses for Z_ρ but rather in the range of values for the null hypotheses for ρ which could not have been rejected on the basis of the evidence from the sample. The solution to this problem is easier than to many. It simply involves looking in the table for the values of ρ that correspond to the already computed values of Z_{ρ_L} and Z_{ρ_U}. These values turn out to be $\rho_L = +0.08$ and $\rho_U = +0.88$. The 99 percent confidence interval for the above problem, therefore, is .08 to .88.

In both the hypothesis testing and confidence interval situations, there are two advantages to retransforming values of Z_r or Z_ρ to the corresponding r and ρ values. One is that the association in the original problem is a Pearson's r and the problem should be understood in terms of the actual relation that is being investigated. The second is that the interpretation of the degree of association (for example in terms of the percent of variance that is predicted) is more easily accomplished for Pearson's r.

9

INFERENTIAL TESTS
FOR NOMINAL DATA

INTRODUCTION

To this point the only inferential tests that have been presented have dealt with data that were at least intervally scaled.

In many problems the data are of a lower level. In the sections that follow, situations will be discussed that deal with data that are only at the level of nominal scaling. In nominal scaling the only measurement on the elements that is possible is their classification. Two elements can be evaluated relative to each other only in terms of whether they are the same or are different. For example, people as elements might be measured in terms of political party affiliation or of hair color. If automobiles were the elements they might be measured (classified) in terms of make of car. In order to examine carefully the inferential tests for nominal data it will be necessary to utilize the elementary notions of probability presented in Chapter 3.

THE BINOMIAL

Consider situations in which samples are taken from populations that are measured on a nominal scale.

The simplest case of interest is that in which the observations may fall into one or the other of two mutually exclusive and exhaustive classes. This is the *binomial* case. For example, if a sample of people is drawn and the people are measured as to their sex, an observation can fall into one and only one of the two categories. No single observation can be both a male and a female, so the categories are mutually exclusive. Further, every observation is either a male or a female, so the categories are exhaustive. Or consider the drawing of a sample with regard to party affiliation (and for simplicity suppose there are only Democrats and Republicans). Again, observations can fall into one or the other of two mutually exclusive classes, and only into these.

The reason for sampling from the population is the same as always. It is not possible, generally, to know all of the scores for all of the elements of the population. In the case of nominal data, the question concerns the *proportion* of cases in the population that fall into each category. For the two category case, one category is arbitrarily labeled success and the other failure. The *parameter* is the proportion of successes in the population, symbolized p. The proportion of failures is symbolized q. Since the two categories are exhaustive then $p + q = 1$, that is, an observation must be in one or the other category. Thus, only one value, p, need be specified, since this value determines the value of q, that is, $q = 1 - p$.

The statistic can either be the number in the sample that were successes (f) or the proportion of successes in the sample (P). Both definitions of the statistic will be examined in the text. It is apparent that they are not really very different from each other since the proportion of successes in the sample is obtained by merely dividing the number of successes in the sample by the total number of people in the sample. Hence, $P = f/n$ (in the sample $P + Q = 1$, of course).

Although the statistic is different from those which have been examined thus far, the question that is asked is precisely the same as before. For any given value of the statistic, what is the probability that values as deviant or more so from the expected value would occur just by chance, if the hypotheses about the population are really true? In the present situation the question will be about the probability that a particular proportion or particular number of successes would deviate at least as much as it does from the expected proportion or expected number of successes.

The primary difference between the sampling distribution of the statistic now under consideration and those that have previously been discussed is that the distribution of the number or proportion of successes in the sample is discrete. There are only a finite number of points to the distribution. Further, the actual computations by which the probabilities are obtained can be performed. As a result, it will not be necessary to resort to tables.

In order to compute the probabilities for the binomial sampling distribution, it will be necessary to use the two basic rules of probability that were presented earlier. The development of these computations is the goal of the next section.

Exact Probabilities for the Binomial Statistic

For purposes of simplicity, sampling will first be done using a coin. The population in this case is all of the possible tosses of the coin with respect to the side that comes up each time. This population is infinite. If the coin is assumed to be a fair one, then the p (Heads) $= p$ (Tails) $= 1/2$. For heads considered to be the success, the assumed value of the parameter would be $p = 1/2$. The two categories are mutually exclusive and the trials or tosses of the coin are independent of each other.

These conditions can be formally stated in terms of a model about the population. The model consists of the following assumptions:

1) $p = 1/2$
2) Sampling random and independent
3) $p(S \cap F) = 0$
4) $p(S \cup F) = 1$

The third and fourth assumptions together state that the categories are mutually exclusive and exhaustive. $p(S \cap F) = 0$ is the formal definition of mutually exclusive, that is, the probability that an event is both a success and a failure is 0.

$p(S \cup F) = 1$ is the formal statement that the categories are exhaustive, that is, that every event can be classified as either a success or a failure.

The conditions stated above determine the expected value of the statistic $E(f)$ and allow the computation of the probability for each value of the statistic for the unique samples of a specified size from the population. In order to illustrate this suppose that a sample were taken that consisted of 8 tosses of the coin. Assume that the coin is fair. This is translated to $p = 1/2$ and $q = 1 - p = 1/2$. The only possible values that the statistic could have in a sample of size 8 would be 0 successes, or 1 success, or 2 successes or $\cdots$ or 8 successes. Of course the values of the statistic in terms of proportions would be .000 or .125 or .250 or $\cdots$ or 1.00. For this example, the number of successes, f, will be used as the statistic.

The expected number of successes in the sample is represented as F so that $E(f) = F$. The value of F is determined by n, the sample size and p, the probability of success. The exact relationship is

$$np = F$$

In order to generate the sampling distribution, it is necessary to compute the probability associated with each value of the statistic. That is, over all the unique samples of size 8 (or equivalently, upon repeated random and independent sampling of samples of size 8) what is the probability of getting exactly 0 successes, what is the probability of getting exactly 1 success (and so forth)?

First consider exactly 0 successes. In order for this to occur, 8 failures in a row must be obtained. There is only one way for this to happen, namely, *FFFFFFFF*. Since each toss is independent and $q = 1/2$, the rule for independent events states that the probability of eight failures in a row is

$$q^8 = \frac{1}{2} \cdot \frac{1}{2} \cdot \cdots \cdot \frac{1}{2} = \left(\frac{1}{2}\right)^8 = \frac{1}{256}$$

The next problem is to compute the probability of exactly one success. One way to get exactly one success is by getting a success on the first trial and failures on all of the others, that is, *SFFFFFFF*. Again this is a series of independent events for which the probability is

$$(p)^1 (q)^7 = \left(\frac{1}{2}\right)^1 \cdot \left(\frac{1}{2}\right)^7 = \left(\frac{1}{2}\right)^8 = \frac{1}{256}$$

This, however, is not the only way that exactly one success can be obtained; another sequence might be *FSFFFFFF*. The probability for this sequence remains the same since the same numbers can be multiplied together in any order and the product will not be changed. However the second sequence is mutually exclusive with regard to the first sequence. That is, if 8 tosses of a coin yield *SFFFFFFF*, it excludes the possibility that the same sequence of tosses could have also been *FSFFFFFF*. Therefore, the probability of getting exactly one success by *either* the first sequence *or* the second sequence is $1/256 + 1/256 = 2/256$. This does not yet give the probability of exactly 1 success in 8 trials since there are other sequences that also give exactly 1 success. Fortunately, these other sequences are mutually exclusive with each other and the above sequences. If the total number of mutually exclusive sequences were known, it would be easy to compute the probability of exactly one success. This would simply be the number of sequences in which one success occurs multiplied by the probability of a single success in one specific sequence.

Fortunately there is a formula that will provide this answer. The question is equivalent to asking how many different combinations there are of 8 events in which there is exactly one success and the rest are failures. The formula is

$$\binom{8}{1} = \frac{8!}{1!\,(8-1)!} = \frac{8!}{1!\,7!} = \frac{8 \times 7 \times 6 \times 5 \times 4 \times 3 \times 2 \times 1}{1\,(7 \times 6 \times 5 \times 4 \times 3 \times 2 \times 1)} = 8$$

where $n!$ (which is read as n factorial and without exclamation) is defined as $n\,(n-1) \cdots 2 \cdot 1$.

Since the probability of exactly one success in one specific sequence was $1/256$, the probability for exactly one success without regard to the sequence in which it occurred is

$$8 \times \frac{1}{256} = \frac{8}{256}$$

The procedure for solving the probability of exactly two successes without regard to order is the same as above. First, it is necessary to compute the probability of exactly two successes in some particular sequence. Next the number of sequences in which exactly two successes can occur must be computed. Finally the number of sequences times the probability must be calculated. Thus, the probability of exactly two successes in some specific sequence is given by

$$p(f = 2) = \left(\frac{1}{2}\right)^2 \left(\frac{1}{2}\right)^6 = \left(\frac{1}{2}\right)^8 = \frac{1}{256}$$

The number of ways to get exactly two successes in 8 trials is given by

$$\binom{8}{2} = \frac{8!}{2! \ (8 - 2)!} = 28$$

Hence, the probability of exactly two successes in any sequence of 8 trials is

$$28 \cdot \frac{1}{256} = \frac{28}{256}$$

Before computing the rest of the probabilities, the general form of the binomial will be given. For exactly f number of successes in n trials the probability is given by

$$\binom{n}{f} p^f \, q^{(n-f)} \quad \text{where} \quad \binom{n}{f} = \frac{n!}{f! \ (n - f)!}$$

is the number of sequences of n observations that yield exactly f successes, p is the probability of success, q is the probability of failure, f is the number of successes and $(n - f)$ is the number of failures. The portion of the expression consisting of $p^f \, q^{(n-f)}$ represents the probability of exactly f successes in n trials for one of the sequences. Since the trials are independent $p^f \, q^{(n-f)}$ merely represents the products of the separate probabilities.

Using the above formula, the probability of exactly three successes is:

$$\binom{8}{3} \left(\frac{1}{2}\right)^3 \left(\frac{1}{2}\right)^5 = \frac{8 \times 7 \times 6}{1 \times 2 \times 3} \cdots \left(\frac{1}{2}\right)^8 = \frac{56}{256}$$

For exactly 4 successes the probability is:

$$\binom{8}{4} \left(\frac{1}{2}\right)^4 \left(\frac{1}{2}\right)^4 = \frac{70}{256}$$

For exactly 5 successes the probability is:

$$\binom{8}{5} \left(\frac{1}{2}\right)^5 \left(\frac{1}{2}\right)^3 = \frac{56}{256}$$

For exactly 6 successes the probability is:

$$\binom{8}{6}\left(\frac{1}{2}\right)^6\left(\frac{1}{2}\right)^2 = \frac{28}{256}$$

For exactly 7 successes the probability is:

$$\binom{8}{7}\left(\frac{1}{2}\right)^7\left(\frac{1}{2}\right)^1 = \frac{8}{256}$$

For exactly 8 successes the probability is:

$$\binom{8}{8}\left(\frac{1}{2}\right)^8\left(\frac{1}{2}\right)^0 = \frac{1}{256}$$

Note that these are the only values that the statistic can have. In 8 trials from a two category population the number of successes must either be 0, or 1, or 2, or $\cdots$ or 8. Since the events defined by those outcomes that give a particular value of the statistic are mutually exclusive, the probability of either 0 successes, or 1 success, or 2, or $\cdots$ or 8 successes must be $p(0) + p(1) + p(2) + \cdots + p(8)$. This is $1/256 + 8/256 + 28/256 + 56/256 + 70/256 + 56/256 + 28/256 + 8/256 + 1/256 = 256/256 = 1$. That is, the values 0 through 8 exhaust the values of the statistic.

It is important to realize that in drawing a sample, the experimenter is not interested in the sequence which gave rise to the particular value of the statistic, but merely the value itself and how deviant it is from the expected value. This is no different from the situation that existed before. If IQ were being studied and the sample drawn gave a mean value of $\bar{X} = 110$, the question of the order in which the scores were selected was never considered. If the sample size were $n = 3$, it did not make any difference whether the scores drawn were in the order 110, 105, 115, or in the order 115, 110, 105. Further, it did not make any difference if the value of $\bar{X} = 110$ were obtained by the scores 110, 105, 115, or 108, 109, and 113. The problem was merely to determine the value of the statistic and then find the probability that values of the statistic at least this extreme could have occurred by chance. The point of all of this is that the binomial situation is precisely the same in terms of the question that is asked about the value of the statistic.

The diagram of the sampling distribution that was computed above is given in Figure 9.1.

In any particular problem it is not actually necessary to compute the whole sampling distribution. The probabilities, for points as extreme or more so from the expected as the obtained one, are computed and the other values in the diagram may be sketched in. This is because the diagram is only used as a reference guide in actually solving a problem.

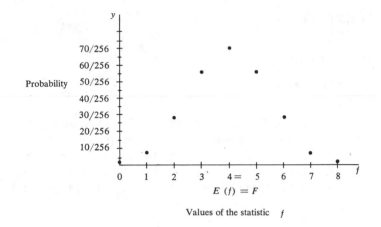

Values of the statistic f

Figure 9.1

Examples

A Two-Tailed Binomial Problem

A group of tire manufacturers claim that 90 percent of the tire failures occur during the last one fifth of tread wear. A check on this figure was obtained by selecting, randomly and independently, 20 tires. Of these 15 went flat during the last one fifth of tread life. Was the claim incorrect?

In this problem $p = 9/10$ and represents the probability of a tire going flat during the last one fifth of tread wear. $q = 1/10$ and represents the probability that a tire will go flat during some time other than the last one fifth of tread wear, that is, that it will go flat during the first four fifths of tread wear.

The expected number of tires going flat during the last one fifth of tread wear, $E(f)$, is $np = 20 \cdot 9/10 = 18$. The observed number of tires that went flat during this period, f_o, was 15. The question is whether 15 is so deviant from 18 that results as extreme or more so from the expected as 15 are unlikely to occur just by chance.

The computation that is desired is the probability of getting 15 or fewer successes in 20 trials when the probability of success is $9/10$. Since the alternative, $H_A : p \neq 9/10$ is two-tailed, this will only represent one half of the deviant cases. There are also cases as deviant from 18 but which lie above it. Hence the computed probability will have to be doubled in this case.

The model of the population and the decision model are:

Model for generating the sampling distribution:
  1) $H_0: p = 9/10, q = 1/10$
  2) Sampling random and independent

3) $p(S \cap F) = 0$
4) $p(S \cup F) = 1$

Decision Model:

1) $H_A : p \neq 9/10$
2) $\alpha = .05$

Note that the population is not of all tires, but of all tires that go flat. Since $f_o =$ the observed number of successes, the computation is for $p (f \leq f_o)$ which in this case is $p (f \leq 15)$. In order to compute this number, the probability of exactly 15 successes would have to be computed, this would then be added to the probability of exactly 14 successes, and these added to 13, and so on. That is

$$p(f \leq 15) = \sum_{f=0}^{15} \binom{n}{f} p^f q^{(n-f)}$$

This lengthy computation can be shortened by noting that $p(0 \leq f \leq 20) = 1$. That is, it is certain that the value of the statistic will be either 0, or 1, or $\cdots$ or 20 successes if the sample size is 20.

However, $p (0 \leq f \leq 20)$ can be divided into two parts. Thus, $p(0 \leq f \leq 20) = p (0 \leq f \leq 15) + p (16 \leq f \leq 20)$. Verbally all this says is that the probability that the number of successes is between 0 and 20 equals the probability that it is either between 0 and 15 or between 16 and 20. Since $p(0 \leq f \leq 20) = 1$, then $p(0 \leq f \leq 15) + p(16 \leq f \leq 20) = 1$. Therefore, $p(0 \leq f \leq 15) = 1 - p(16 \leq f \leq 20)$.

It is only necessary to compute $p(16 \leq f \leq 20)$ and subtract this from 1 to get the correct answer.

The computation is:

$$p(16 \leq f \leq 20) = \sum_{f=16}^{20} \binom{n}{f} p^f q^{(n-f)} = \binom{20}{16}\left(\frac{9}{10}\right)^{16}\left(\frac{1}{10}\right)^4$$

$$+ \binom{20}{17}\left(\frac{9}{10}\right)^{17}\left(\frac{1}{10}\right)^3 + \binom{20}{18}\left(\frac{9}{10}\right)^{18}\left(\frac{1}{10}\right)^2$$

$$+ \binom{20}{19}\left(\frac{9}{10}\right)^{19}\left(\frac{1}{10}\right)^1 + \binom{20}{20}\left(\frac{9}{10}\right)^{20}\left(\frac{1}{10}\right)^0$$

$$= 4845 \times \frac{1.848 \times 10^{15}}{10^{20}} + 1140 \times \frac{1.663 \times 10^{16}}{10^{20}}$$

$$+ 190 \times \frac{1.497 \times 10^{17}}{10^{20}} + 20 \times \frac{1.338 \times 10^{18}}{10^{20}}$$

$$+ 1 \times \frac{1.205 \times 10^{19}}{10^{20}}$$

$$= 8.954 \times \frac{10^{18}}{10^{20}} + 1.906 \times \frac{10^{19}}{10^{20}} + 2.84 \times \frac{10^{19}}{10^{20}}$$

$$+ 2.68 \times \frac{10^{19}}{10^{20}} + 1.205 \times \frac{10^{19}}{10^{20}}$$

$$= .08954 + .1906 + .284 + .268 + .121 = .954$$

Therefore, $p(0 \leq f \leq 15) = 1 - .954 = .046$, and $2p(0 \leq f \leq 15)$ $= 2 (.046) = .092$. (This step doubles the probability which is necessary for the two-tailed test.) If α were .05, then the null hypothesis that $p = 9/10$ could not be rejected on the basis of the evidence from the sample.

A sketch of the sampling distribution of the statistic for the above problem is given in Figure 9.2.

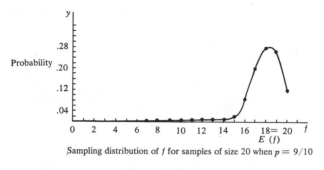

Sampling distribution of f for samples of size 20 when $p = 9/10$

Figure 9.2

Since the sampling distribution consists of a limited number of points, the computation was not in terms of areas but in terms of the exact probabilities of the points under consideration.

Notice (it can hardly be avoided), that the distribution is sharply skewed to the left. This results from the fact that the probability of a success was not $1/2$ but $9/10$. Therefore, in a sample of size 20 the expected number of successes was not 10 (from $np = 20 \cdot 1/2$) but 18 (from $np = 20 \cdot 9/10$). It was possible, given this population, to get sample results that deviated by far fewer number of successes than was expected but it was not possible to get samples that had a number of successes that were far greater in number than the expected. How then can a two-tailed computation be made? That is, the observed number of successes was 15. This is 3 less than the expected number of successes. Shouldn't values of the statistic as deviant in the high direction from the expected as 15 is in the low direction be those values of the statistic that are 21 or greater? If this were the case then there would be no possible values of the statistic that could fulfill this requirement when $n = 20$. However, this is not what is meant by deviance. Deviance is defined in terms of probabilities. Values of a statistic are equally deviant when the classes of events they define are equally unlikely to occur. Thus, if $p(f \leq 15) = .046$, then values of the statistic above the expected value are as deviant if they are just as unlikely to occur. It is not even necessary to identify them. They are whatever values or fraction of values that occur as infrequently. Hence, for a two-tailed test in which the observed value of the statistic falls to one side of the expected value, the first step is to compute the probability that values this extreme or more so would occur by chance *in the same direction as the observed result*. This is the class of events defined by the observed value. Then, the probability of results as extreme or more so than this one *in either direction* is twice the computed probability.

Note that in the case of the binomial all of the computations are performed directly in terms of the sampling distribution of the statistic.

A One-Tailed Binomial Problem

Suppose a manufacturer maintains that 75 percent of the housewives in the country use his brand of soap. A competitor thinks that this claim is false and decides to take a sample. Out of ten housewives that were randomly and independently selected, four used the product for which the 75 percent claim had been made. What did the competitor conclude?

It is apparent in this problem that the competitor wishes to prove that a false claim has been made. If the proportion of people in the sample that used the product would have turned out to be greater than 75 percent, no complaint against the manufacturer could have been lodged. Clearly the test is being run to conclude that if the true proportion in the population that use the product is not 75 percent, the population value must be less than 75 percent.

The model for the problem then becomes:

1) $H_0 : p = 3/4, q = 1/4$
2) Sampling random and independent
3) $p (S \cap F) = 0$
4) $p (S \cup F) = 1$

The decision model is:

1) $H_A : p < 3/4$
2) $\alpha = .01$

Since the number of successes was 4, it is necessary to find:

$$p(f \leq 4) = \sum_{f=0}^{4} \binom{n}{f} p^f q^{(n-f)}$$

This is:

$$\binom{10}{0}\left(\frac{3}{4}\right)^0\left(\frac{1}{4}\right)^{10} + \binom{10}{1}\left(\frac{3}{4}\right)^1\left(\frac{1}{4}\right)^9 + \binom{10}{2}\left(\frac{3}{4}\right)^2\left(\frac{1}{4}\right)^8 + \binom{10}{3}\left(\frac{3}{4}\right)^3\left(\frac{1}{4}\right)^7$$

$$+ \binom{10}{4}\left(\frac{3}{4}\right)^4\left(\frac{1}{4}\right)^6 =$$

$$1 \times \frac{1}{1,052,576} + \frac{10 \times 3}{1,052,576} + \frac{45 \times 9}{1,052,576} + \frac{120(27)}{1,052,576} + \frac{210(81)}{1,052,576} =$$

$$\frac{30,686}{1,052,576} = .03 > .01 = \alpha.$$

The experimenter must, therefore, conclude that the evidence from the sample is insufficient to reject the null hypothesis that 75 percent of the housewives do use the product.

The sketch of the sampling distribution of the statistic is given in Figure 9.3.

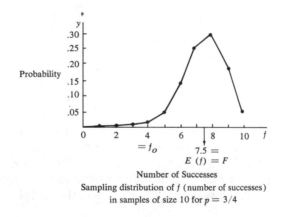

Figure 9.3

The Normal Approximation to the Binomial

It is apparent that the computational problems involved for the binomial become vast as the sample size increases. For example, if the problem were a two-tailed binomial with $p = 1/2$, $n = 100$ and $f_o = 15$, the computation would be:

$$2p(f \le 15) = 2\sum_{f=0}^{15} \binom{100}{f}\left(\frac{1}{2}\right)^f\left(\frac{1}{2}\right)^{(100-f)}$$

This would take a lot of work. Larger samples and different values for p would involve even more work. In the never ending search to avoid work, an approximation to the binomial has been discovered. This approximation is based on the same general theorem that has been the basis of the previous inferential tests, namely, that for many statistics the sampling distribution approaches normality as the sample size increases, even if the distribution of the population was not normal.

In the case of the binomial it is certainly true that the distribution of the population is not normal. In fact, there are only two points to the population distribution. For example, the distribution of a binomial population in which $p = 7/10$ and $q = 3/10$ appears as in Figure 9.4.

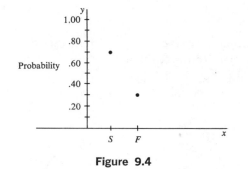

Figure 9.4

This distribution is not normal. However, the number of values that the statistic, f, may take increases as the sample size increases. Thus, for a sample of size five from a binomial population there are 6 possible values that the statistic may have. For samples in which $n = 25$, there are 26 possible values of the statistic. Further, although the individuals in the binomial population are only scored on a nominal scale, the values of the statistic are scored on a ratio scale. If a sample has 8 successes, this is twice as great a number of successes as occurs in a sample in which there are only 4 successes. As a consequence, the sampling distribution of the number of successes (or, equivalently, of the proportion of successes) approaches a normal distribution as the sample size increases.

It may already be clear that the rapidity with which the sampling distribution approaches normality depends not only on the sample size, but also on the values of p and q.

For example, consider two cases, one in which $p = 1/2$ and the other in which $p = 3/4$. First consider the sampling distribution of the number of successes in each case for samples of size five which are given in Figure 9.5.

In neither of these cases would the distributions be considered normal. However, the distribution of the statistic for $p = 1/2$ is certainly closer to normal than is that for $p = 3/4$.

Consider next the sketches of the sampling distribution where $n = 10$ which are given in Figure 9.6.

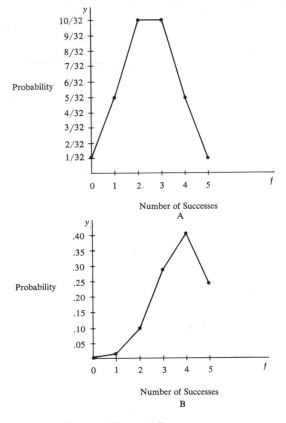

Figure 9.5

Now the sampling distribution for $p = 1/2$ is close to normal, but the distribution for $p = 3/4$ still does not appear as a normal distribution, although it is closer to one than that for $p = 3/4$ and $n = 5$. In order for the sampling distribution to be approximately normal when $p = 3/4$, the sample size would have to be larger than ten. As the sample size were increased, however, the distribution of the statistic would approach a normal distribution. The sketch of the distribution when $p = 3/4$ and $n = 35$ is given in Figure 9.7.

Now the distribution of the statistic is very close to a normal distribution. It is true that this curve is skewed to the left, but the probabilities represented in the skewed portion of the curve are extremely small.

Of course, the normal curve is always only an approximation to the binomial, even when the discrepancy between the two is very small. The binomial sampling distribution always consists of a finite number of

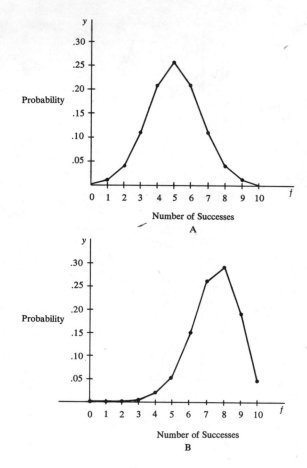

Number of Successes

A

Number of Successes

B

Figure 9.6

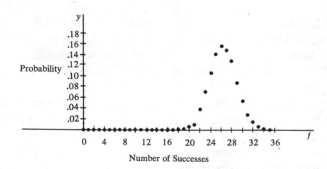

Number of Successes

Figure 9.7

points. Even if the sample is of size 1000, there are only 1001 possible values that the statistic could have. On the other hand, the normal curve consists of an infinite number of points, so that when it is used instead of the exact binomial distribution it must be an approximation. The approximation becomes extremely good however as the sample size increases.

The general rule for determining when the normal curve is a good enough approximation to the binomial is: *If both np and nq $\geq$ 5, the normal may be used as an approximation to the binomial.*

To illustrate this, consider the case where $p = 1/2 = q$ and $n = 11$. Here $np = nq = 5.5 > 5$ and the rule says the normal distribution may be used to approximate the exact binomial distribution of the statistic.

In order to demonstrate this, the probabilities will be obtained both ways. The binomial computations are by now familiar to you. In order to perform the computations using the normal curve it is necessary to realize that the value of exactly f number of successes cannot be computed on the normal curve. Since the normal curve is continuous, the area under the curve that falls under any point is taken to be zero.

The value of exactly f successes is, therefore, represented on the continuous normal curve as the proportion of the total area that falls under the curve between $f - \frac{1}{2}$ and $f + \frac{1}{2}$. Thus, to find the probability of exactly 7 successes on the normal curve, it will be necessary to compute the proportion of the total area that falls between the points $6\frac{1}{2}$ and $7\frac{1}{2}$. Since the curve is a normal distribution this means finding the area between the two z scores, that obtained for the point $6\frac{1}{2}$ and that for $7\frac{1}{2}$.

From previous discussions the z score is obtained as follows:

$$z = \frac{\text{score} - \text{mean}}{\text{standard deviation}}$$

In the case under discussion this becomes:

$$z_f = \frac{f - E(f)}{\sigma_f}$$

where the z scores are known to fall on a normal curve.

The only value that is not known is σ_f which is the true standard error of the statistic. Fortunately, this value is readily determined. It is only a function of the size of the sample and p. The formula is $\sigma_f = \sqrt{npq}$ where p and q are the *population values*. It is important to note that this is the first instance in which the standard error of the statistic depends on the value of the population parameter. As a result, even though the sample size remains constant, the variability of the sampling distribution changes if the proportion of successes in the population changes. For example, for samples of size 100, $\sigma_f = 5$ when $p = 1/2$ and $\sigma_f = 4.33$ when $p = 3/4$.

The formula, $\sigma_f = \sqrt{npq}$, holds even if the sample is not large enough to result in a normal distribution for the statistic. However, its value is particularly useful when the distribution is one for which the areas under the curve between the various points are known. In the present case this means the normal curve.

In the example being considered, $n = 11$ and $p = 1/2$ so that $E(f) = 11(1/2) = 5.5$. What is the probability of exactly four successes?

Using the normal approximation this requires finding the area under the curve between 3.5 and 4.5:

$$z_{f=3.5} = \frac{3.5 - 5.5}{\sqrt{(11)(\frac{1}{2})(\frac{1}{2})}} = \frac{-2}{\frac{1}{2}\sqrt{11}} = \frac{-2}{1.66} = -1.20$$

$$z_{f=4.5} = \frac{4.5 - 5.5}{1.66} = -\frac{1}{1.66} = -0.60$$

The area then is obtained from the tables as:

$$.3849 - .2257 = .1592$$

The exact computation using the binomial is:

$$\binom{11}{4}\left(\frac{1}{2}\right)^4\left(\frac{1}{2}\right)^7 = \frac{330}{2048} = .161$$

which compares favorably with the above computations using the normal approximation.

The table for all of the probabilities is given in Table 9.1.

Table 9.1

**Probabilities Obtained from the Binomial and
from the Normal Approximation to the Binomial**

Successes	Probability From Normal Approximation	From the Binomial
0	.001	.000
1	.007	.005
2	.027	.026
3	.079	.081
4	.159	.161
5	.226	.226
6	.226	.226
7	.159	.161
8	.079	.081
9	.027	.026
10	.007	.005
11	.001	.000

Obviously, as the values of np and nq get larger, the normal becomes a better and better approximation to the binomial.

The z ratios are identical if proportions are dealt with instead of the number of successes since $P = f/n$. The formula then becomes:

$$z_P = \frac{P - p}{\sigma_P} \quad \text{where} \quad \sigma_P = \sqrt{\frac{pq}{n}}$$

The two formulas are equal. That is:

$$z_f = \frac{f - E(f)}{\sigma_f} = z_P = \frac{P - p}{\sigma_P}$$

Their equivalence is easily shown:
Since $P = f/n$, then $f = nP$ and $E(f) = np$, so

$$z_f = \frac{f - E(f)}{\sqrt{npq}} = \frac{nP - np}{\sqrt{npq}} = \frac{n(P - p)}{\sqrt{npq}}$$

Dividing numerator and denominator by n gives:

$$z_f = \frac{(P - p)}{\dfrac{\sqrt{npq}}{n}}$$

Bringing the n under the radical sign results in:

$$\frac{(P - p)}{\sqrt{\dfrac{npq}{n^2}}} = \frac{(P - p)}{\sqrt{\dfrac{pq}{n}}} = z_P$$

The z_f statistic is probably a little easier to use in terms of adjusting a specific value of f_o to the continuous normal curve, that is, to $f_o \pm \frac{1}{2}$.

An Example

The use of the normal approximation to the binomial is exactly analogous to its use in the z test for the true mean. The situation includes, in both cases, an observed value of the statistic, an expected value of the statistic, and the true standard error of the statistic.

For example, suppose that it is hypothesized that two candidates have equal support from the voters. Suppose that this proposition is tested by drawing, randomly and independently, a sample of 100. The results indicate 57 people favor candidate A and 43 favor candidate B. What is the conclusion?

No direction is implied. The model for generating the sampling distribution is:

1) $H_0 : p = 1/2$
2) Sampling random and independent

3) Categories are mutually exclusive and exhaustive (i.e., $p (S \cap F)$ $= 0$ and $p (S \cup F) = 1$).
4) Sampling distribution of f normal

The Decision Model is:

1) $H_A : p \neq 1/2$
2) $\alpha = .05$

The z score for the statistic is:

$$z_{f_o} = \frac{f_o - E(f)}{\sigma_f} = \frac{57 - 50}{\sqrt{100 \cdot \frac{1}{2} \cdot \frac{1}{2}}} = \frac{7}{5} = +1.4$$

and the probability evaluation is:

$$p (|z| \geq 1.4) = 2 (.081) = .162 > .05 = \alpha$$

The conclusion, therefore, is that the hypothesis that the two candidates have equal support cannot be rejected. Obviously, there is a chance that the hypothesis is really false and that the investigator has failed to reject a false hypothesis. That is, although the sample result is not unlikely if $p = 1/2$, it is also not unlikely if $p = .57$, or if p equals any one of a number of other values.

In this case the population consists of the registered voters with respect to their stated preferences, and this most likely is not the same population that consists of the actual voters and their preferences as expressed in their votes. Hence, even had the evidence been such that the hypothesis would have been rejected, it would not have been possible to say that among those who do vote, there is not equal support.

The diagrams of the actual statistic and the transformed statistic are given in Figure 9.8.

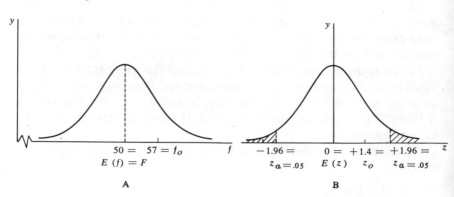

Figure 9.8

In the above computations, the adjustment for the continuous distribution was not made. Since $f_o = 57$, then on the continuous distribution the observed value of the statistic must be interpreted as the interval from 56.5 to 57.5. 56.5 then defines the class of events that are deviant from $E(f) = 50$.

The computation of z then would be

$$z = \frac{56.5 - 50}{5} = \frac{6.5}{5} = +1.3$$

The probability evaluation would be

$$p\,(|z| \geq 1.3) = 2\,(.097) = .194 > .05 = \alpha$$

Thus even with a large n, the *correction for continuity* altered the probability from .162 to .194. This is a fairly large change, although it did not affect the decision to fail to reject the null hypothesis. It must be apparent that only the numerator is affected by the correction and, therefore, the larger that $|f_o - E(f)|$ is, the less important the correction is. To be safe it is best to use the correction except for extremely large samples.

Confidence intervals for p

Although it is possible to compute the range of nonrejectable null hypotheses based on the evidence from the sample, the problem is more complicated than previously. This is due to the fact that the value of the standard error of the statistic, σ_f, is not independent of the parameter since $\sigma_f = \sqrt{npq}$. Thus, the sampling distribution for p_L will not be the same as that for p_U. Because of the relatively complicated algebra involved, the solution to the confidence interval problem will not be presented although the student should be aware of the fact that a solution does exist.

THE CHI-SQUARE DISTRIBUTIONS

Chi-Square Goodness of Fit

Frequently there are more than two categories into which observations may fall. For example, hair color may fall into any one of several categories — blond, grey, redhead, brunette. Types of automobiles also form a nominal scale of several categories as do the states of the Union in which people may live. The binomial test is only appropriate for nominal scales of two mutually exclusive categories. This section will develop a method for dealing with data that fall into a nominal scale consisting of two *or more* mutually exclusive categories. As in the case of the binomial there will be a set of hypothesized proportions for each category and the problem will be to determine how likely results like the observed are under the hypotheses.

The sampling distribution that is appropriate for the evaluation of the statistic is the chi-square distribution. As with t, the chi-square distribution varies depending on the degrees of freedom. The statistic that measures the sample is not, precisely speaking, a value of chi-square. But the values of the statistic, under certain conditions, are distributed as chi-square. This is analogous to the situation where the values of the binomial statistic, under certain conditions, were distributed normally. χ_ν^2 will be the symbol for chi-square with ν degrees of freedom. χ is the Greek letter chi.

The Chi-Square Distribution

To understand the chi-square distribution, it is easiest to consider the generation of the distribution based on repeated random and independent samples.

Consider first the chi-square distribution with one degree of freedom. This distribution is obtained by sampling from a normal curve of z scores. Each sample consists of only one z score randomly and independently selected from a normal distribution of z scores. This z score is then squared to give the value of the statistic. Hence, the distribution of chi-square with one degree of freedom is the distribution of the values of a squared z score obtained from repeated random and independent sampling of a single z score selected from a normal distribution.

The chi-square distribution with two degrees of freedom is obtained as follows. Randomly and independently two z scores from a normal distribution are selected, each is squared and the two are added together. This gives one value of the statistic. Hence, the various values of the statistic are based on the sum of the squares of two randomly and independently selected normal z scores. The definition of the chi-square statistic with ν degrees of freedom is: The sum of the squares of ν randomly selected normal z scores. A single value of chi-square with ν degrees of freedom is then obtained from the sum of ν squared normal deviates each of which is randomly and independently selected.

For example, suppose chi-square with 5 degrees of freedom is being considered. Then to obtain a single value of the statistic, five z scores from a normal curve would be randomly and independently selected. Suppose these values turned out as follows: $z_1 = 1.0$, $z_2 = -3.2$, $z_3 = .64$, $z_4 = .50$, and $z_5 = -1.2$. Then $\chi_5^2 = (1.0)^2 + (-3.2)^2 + (.64)^2 + (.50)^2 + (-1.2)^2 = 1.00 + 10.24 + .41 + .25 + 1.44 = 13.34$, and this is one value of the statistic.

By repeated random and independent sampling of 5 normal deviates which were squared and then summed, the distribution of χ_5^2 would be obtained. Of course, the procedure for obtaining the χ^2 distribution is equivalent to going through the squaring and summing process for all of the unique samples of five z scores from the normal curve.

The Problem

Suppose an investigator had a hypothesis that on a particular college campus, blond and brunette girls are each twice as common as redheads. He then selected 100 coeds and found that 10 were redheads, 30 were blonds and 55 were brunettes. What did he conclude about his hypothesis?

This problem involves nominal scaling of elements onto a three category variable of hair color. (For the purposes of this problem, it will be supposed that there were no grey-haired, bald, or other types of coeds.)

The hypothesis about the parameter deals with the proportions of coeds that are in each category. This is analogous to the situation in the binomial except that there are three categories instead of two. Translating the experimenter's hypothesis, the following is obtained:

$$p_r = .20, \; p_{bl} = .40, \text{ and } p_{br} = .40$$

These proportions are obtained from the verbal hypothesis by letting $x =$ the probability of a redhead. Then, by the statement of the problem, the probability of a blond must be $2x$ as must be the probability of a brunette. However, the probability that an observation will be in any one of the categories must be 1.00. Therefore, $x + 2x + 2x = 1.00$ from which $x = .20$ and $2x = .40$.

The question remaining is: how well does the observed data compare to that which was expected under the hypotheses. To compute the observed value of the statistic it is necessary to deal with the hypothesized and observed frequencies in the categories rather than the proportions. The frequency expected under the null hypothesis for category i is simply $F_i = np_i$. The expected and observed results are summarized in the following table:

HAIR COLOR

	Redhead	Blonde	Brunette	
Observed (f)	15	30	55	100
Expected (F)	20	40	40	100

The statistic that is computed is the following:

$$\sum_{i=1}^{k} \frac{(f_i - F_i)^2}{F_i}$$

where k is the number of categories, F_i is the expected frequency in category i and f_i is the observed frequency in category i. For the above problem the computation is:

$$(20 - 15)^2/20 + (40 - 30)^2/40 + (40 - 55)^2/40 = 25/20$$

$$+ 100/40 + 225/40 = \frac{375}{40} = 9.4$$

The value of the statistic is 9.4. What does this mean?

Fortunately, the values of the statistic as defined above are distributed as χ_2^2. That is, the computation of the statistic

$$\sum_{i=1}^{k} \frac{(f_i - F_i)^2}{F_i}$$

based on repeated random and independent samples results in values that are distributed as the chi-square statistic whose degrees of freedom are one less than the number of categories. Before completing the problem it would be well to examine the concept of the degrees of freedom and the relationship between the above statistic and χ_{k-1}^2.

Degrees of Freedom

The reason that the degrees of freedom are one less than the number of categories is as follows. For any sample of size n, the number of observations in any two of the categories are free to vary. However, once the numbers in two of the categories are fixed, the third category must have whatever number is required to complete the sample size. In the previous example, the sample size was 100. Only two of the observed frequencies are free to vary from the expected. That is, the observed frequency in cell 1 (redheads) could be any one of many values as could the frequency in cell 2 (blondes). Once these numbers are fixed, however, the deviation of the observed frequency from the expected in cell 3 is determined. Of course, any two cells can be considered free to vary (like 1 and 3). The point is that the last cell's frequency is determined by the sample size and the frequencies in two other cells. Equivalently, since $np_i = F_i$, the expected proportions in the cells are free to vary up to the last one. This last proportion must be such that the sum of all of the proportions is 1.00.

Why the Statistic Is Distributed as χ^2

As previously discussed, the χ^2 statistic is based on the sum of the squares of a number of normal deviates. In fact χ_ν^2 is defined as the sum of the squares of ν randomly and independently selected normal deviates.

Why is the statistic that is computed using the frequencies distributed as χ^2_{k-1}?

The answer to this question will be presented by an argument that parallels the argument for the normal as an approximation to the binomial.

The statistic

$$\sum_{i=1}^{k} \frac{(f_i - F_i)^2}{F_i}$$

only approximates the χ^2 distribution under certain conditions. As with the binomial, the categories must be mutually exclusive and the probability of an observation falling into some one of the categories must be 1.00. In addition, *the observed frequencies must be normally distributed about the expected frequencies for every cell.* This condition will have been considered to have been met when, in each cell, the expected frequencies are greater than or equal to 5 if the degrees of freedom are less than or equal to 4, or if the expected frequencies for each cell are greater than or equal to 3 if the degrees of freedom are greater than 4. Symbolically, this can be presented as $F_i \geq 5$ for every i when $\nu \leq 4$ and $F_i \geq 3$ for every i when $\nu > 4$. Since the expected frequency is obtained from np_i, this requirement exactly corresponds to the requirement that the normal approximates the binomial only if both np and $nq \geq 5$. (Since χ^2 is appropriate for 2 or more cells, the binomial condition should be equivalent to the χ^2 requirement when there are only 2 cells, and it is.)

For expected frequencies less than 5 it is not possible for the observed frequencies to be normally distributed about the expected frequency. For example, if $F = 2$, then f can equal, upon repeated sampling, values far above 2, but only 0 or 1 below 2. Hence the sampling distribution of f about the expected value of the distribution, F, would appear approximately as given in Figure 9.9.

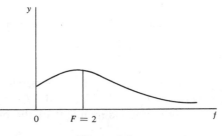

Figure 9.9

It is easily seen that the distribution is skewed to the right.

On the other hand, if F is at least 5, the sampling distribution of f can approach normality as is illustrated in Figure 9.10.

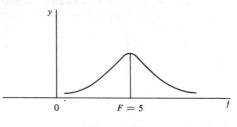

Figure 9.10

When the sampling distribution of f_i is normal about F_i for every i (that is, for every cell), the computation of the statistic

$$\sum_{i=1}^{k} \frac{(f_i - F_i)^2}{F_i}$$

is similar to the computation of a value of χ^2. Instead of adding up squared z scores from a normal curve, the addition is of the squared deviations of $(f_i - F_i)$ where f_i is drawn from a normal distribution. Dividing by F_i is related to dividing by the SD in a z score since the variability of the sampling distribution of f is dependent on F. If F were 50, one would expect that the f's would vary more from each other on the average than if F were 5. Remember that the sampling distribution of f about F is based on repeated random samples of a given size from a population with a stated value of F for a cell. Due to sampling error, the observed frequencies, f, would be expected to vary from each other. Fortunately, when $F \geq 5$, this sampling distribution of f is approximately normal.

It should be understood that $(f_i - F_i)^2/F_i$ is not a squared normal deviate but is similar to one. As was indicated in the normal approximation to the binomial, $z = (f_i - F_i)/\sqrt{npq}$. Thus $z^2 = (f_i - F_i)^2/npq$ $= (f_i - F_i)^2/F_iq$ and this approaches $(f_i - F_i)^2/F_i$ as q approaches the value 1. The above discussion, therefore, is merely to indicate that

$$\sum_{i=1}^{k} \frac{(f_i - F_i)^2}{F_i}$$

is similar to adding up a series of normal deviates. However, the mathematical differences between $(f_i - F_i)^2/F_i$ and $(f_i - F_i)^2/F_iq$, and the fact that the last category is not independent of the others leads to the distribution of

$$\sum_{i=1}^{k} \frac{(f_i - F_i)^2}{F_i} \quad \text{as} \quad \chi^2_{k-1}$$

The formal model for the χ^2 goodness-of-fit test is

1) $H_0 : p_1 = a_1, p_2 = a_2, \cdots p_k = a_k$
2) $p_1 + p_2 + \cdots + p_k = 1$ (categories exhaustive)
3) $p \, (S_i \cap S_j) = 0$, for every $i \neq j$ (categories mutually exclusive)
4) Sampling random and independent
5) $df = k - 1 = \nu$ where k is the number of categories
6) f_i normal about F_i, for every i

In terms of the problem presented earlier, the computed value of the statistic was 9.4 and this must be evaluated using the χ^2 distribution with two degrees of freedom. The other conditions of the model have been fulfilled so the decision will be either to reject the null hypothesis in favor of the alternative or to fail to reject the null hypothesis. The decision model is:

1) $H_A : p \neq a_1$ and/or $p_2 \neq a_2$, and/or $\cdots$ and/or $p_k \neq a_k$
2) $\alpha = .05$

Notice that the alternative hypothesis is merely that at least one of the assumed proportions is false.

The χ_2^2 distribution is given in Figure 9.11. The symbol $\chi_{2\alpha}^2$ is a value of χ_2^2 such that $p \, (\chi_2^2 \geq \chi_{2\alpha}^2) = \alpha$.

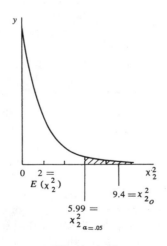

Figure 9.11

The $p \, (\chi_2^2 \geq 9.4) < .01 < .05 = \alpha$. Therefore, the conclusion is to reject the null hypothesis in favor of the alternative. In terms of the original problem this would mean to reject the hypothesis that the proportions of blondes and brunettes in the population were both twice as great as that of redheads. It is impossible to state which of the proportions is actually false. The conclusion that is made when the alternative hypothesis is accepted is merely that at least one of the stated proportions is wrong.

χ^2 a Two-Tailed Test

The χ^2 test is a two-tailed test. Deviations may contribute to a large value of χ^2 either because they are large negative values (the observed frequency is much smaller than the expected frequency) or large positive values (the observed frequency is much greater than the expected). There is no way to specify that only one direction be considered when the number of cells is greater than two. For example, in the above problem even if the experimenter wanted the alternative to be $p_1 < .20$, which implies $f_1 < F_1$, the probability evaluation of the statistic would have been unclear since p_2 could have been either less than or greater than .40 (that is, a deviation would have counted if $f_2 < F_2$ or if $f_2 > F_2$). As the number of cells increases, the specification of a one-tailed test becomes even more difficult. In fact, with more than two categories, there are theoretically three types of tests that might be considered: 1) one-tailed tests in which all cells have the direction specified in which deviations may count, 2) two-tailed tests in which the deviations of observed frequencies from the expected may be in either direction, 3) mixed tests in which deviations may occur in only one direction in some cells but in either direction in the other cells.

For many reasons, only the two-tailed situation is dealt with. One of these reasons is that the probability that all deviations would be in a predicted direction is not $1/2$ of the probability of the two-tailed situation and the relationship changes depending on the degrees of freedom. Of course, if there are only two cells, a direction can be specified to the alternative hypothesis since there is only one degree of freedom. Thus, predicting that $f_1 < F_1$ in cell 1 automatically implies $f_2 < F_2$ in cell 2. This is exactly what is done in the one-tailed alternative hypothesis of the z test for the true proportion. Because of the complications involved in interpretation it is recommended that all one-tailed tests with the two category nominal situation be performed with z_P or z_f, that is, the normal approximation to the binomial.

To summarize, the χ^2 test is a two-tailed test because deviations contribute to the value of the statistic when they are either greater than the expected or less than the expected.

To examine briefly why only one tail of the χ^2 distribution is used even though it is a two-tailed test, it must be realized that the extreme righthand values of the distribution represent large values of χ^2. These occur when the observed frequencies are greatly deviant from the expected values. In this case, one would be inclined to reject the hypotheses. However, the extreme lefthand values of the distribution represent very small values of χ^2. These values occur when the observed frequencies are extremely close to the expected values. Even if the observed frequencies are so close to the expected frequencies that they could occur by chance rarely, one would certainly not reject the hypothesis that led to the expected frequencies. If observations are close to expected ones they are certainly not evidence against the hypotheses. Hence, *in the χ^2 distributions, the extreme righthand side of the curve represents low probability two-tailed values of the statistic that result from large deviations from the expected.*

Shapes of the χ^2 Distributions and Their Expected Values

The distribution's shape is a function of the degrees of freedom. For one degree of freedom, the χ^2 distribution is somewhat similar to the right half of the unit normal curve. This may easily be seen by referring to the unit normal distribution in Figure 9.12.

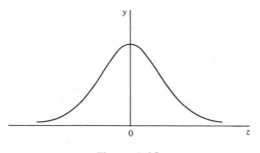

Figure 9.12

It will be recalled that χ_1^2 is obtained by taking one z score at a time from a normal curve and squaring it. If this process is repeated for the whole curve above, all of the values below 0 will be eliminated by the process of squaring. This will make the values above 0 twice as common. However, the curve will not be the same as one that is twice as high as the positive half of the normal curve because the z scores are squared and large values when squared increase more than do small values. The distribution of χ_1^2 is as drawn in Figure 9.13.

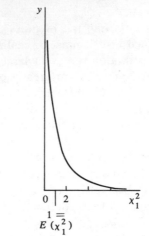

Figure 9.13

When two z scores are squared and added together, as is done to obtain χ_2^2, the distribution is as in Figure 9.14.

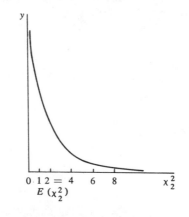

Figure 9.14

As the degrees of freedom increase, the distribution of χ^2 approaches a normal distribution. The expected value of the χ^2 distribution is always equal to the degrees of freedom. Thus, for χ_{15}^2 the expected value of the distribution is 15 and the diagram is as in Figure 9.15.

The reason that the expected value is equal to the degrees of freedom may be seen by considering the variance of a set of z scores. Since $\bar{z}$ for a distribution of z scores is always 0, and the variance of a distribution of z scores is 1, then by the definition of a variance,

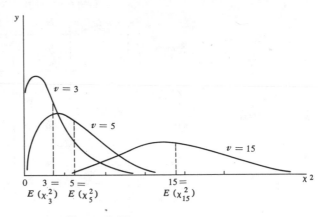

Figure 9.15

$$\sum_{i=1}^{N} (z_i - \bar{z})^2/N = \sum_{i=1}^{N} (z_i - 0)^2/N = \sum_{i=1}^{N} (z_i)^2/N = 1$$

But this is simply the average value of chi-square with 1 degree of freedom, which is the definition of $E(\chi_1^2)$. Since χ^2 with larger degrees of freedom is obtained by adding together a number of squared z scores, the average value is based on the sum of a set of variances. Since these variances are of distributions of z scores and each distribution has an average value of 1, the average of the sum is equal to the number of squared z scores. Hence $E(\chi_\nu^2) = \nu$.

χ^2 Test of Association

A test for the significance of the association between two nominally scaled variables is the χ^2 test of association. This χ^2 test differs from φ in two important ways. The most important one is that φ is simply a measure of the degree of association between two nominally scaled variables whereas χ^2 is a test for the statistical significance of association. Additionally, the χ^2 test of association may be used no matter how many categories there are on each variable whereas φ is limited to measuring the degree of association for two nominal variables each of which has exactly two categories.

An Example

Consider a test to determine if there is an association between the type of magazine a person prefers and his level of education. A sample of 160 might give the following results:

LEVEL OF EDUCATION

		College	H.S.	Gr. S.	
	Sports	12	20	8	40
		a	b	c	
TYPE OF MAGAZINE	Business	16	10	4	30
		d	e	f	
	News	6	66	8	80
		g	h	i	
	Arts	6	4	0	10
		j	k	l	
		40	100	20	160

The null hypothesis in the χ^2 test of association is that there is no association between the two variables. Translating this mathematically, the null hypothesis becomes:

$$H_0 : p_{r_i c_j} = p_{r_i} p_{c_j} \text{ for every } i, j \text{ pair}$$

The argument for phrasing the null hypothesis this way is based on the probability rule for independent events. It will be recalled that if two events are independent, the probability that they will both occur is the product of their probabilities. The argument is that being in a particular row is an event, and being in a particular column is an event. If there is no association between the two variables, then the row category that a person is in is independent (or unassociated with) the column category that he is in. That is, rows are independent of columns. Hence, the probability of being in a given row and a given column should be the probability of being in that row times the probability of being in that column, and this should hold for every row-column pair. This is the statement presented in the null hypothesis.

The full model for the χ^2 of association test is:

1) $H_0 : p_{c_i r_j} = p_{c_i} p_{r_j}$ for every i and j

2) $\sum_{i=1}^{r} \sum_{j=1}^{k} p_{c_i r_j} = 1$

3) $p(r_1 \cap r_2), p(r_1 \cap r_3) \cdots p(r_{r-1} \cap r_r) = 0$
$p(c_1 \cap c_2), p(c_1 \cap c_3) \cdots p(c_{k-1} \cap c_k) = 0$

4) R and I

5) $df = (r - 1)(k - 1) = c$

6) f_{ij} normal about F_{ij} for every ij

The ij subscript denotes a particular cell. Thus F_{23} is the expected frequency in that cell which is in row two and column three.

The second condition merely states that the cells of the table are exhaustive. That is, an observation must fall into some one of the cells. Condition three is the requirement that each of the variables consists of categories that are mutually exclusive. The fourth condition is the familiar one that the sampling be done randomly and independently. The fifth condition is the degrees of freedom. Note that in x^2 for association, the degrees of freedom are obtained by multiplying the number of row cells less one by the number of column cells less one. In the example presented above, the degrees of freedom are $(4 - 1)(3 - 1) = 6$. The number of observations in as many as 6 cells can be freely chosen, but then the number of observations in the remaining cells are determined. Another way to state this is to say that the row marginals force the last cell in each row to have whatever number of observations are needed to add up to the number of observations in the marginal for that row. Of course, the same restriction is forced on the last cell in each column by that column marginal.

The last condition is the same as the requirement in the x^2 goodness of fit test that the distribution of the observed frequencies must be normal about the expected frequencies. The same rule applies for determining when this occurs, namely, if $df \leq 4$, then $F \geq 5$ and if $df > 4$, $F \geq 3$. (The student should realize that this rule is quite arbitrary, just as was the requirement that $n \geq 30$ for $\bar{X}$ to be approximately normal in the z test for the true mean and that both np and nq be at least 5 for f to be approximately normal in the normal approximation to the binomial. Other authors, who are somewhat more conservative, require np and nq to both be at least 10 for the normal to be an approximation to the binomial and also that $F \geq 10$ if $df \leq 4$ and $F \geq 5$ if $df > 4$ for the x^2 tests. Obviously, the stricter the requirements are, the closer the approximations come to the theoretical distribution.)

The expected frequencies in the x^2 for the association test are obtained from the marginals. This differs from their determination in the goodness of fit test where they were obtained directly from the null hypothesis.

The argument for computing the expected frequencies is as follows. Consider cell a. Under the null hypothesis that the rows are independent of the columns the probability of an observation being in both row one and column one is the probability of its being in row one times its probability of being in column one. From the marginals, 40 of the cases were in row one out of the total number of observations of 160. Hence the probability of being in row one is $40/160 = 1/4$. Similarly, the probability of being in column one is $40/160 = 1/4$. Therefore, if rows and columns are independent, p (cell a) $= p_{r_1 c_1} = p_{r_1} p_{c_1} = (1/4)(1/4) = 1/16$. The expected frequency then is obtained from $F_{11} = (p_{r_1 c_1})(n) = (1/16)(160) = 10$.

For cell b the expected frequency is $F_{12} = p_{r_1 c_1} \cdot n = p_{r_1} p_{c_2} \cdot n = (1/4)(5/8)(160) = (5/32)(160) = 25$.

For cell d: $F_{21} = p_{r_2 c_1} \cdot n = p_{r_2} p_{c_1} \cdot n = (3/16)(1/4)(160) = 7.5$.

For cell e: $F_{22} = p_{r_2 c_2} \cdot n = p_{r_2} p_{c_2} = (3/16)(5/8)(160) = 75/4 = 18.75$.

Finally cells g and h are computed: $F_{31} = (1/2)(1/4)(160) = 20$ and $F_{32} = (1/2)(5/8)(160) = 50$.

The other cell frequencies are determined by these numbers. That is, F_{13} must be 5 since the marginal for row 1 is 40 and $F_{11} + F_{12} = 35$. Similarly F_{23} must be 3.75, F_{33} must be 10, $F_{41} = 2.50$, $F_{42} = 6.25$, and $F_{43} = 1.25$.

These results are summarized in the following table:

| | | | LEVEL OF EDUCATION | | | | |
			College	H.S.	Gr. S.		
	Sports	f	12	20	8		40
		F	10	25	5		
TYPE	Business	f	16	10	4		30
OF		F	7.5	18.75	3.75		
MAGAZINE	News	f	6	66	8		80
		F	20	50	10		
	Arts	f	6	4	0		10
		F	2.50	6.25	1.25		
			40	100	20		160

Notice that condition 6 has not been met since all of the F_{ij} are not at least 3 which is required when $df > 4$.

One way to overcome this problem is to collapse categories. For example, if the first and third columns were combined the result would be the following 2 x 4 table in which all of the expected frequencies are at least 3:

| | | | LEVEL OF EDUCATION | | | |
			Coll. and Gr. S.	H.S.		
	Sports	f	20	20		40
		F	15	25		
TYPE	Business	f	20	10		30
OF		F	11.25	18.75		
MAGAZINE	News	f	14	66		80
		F	30	50		
	Arts	f	6	4		10
		F	3.75	6.25		
			60	100		160

Note that the degrees of freedom are reduced from $(4 - 1)(3 - 1) = 6$ to $(4 - 1)(2 - 1) = 3$. As a result, although all of the expected frequencies are now greater than 3 they are not greater than 5, which is needed when $df \leq 4$. Further, the collapsing of the college and grade school categories does not make much sense. Similarly, row categories could also be collapsed to obtain the required level for the expected frequencies. For example if rows 3 and 4 were combined the results would be:

LEVEL OF EDUCATION

		College	H.S.	Gr. S.	
	Sports	12	20	8	40
		10	25	5	
TYPE					
OF	*Business*	16	10	4	30
MAGAZINE		7.5	18.75	3.75	
	News aud Arts	12	70	8	90
		22.5	56.25	11.25	
		40	100	20	160

Again the decision to collapse cells partly hinges on the sense that the new categories make.

While the above solution to the problem is a possibility, another and preferable way to achieve the desired results is to increase the sample size. Suppose therefore that 400 cases had been selected with the following results:

LEVEL OF EDUCATION

		College	H.S.	Gr. S.	
	Sports	20	60	40	120
		24	72	24	
TYPE	*Business*	30	38	12	80
OF		16	48	16	
MAGAZINE	*News*	20	133	27	180
		36	108	36	
	Arts	10	9	1	20
		4	12	4	
		80	240	80	400

It should be apparent that if the sample size were to be increased from 160 to 400, the results would not be exactly 2.5 times the original results for all of the marginals and the cells because of sampling error.

The statistic,

$$\sum_{i=1}^{r} \sum_{j=1}^{k} \frac{(f_{ij} - F_{ij})^2}{F_{ij}}$$

is distributed as χ^2 with $(r-1)(c-1)$ degrees of freedom. The double summation and subscript notation merely indicates that the process must be carried out across all of the rows and columns. The computation for the example then becomes:

$$\chi_6^2 = \sum_{i=1}^{4} \sum_{j=1}^{3} \frac{(f_{ij} - F_{ij})^2}{F_{ij}}$$

$$= \frac{(20-24)^2}{24} + \frac{(60-72)^2}{72} + \frac{(40-24)^2}{24} + \frac{(30-16)^2}{16}$$

$$+ \frac{(38-48)^2}{48} + \frac{(12-16)^2}{16} + \frac{(20-36)^2}{36} + \frac{(133-108)^2}{108}$$

$$+ \frac{(27-36)^2}{36} + \frac{(10-4)^2}{4} + \frac{(9-12)^2}{12} + \frac{(1-4)^2}{4}$$

$$= 55.81$$

Evaluation of this value by use of Table V in the Appendix indicates that $p(\chi_6^2 \geq 55.70) < p(\chi_6^2 \geq 16.81) = .01$. This is diagrammed in Figure 9.16.

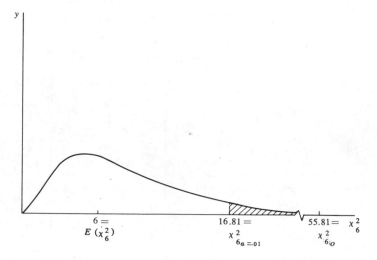

Figure 9.16

Thus even for an α level as low as .01, the null hypothesis would have had to have been rejected in favor of the alternative. In the case of χ^2 for association, the alternative hypothesis is simply $H_A : p_{r_i c_j} \neq p_{r_i} p_{c_j}$ for some i,j. That is, all that is implied in accepting the alternative is that somewhere in the table there is a lack of independence between rows and columns. It may have been, for example, merely a much larger proportion of high school graduates who read news magazines compared to what was expected under the assumption of independence, that led to the significant value of the statistic.

In this example, the verbal conclusion would be that there is a statistically significant association between the highest degree that a person earned and the type of magazine that he preferred.

10

MATCHED GROUPS. z AND t TESTS

z TEST FOR THE DIFFERENCE BETWEEN MEANS BASED ON MATCHED GROUPS

The discussion that follows resembles closely the presentation of Chapter 5 on the difference between means. The major change that will be considered here is that individuals in one sample are matched with those in the other on a relevant variable. Hence individuals in the samples are not drawn independently of each other.

In order to investigate further the z test for the difference between means using matched groups it is probably best to consider an example.

Consider an experiment to determine whether or not a particular drug affects learning ability. Since IQ is generally considered related to the ability to learn, the experimenter might well consider matching the individuals on IQ. That is, for a particular IQ level, one person at that level would be placed in each group, for example, one in the control group and one in the group that took the drug. Thus individuals in one group would be *matched* with those in the other group. The effect of such matching should be to reduce the differences between the two groups since each individual in one group has a "twin" in the other group. This does not mean that the experimental group will not differ from the control group. It merely means that a difference between the two groups is more important since the two groups are more alike than they would have been if they both had been randomly and independently drawn.

Consider a situation where the experimenter draws four pairs of individuals who are matched on IQ. Suppose that for each pair there is a random assignment of one individual to the control group and one to the experimental group. Consider the following results in terms of scores on a learning task:

Drugs	No Drugs	IQ
2	4	90
6	9	95
7	8	98
11	10	100

This table indicates that of the two people that were selected with an IQ of 90, the one that took the drug scored 2 while the person in the control group scored a 4 on the same task.

In order to determine if the experimental condition was effective and at the same time take into consideration the effect of matching, it will first be necessary to examine the population that is being dealt with.

Essentially there are three populations to consider. First, there are all of the people who do not undergo the drug treatment with respect to how they do on the learning task. Secondly there are all of the people who take the drug with respect to how they perform on the task. Finally, there is the population of individuals with respect to their IQ scores. These three distributions are presented in Figure 10.1.

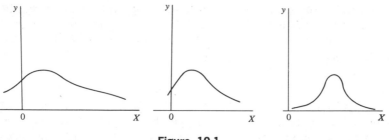

Figure 10.1

The experimental data can be considered to have come about as follows: From the distribution of IQ scores pairs of individuals with the same IQ are selected. One member of each pair is randomly assigned to the control group and another member to the experimental group. Hence, under these circumstances the distributions of learning scores in the populations are not independent of each other. Each person in the distribution of scores that represents the no drug condition has a mate in the population of scores under the drug condition. Scores, therefore, cannot be independently selected from each of the two distributions. However, pairs matched on IQ can be randomly and independently selected.

Effect of Matching on the Standard Error

The statistic in the test for the difference between means based on matched groups is $(\bar{X}_1 - \bar{X}_2)$. The question arises as to how the matching affects the standard error. The answer to this is rather easily seen by recalling that when there is no matching, the members of each sample are drawn independently of each other. In the matched case, each observation in one sample is matched or paired with an observation in the second sample. If the variable on which the matching occurs is relevant to the task, members in the two samples should be more like each other than are members in two samples in which the members of one sample have been selected independently of the members in the other sample. As a result, given two experimental conditions (or a control condition and an experimental condition), the two means should differ less from each other on the average when there is matching than when there isn't. Another way to see this is to realize that, without matching, the two means could differ from each other not just due to the different effects of the two experimental conditions, but also because the two samples differed from each other in terms of the IQ's of the members. In effect, matching on a relevant variable reduces one source of sampling variability. It is possible to match on more than one variable. If several relevant variables have all been matched, like IQ, age, education, and so on, even more of the sampling variability is eliminated. The effect of eliminating sampling variability is to make the difference between the two sample means almost completely a result of the difference in the effects of the two experimental conditions. Obviously, the best match would be one in which a person were matched with himself. One of the major problems here is that an effect that appears may be due to the learning from the first task and not due to the changed condition. Even if learning can be controlled, the investigator may be more interested in the changes that occur among persons under the two conditions rather than the changes that occur within persons. If this were the case, it would be necessary to match using different individuals.

The formula for the standard error for matched groups is:

$$\sigma_{(\bar{X}_1 - \bar{X}_2)} = \sqrt{\frac{\sigma_{X_1}^2 + \sigma_{X_2}^2 - 2\rho_{X_1 X_2}\sigma_{X_1}\sigma_{X_2}}{n}}$$

where σ_{X_1} and σ_{X_2} are the standard deviations of the two populations and $\rho_{X_1 X_2}$ is the correlation between the scores under the control conditions and those under the experimental conditions across all of the matched pairs in the population. It will be recalled that when there is no matching the standard error is given by:

$$\sigma_{(\bar{X}_1 - \bar{X}_2)} = \sqrt{\frac{\sigma_{X_1}^2}{n_1} + \frac{\sigma_{X_2}^2}{n_2}}$$

For equal sized samples this becomes:

$$\sigma_{(\bar{X}_1 - \bar{X}_2)} = \sqrt{\frac{\sigma_{X_1}^2 + \sigma_{X_2}^2}{n}}$$

Thus the difference between the two standard errors is determined by the factor $-(2\rho_{X_1X_2}\,\sigma_{X_1}\sigma_{X_2})/n$ which is subtracted from the standard error for the unmatched case. Obviously, if $\rho_{X_1X_2} = 0$ the formula for the matched case reduces to that in the unmatched case. If $\rho_{X_1X_2} = 0$, then the variable that was selected was not relevant. The larger the correlation, the smaller $\sigma_{(\bar{X}_1 - \bar{X}_2)}$ becomes.

The Model

The conditions that must be met for the z test for the difference between the means using matched groups are exactly the same as the conditions for the difference between means of unmatched groups. They are:

1) $H_0 : \mu_1 - \mu_2 = a$
2) $\sigma_{(\bar{X}_1-\bar{X}_2)} = b$
3) R and I
4) $(\bar{X}_1 - \bar{X}_2)$ normal

t TEST FOR THE DIFFERENCE BETWEEN MEANS—MATCHED GROUPS

As with the z test above, the major difference in the matched groups t test compared with the independent groups t test is the standard error. Of course in a t test the standard error is estimated. This means that the estimate for matched groups is smaller than it would be for unmatched groups. It will be recalled that,

$$est\ \sigma_{(\bar{X}_1-\bar{X}_2)} = \sqrt{\frac{n_1 SD_1^2 + n_2 SD_2^2}{n_1 + n_2 - 2}\left(\frac{n_1 + n_2}{n_1 n_2}\right)}$$

This became

$$est\ \sigma_{(\bar{X}_1-\bar{X}_2)} = \sqrt{\frac{SD_1^2 + SD_2^2}{n - 1}}$$

when the two groups were of equal size. Since $est\ \sigma^2_{\bar{X}_1} = SD_1^2/(n - 1)$ and $est\ \sigma^2_{\bar{X}_2} = SD_2^2/(n - 1)$ this could also be written as $est\ \sigma_{(\bar{X}_1-\bar{X}_2)} = \sqrt{est\ \sigma^2_{\bar{X}_1} + est\ \sigma^2_{\bar{X}_2}}$. For the case where the groups have been matched, the estimate of the standard error is reduced by $2\,r_{X_1X_2}\,est\ \sigma_{\bar{X}_1}\,est\ \sigma_{\bar{X}_2}$ so that the formula for the standard error becomes:

$$est\ \sigma_{(\bar{X}_1-\bar{X}_2)} = \sqrt{est\ \sigma^2_{\bar{X}_1} + est\ \sigma^2_{\bar{X}_1} - 2\,r_{X_1X_2}\,est\ \sigma_{\bar{X}_1}\,est\ \sigma_{\bar{X}_2}}$$

where $r_{X_1X_2}$ is the correlation that exists in the sample between the scores obtained under the X_1 treatment and those obtained under the X_2 treatment. The t ratio then becomes:

$$t_{n-1} = \frac{(\bar{X}_1 - \bar{X}_2) - (\mu_1 - \mu_2)}{est\ \sigma_{(\bar{X}_1-\bar{X}_2)} = \sqrt{est\ \sigma^2_{\bar{X}_1} + est\ \sigma^2_{\bar{X}_2} - 2r_{X_1X_2}\,est\ \sigma_{\bar{X}_1}\,est\ \sigma_{\bar{X}_2}}}$$

where n is the *number of pairs*. Thus, if there are six pairs of matched individuals, the degrees of freedom equal 5. Note that if the samples had been randomly and independently drawn instead of being matched the degrees of freedom would have been $n_1 + n_2 - 2$ or 10. Thus, matching reduces the degrees of freedom.

This reduction in the degrees of freedom is an important point. It will be recalled from Figure 5.3 that as the degrees of freedom become smaller, the t distribution becomes more sharply peaked. As a consequence more of the scores fall in the tails of the t distribution when there are fewer degrees of freedom. The result of this is that, for a given α level, the t ratio must be larger when there are fewer degrees of freedom. It thus would appear that matching has made it more difficult to obtain significance. However, the decrease in degrees of freedom can be compensated for by the correlation. Since the standard error of the difference between the sample means is reduced by $-2 r_{X_1 X_2} est \, \sigma_{\bar{X}_1} est \, \sigma_{\bar{X}_2}$, a given difference in $(\bar{X}_1 - \bar{X}_2)$ results in a larger t ratio when matching on a relevant variable has occurred. This matching reduces the size of the denominator which of course increases the size of the ratio. Whether or not matching has been worthwhile (in terms of making it easier to achieve significance) depends on the size of the correlation. It must at least be large enough to compensate for the loss in degrees of freedom. Similarly, matching on an irrelevant variable makes it more difficult to achieve statistical significance. In this case the correlation is close to 0. As a result $est \, \sigma_{(\bar{X}_1 - \bar{X}_2)}$ is not reduced. But matching reduces the degrees of freedom so that a larger t ratio is needed to obtain significance. Thus the experimenter, if he matches on a variable unrelated to the task, makes it more difficult to reject the null hypothesis. This problem becomes of less importance as the degrees of freedom increase, since, for example, $t_{25 \alpha = .05} = 2.06$ and $t_{\infty \alpha = .05} = 1.96$.

MATCHED GROUPS AND DIFFERENCES

An algebraically equivalent way of approaching the matched groups problem is to consider the population of differences that are formed on the basis of the matched pairs. Although there are two populations, the two samples are not randomly and independently selected. Instead, it is the matched pairs that are randomly and independently selected. The situation is diagrammed in Figure 10.2.

For a score selected at random from Population 1, say X_1, a particular person, say Y_1, must be selected from Population 2. The selection is of course determined by the score on the matching variable or set of variables. Thus if the matching is on IQ and X_1 has an IQ of 97, this determines that a person from the second population with an IQ of 97 must also be selected. As a result it is possible to consider every person in

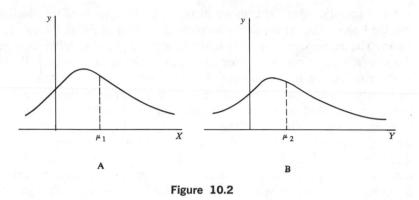

Figure 10.2

Population 1 matched with a person from Population 2. This set of pairs can be considered to be a new population with the score for a pair being the difference between the two scores. This yields a population of differences. The mean of this population δ is equal to $\mu_1 - \mu_2$, the difference between the means of the two original populations.

The individual differences would be obtained as follows:

Pair No.	Scores of Individuals Under Condition 1.	Scores of Individuals Under Condition 2.	Differences Between Matched Pairs
1	X_1	Y_1	$D_1 = X_1 - Y_1$
2	X_2	Y_2	$D_2 = X_2 - Y_2$
3	X_3	Y_3	$D_3 = X_3 - Y_3$
.	.	.	.
.	.	.	.
.	.	.	.
N	X_N	Y_N	$D_N = X_N - Y_N$

For $\mu_1 - \mu_2 = a$, the diagram of the population of differences is given in Figure 10.3.

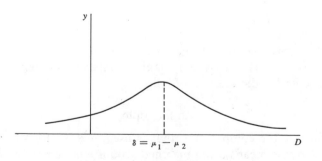

Figure 10.3

Since sampling from the above distribution is equivalent to selecting matched pairs, the problem can be reduced to that of a test for the true mean. The single sample that is selected is a sample of differences from the above population. The observed value of the statistic is then $\bar{D}$, the average difference in the sample. This of course is equal to $(\bar{X}_1 - \bar{X}_2)$. As a result the computations reduce to those of a test for the true mean. If σ_D, the standard deviation of the population of differences is known, then $\sigma_{\bar{D}}$, the standard error of the statistic, is equal to $\sigma_D/\sqrt{n}$. In this case a z test is performed. If the value of $\sigma_{\bar{D}}$ cannot be determined precisely then it must be estimated from the standard deviation of the sample. As usual $est\ \sigma_{\bar{D}} = SD_D/\sqrt{n-1}$. Note that except for subscript notation, the computation is precisely that of a test for the true mean. This should not be surprising since the problem has been reduced to a true mean problem. To understand this more fully it is only necessary to consider that there is a population of scores; from this population a single sample has been selected. The mean of the sample is computed and the question is whether or not this observed mean is consistent with the assumed mean of the population. The fact that the scores in the population are differences, and that the mean of the sample is, therefore, an average difference, makes no difference in the formal analysis of the problem. Likewise, the models that are appropriate are precisely those which were appropriate in the z and t tests for the true mean. They are:

z test for the difference between population means using matched groups:

1) $H_0 : \delta = a$
2) $\sigma_{\bar{D}} = b$
3) R and I
4) $\bar{D}$ normal

t test for the difference between population means using matched groups:

1) $H_0 : \delta = a$
2) $est\ \sigma_{\bar{D}} = SD_D/\sqrt{n-1} = b$
3) R and I
4) D normal ($\bar{D}$ normal in alternate model)
5) $df = (n-1) = c$ (where n is the number of differences which of course is also the number of pairs).

An Example

To illustrate the computation that is used, a t test for the difference between the true means using matched groups will be presented.

Consider a study to determine if a particular drug affects learning. Suppose that a control group is also used in which the individuals are matched on the basis of IQ. IQ would seem to be a reasonable variable on which to match since the scores in the experiment are on a learning task. The results are:

Pair No.	X Under Drug	Y No Drug	IQ
1	2	4	90
2	6	9	95
3	7	8	98
4	11	10	100
5	13	13	109

The IQ scores do not enter into the computations but merely indicate that the first pair consists of persons each with an IQ of 90, the second pair each had IQ's of 95, and so forth.

In order to treat the problem computationally as a t test for the true mean, it is necessary to first obtain the differences between the pairs. These are:

$X - Y = D$	$-\bar{D} = d$	d_2
-2	$-(-1) = -1$	1
-3	$-(-1) = -2$	4
-1	$-(-1) = 0$	0
$+1$	$-(-1) = +2$	4
0	$-(-1) = +1$	1

$$\bar{D} = -5/5 = -1 \qquad\qquad SD_D = \sqrt{10/5} = \sqrt{2} = 1.4$$

Under a null hypothesis of no difference the model for the problem becomes:

1) $H_0 : \mu_1 - \mu_2 = \delta = 0$
2) $est\ \sigma_{\bar{D}} = SD_D/\sqrt{n-1} = 1.4/\sqrt{4} = 1.4/2 = 0.7$
3) Random and independent sampling
4) $\bar{D}$ normal
5) $df = (n-1) = 4$

Because the sample only consists of five pairs, there is no guarantee that the sampling distribution of the statistic, $\bar{D}$, is normal, unless the underlying distribution of differences, D, are normal. This will be assumed to be the case in order to demonstrate the computations.

The computed value of t is:

$$t_{4_o} = \frac{\bar{D}_o - E(\bar{D})}{est\ \sigma_{\bar{D}}} = \frac{-1 - 0}{0.7} = -1.4$$

The problem as worded indicates a two-tailed alternative $H_A : \delta \neq 0$. α for this problem will be taken to be equal to .10.

The diagram of the sampling distribution of the statistic is shown in Figure 10.4.

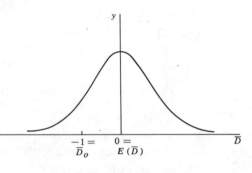

Figure 10.4

The diagram of the t distribution is shown in Figure 10.5.

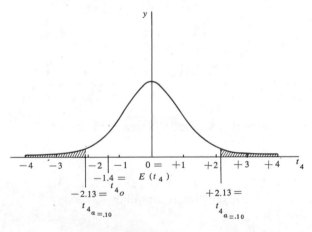

Figure 10.5

The probability of a chance occurrence of a value of t_4 as deviant or more so from the expected as t_{4_o} is given by:

$$p \, (|t_4| \geq 1.4) > p \, (|t_4| \geq 2.13) = .10 = \alpha$$

Therefore, the null hypothesis could not be rejected and the conclusion would be that the evidence was insufficient to demonstrate that the drug had an effect on learning ability of the task.

The computation of $est\ \sigma_{\bar{D}} = SD/\sqrt{n-1}$, while simpler than the computation of

$$est\ \sigma_{(\bar{X}_1 - \bar{X}_2)} = \sqrt{est\ \sigma^2\bar{x}_1,\ est\ \sigma^2\bar{x}_2 - 2\ r_{X_1 X_2}\ est\ \sigma\bar{x}_1\ est\ \sigma\bar{x}_2}$$

is algebraically equivalent to it. The number obtained from the computation will be the same whether the first formula is used or the second one is. Using the differences instead of the scores in the two separate samples automatically takes into account the two standard errors and the degree of correlation between the two sets of scores.

Similarly, in the z test for the difference between means based on matched groups:

$$\sigma_{\bar{D}} = \frac{\sigma_D}{\sqrt{n}} = \sigma_{(\bar{X}_1 - \bar{X}_2)} = \sqrt{\frac{\sigma^2 x_1 + \sigma^2 x_2 - 2\rho_{X_1 X_2}\sigma_{X_1}\sigma_{X_2}}{n}}$$

That is, the two computations are equivalent. Conceptually, however, it is again easier to consider the sample as a single group of scores from a population of differences.

It should be apparent to the student that one-tailed tests and confidence intervals in the case of t or z for matched groups are essentially no different than they previously were when the problem was for the true mean (or the difference between means if the formula with the correlation is used).

Note on Interpretation

Although the computation is easier to perform by considering the sample to be a single sample from a population of differences, it is necessary to realize that conclusions are still being made about the difference between two population means. The situation that has been translated concerns the difference between two conditions and the conclusion must also be in these terms.

11

F TEST FOR ONE-WAY ANALYSIS OF VARIANCE

INTRODUCTION

The last inferential test to be considered deals with the case of more than two conditions or experimental treatments. The scores that the individuals receive are on at least an interval scale just as in the t and z tests for the true mean and difference between means. However, in this test there are many samples, and hence many sample means, all of which are to be compared.

It is not legitimate to compare all of the sample means with each other for at least two reasons. First, the probability of obtaining a significant result by pure chance increases as the number of comparisons that are made increases. Therefore, it would be necessary to compute the probability of obtaining at least as many significant comparisons as were actually obtained instead of just the probability for one significant result. This would be necessary since more than one of the many comparisons could be significant. Secondly, and most importantly, not all of the comparisons are independent of each other. For example, suppose there were three experimental treatments and three means were obtained, $\bar{X}_1$, $\bar{X}_2$, and $\bar{X}_3$. If $\bar{X}_1 > \bar{X}_2$ and $\bar{X}_2 > \bar{X}_3$, then it must be true that $\bar{X}_1 > \bar{X}_3$. The last comparison is not independent of the other two. Thus if the first and second comparisons are significant it is certain that the last one is significant. One could not compute the probability of getting three significant results out of three comparisons because all three comparisons are not independent.

Because of these problems, another way of testing for statistical significance has been developed. In order to use this method — the one-way analysis of variance — several assumptions must again be made. Perhaps the most important is that stated in the null hypothesis. The null and the alternative hypotheses are: $H_0 : \mu_1 = \mu_2 = \cdots = \mu_k$ and $H_A : \mu_1 \neq \mu_2$ and/or $\neq \mu_3$ and/or $\neq \cdots$ and/or $\neq \mu_k$.

The null hypothesis states that all of the means of the populations from which the samples are selected are equal, while the alternative merely states that somewhere among the population means, two are not equal. Thus, the test is clearly a two-tailed test since the alternative states no direction to the inequality. Another important condition is that $\sigma_1^2 = \sigma_2^2 = \cdots = \sigma_k^2$ and that $X_1, X_2, \cdots,$ and X_k are normal. These requirements, when taken together, state that the samples all come from identically distributed populations. This conclusion is reached because the populations are all normal with equal means and variances and normal distributions can only differ from each other with respect to their means and/or variances.

The statistic that is evaluated is based on two independent estimates of the population variance. The argument is this: The variance of a population of scores should be reflected in two ways. First, it should be reflected in how much individuals in the sample vary from each other. That is SD_X^2 (or SD_X) should indicate something about the underlying variability of the individuals in the population from which the sample was selected. If the individuals in the population differ greatly from each other, then the SD of the sample should be greater than if they do not differ very much from each other. Secondly, the variability of the sample means should also reflect the underlying variability in the population. The greater σ_X is, the greater also should be the variability among the sample means, $\sigma_{\bar{X}}$.

These considerations lead to the formation of a ratio, the F ratio. The ratio consists of two independent estimates of σ_X^2, the population variance. The first estimate is based on the variability that is observed among the sample means. This is the numerator of the ratio. The second estimate is based on the variability *within* the samples. This estimate becomes the denominator of the ratio.

By requiring that the underlying distributions be normal, these two estimates are independent. This results from the fact that has already been pointed out, that the means and variances of samples drawn from a normal population are independent of each other.

Not only are the two estimates of σ_X^2 independent, but they will be developed in such a way that they are unbiased. This means that if the samples all came from the same population, as is assumed in the model, the two estimates should give the same numerical values, except for sampling error.

This is a consequence of the fact that the variance of a population is a unique number, that is, there is only one value to the variance of a population. By definition, an estimate is an unbiased one if the average value of the estimates based on all of the unique samples of a particular size from the population equals the value of the population parameter. Another way to state this is: If E (statistic) = parameter, the statistic is said to be an unbiased estimator of the population parameter. Now if $E_1 = E$ (estimates based on sample means) $= \sigma_{\bar{X}}^2$ and $E_2 = E$ (estimates based on sample standard deviations) $= \sigma_X^2$, then, of course, the two expected values must be equal. This ratio would then be 1, that is,

$$\frac{E_1}{E_2} = \frac{\sigma_{\bar{X}}^2}{\sigma_X^2} = 1$$

Of course, in any particular situation, the two estimates might not be precisely equal even though, *on the average*, they are equal. Thus, due to sampling error, the ratio might sometimes be greater than 1 and sometimes less than 1, *when the null hypothesis is true*.

Next consider what would happen if $H_0 : \mu_1 = \mu_2 = \cdots = \mu_k$ were not true. In order to simplify the example, consider only four population means so that $H_0 : \mu_1 = \mu_2 = \mu_3 = \mu_4$. In this situation there will be four experimental conditions and four samples, one from each of the populations. Hence there will be four sample means, $\bar{X}_1, \bar{X}_2, \bar{X}_3,$ and $\bar{X}_4$. If the samples all come from normal populations with the same mean and variance, they will differ from each other only because of sampling variability. This will be true even if the samples are not of equal sizes, and for this test they do not have to be of equal sizes. This situation is represented in Figure 11.1.

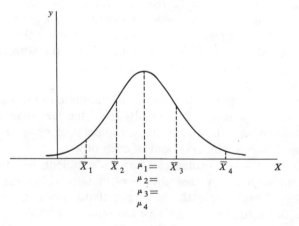

Figure 11.1

Suppose, however, that the null hypothesis is false; that is that $H_A : \mu_1 \neq \mu_2$ and/or $\neq \mu_3$ and/or $\neq \mu_4$ is the true state of affairs. Since $\sigma_{\bar{X}_1}^2 = \sigma_{\bar{X}_2}^2 = \sigma_{\bar{X}_3}^2 = \sigma_{\bar{X}_4}^2$ is a condition that must be met, the four populations will only differ from each other in terms of the values of their means. At least one mean will be different form the others.

The situation under the alternative hypothesis is represented in Figure 11.2. The diagram is for the case where only one of the population means is different form the others.

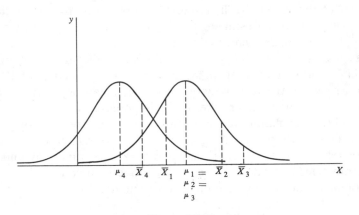

Figure 11.2

Two conclusions should be apparent. The first is that the *SD*'s of the samples are not dependent on the means of the populations. Therefore, estimates of the population variance should be, on the average, the same when only the null hypothesis is false as when it is true. Obviously, variability *within* samples is dependent on the variability of the population of individuals from which the samples were selected, and this population variability does not change when the means of the populations are unequal. As a result, the denominator of the *F* ratio will be the same, on the average, whether the null hypothesis is true or false.

The numerator, however, does not remain the same. It is clear that the sample means differ more from each other on the average when the samples are selected from populations whose means are not all the same than when they are selected from populations whose means are identical.

This statement is true as long as the other conditions remain the same, that is, the populations are still normally distributed with the same variances which are also equal and the samples are of the same sizes under both circumstances.

As a consequence of this increased variability *between* samples when the alternative hypothesis is true, the estimate of $\sigma_{\bar{X}}^2$ based on the sample means should usually be larger than it is when the null hypothesis is true.

This is the key to the *F* test for the one way analysis of variance. If the null hypothesis is false, the *F* ratio should be greater than 1 (because the numerator estimate will be larger but the denominator estimate will not be affected). However, sometimes, even if the null hypothesis is true, the ratio will be larger than 1 just due to sampling variability. The test then is to determine whether or not the ratio is so much greater than 1, that it is unlikely to have occurred by chance from the assumed population (that is, one in which all of the population means are equal).

Of course, if the ratio is less than 1, one cannot possibly reject the null in favor of the alternative hypothesis. The only way to get a ratio less than 1 is to have an estimate based on the variability of the sample means that is smaller than the estimate based on the sample standard deviations. But if the null hypothesis is false, then the numerator estimate should be *larger* than that in the denominator. Rejection of the null hypothesis when the variability of the sample means is too small would have to be in favor of an alternative hypothesis that stated that the means of the population were even closer than they are when they are all equal! This is absurd. (If the sample means are really closer together than is reasonable to expect from samples that are randomly and independently selected from the same population, this could be a clue that the random and independent condition has been violated.)

PRECISE ESTIMATES OF $\sigma_{\bar{X}}^2$

The Numerator of the F Ratio

In order to estimate $\sigma_{\bar{X}}^2$ from the sample means it is necessary to first recall that:

$$est \ \sigma^2_{\bar{x}} = \frac{est \ \sigma_X^2}{n}$$

Solving for the population variance gives:

$$est \ \sigma^2_X = n \ est \ \sigma^2_{\bar{x}}$$

The next problem is to determine *est* $\sigma^2_{\bar{x}}$ from the sample means. In order to do this, consider the population whose elements are samples instead of individuals and where the score for each sample is the mean. The observed sample means then constitute a sample of scores from this population. The problem then is to estimate the variance of this population, that is, to obtain *est* $\sigma^2_{\bar{x}}$. But it is already known that the unbiased estimate of a population variance is obtained from

$$est \ \sigma_X^2 = SD_X^2 \cdot \frac{n}{n-1}$$

In this case the individuals are samples and the scores are means. The estimate of the variance from k samples then becomes:

$$est \ \sigma^2_{\bar{x}} = SD^2_{\bar{x}} \left(\frac{k}{k-1} \right)$$

But $SD^2_{\bar{X}}$ is the variance among the observed sample means. If there are k samples, this becomes by definition of the SD:

$$SD^2_{\bar{X}} = \frac{\sum_{i=1}^{k}(\bar{X}_i - \bar{X}_{\bar{X}})^2}{k}$$

Hence:

$$est\ \sigma^2_{\bar{X}} = \frac{\sum_{i=1}^{k}(\bar{X}_i - \bar{X}_{\bar{X}})^2}{k}\left(\frac{k}{k-1}\right) = \frac{\sum_{i=1}^{k}(\bar{X}_i - \bar{X}_{\bar{X}})^2}{k-1}$$

where $\bar{X}_{\bar{X}}$ is the weighted mean of the sample of k means and $\bar{X}_i$ is a sample mean.

Therefore:

$$est\ \sigma^2_X = n\ est\ \sigma^2_{\bar{X}} = n\ \frac{\sum_{i=1}^{k}(\bar{X}_i - \bar{X}_{\bar{X}})^2}{k-1}$$

where n is the size of the sample. If the samples are not all the same size, then the difference between a particular sample mean and the overall mean of the sample means should be weighted by the number of individuals in the sample. If the sample is large, then the difference between that sample mean and the overall mean should count more than the difference between the overall mean and the mean of a small sample.

The formula for weighting when the samples are of unequal sizes is:

$$est\ \sigma^2_{\bar{X}} = \frac{\sum_{i=1}^{k}n_i(\bar{X}_i - \bar{X}_{\bar{X}})^2}{k-1}$$

The Denominator of the F Ratio

The denominator of the F ratio is the estimate of the population variance based on the standard deviations of the samples. It has already been given that the unbiased estimate of the population variance from the variance of a single sample is:

$$est\ \sigma^2_X = SD^2_X\left(\frac{n}{n-1}\right)$$

In order to make an estimate from the variances of more than one sample, each variance must be considered. In addition, they must be weighted by the size of the sample. It seems reasonable that the variance of a larger sample should be counted more in the estimate than that of a smaller sample.

The formula for estimating the population variance from several samples is:

$$est \ \sigma_{\bar{X}}^2 = \frac{n_1 SD_1^2 + n_2 SD_2^2 + \cdots + n_k SD_k^2}{n_1 - 1 + n_2 - 1 + \cdots + n_k - 1} = \frac{\sum_{i=1}^{k} n_i SD_i^2}{N - k}$$

where n_1 is the number of individuals in the ith sample, $N = n_1 + n_2 + \cdots + n_k$ is the total number of individuals in all of the samples, and k is the number of groups.

The *F* ratio then becomes:

$$F_{k-1,N-k} = \frac{\sum_{i=1}^{k} n_i (\bar{X}_i - \bar{X}_{\bar{x}})^2}{k - 1} \Bigg/ \frac{\sum_{i=1}^{k} n_i SD_i^2}{N - k}$$

where $k - 1$ are the degrees of freedom of the estimate in the numerator and $N - k$ are the degrees of freedom of the estimate in the denominator.

If the samples are all of the same size the formula reduces to:

$$F_{k-1,N-k} = \frac{n \sum_{i=1}^{k} (\bar{X}_i - \bar{X}_{\bar{x}})^2}{k - 1} \Bigg/ \frac{n \sum_{i=1}^{k} SD_i^2}{N - k}$$

$$= \frac{\sum_{i=1}^{k} (\bar{X}_i - \bar{X}_{\bar{x}})^2}{k - 1} \Bigg/ \frac{\sum_{i=1}^{k} SD_i^2}{N - k}$$

DEGREES OF FREEDOM AND DISTRIBUTIONS OF THE *F* RATIO

As noted, the degrees of freedom of the *F* ratio are given for both the numerator and denominator. This is because two independent estimates of the population variance are being made and the *variability* of these estimates depends on the degrees of freedom upon which the estimate is based.

In the numerator there are k observations. But, as usual, the overall mean of the sample uses up one degree of freedom. Hence, the degrees of freedom are equal to $k - 1$.

In the denominator there are N observations, but the estimate is based on the variances of the samples. In order to compute the variance of a sample it is necessary to compute the mean of the sample. Therefore, one degree of freedom is used up in each sample so there are $N - k$ degrees of freedom.

The distribution of *F*, which is the ratio between the two estimates, depends upon the degrees of freedom in both the numerator and denominator, that is, upon both the number of groups and the number of individuals. Just as with the t ratio, there is a different distribution for each combination of degrees of freedom. Of course the expected value of the ratio is always about 1, since the numerator and denominator are always unbiased estimates of the same value. (The ratio does not have an expected value of exactly 1 because the expected value of a ratio does not equal the ratio of the expected values. As the degrees of freedom increase the expected value of F does approach exactly 1.) When there are fewer degrees of freedom, the distribution of F has a larger proportion of cases in the tail so an F ratio much greater than 1 is needed to obtain significance. The F ratio approaches a normal distribution as the degrees of freedom increase and the size of the ratio that is needed to obtain significance at a particular α level decreases. As in the case of the t and χ^2 tables, only a limited number of values are given at each combination of degrees of freedom. Generally these values are limited to those at $\alpha = .01$ and at $\alpha = .05$. Since the alternative hypothesis merely deals with an inequality among population means without specifying the direction of the inequality, these values are of course two-tailed.

RELATIONSHIP BETWEEN t AND F

The t test for the difference between means is closely related to the F test. In this case there are only two groups. To be analogous to the F test, μ_1 and μ_2 must be equal in the null hypothesis so that $\mu_1 - \mu_2 = 0$.

In this case the numerator estimate is based only on two groups so that there is one degree of freedom ($k - 1 = 2 - 1 = 1$). The degrees of freedom in the denominator have been given as $n_1 + n_2 - 2 = N - k$. Thus the t test for the difference between means is similar to the F test with one degree of freedom in the numerator and $N - 2$ degrees of freedom in the denominator. The exact relationship is $t^2_{n_1 + n_2 - 2} = F_{1, N-2}$. Thus, F with one degree of freedom in the numerator is equal to t squared.

An Example

Suppose that three teaching methods are being tested to determine if they differ in effectiveness. The groups are randomly and independently selected and each person is given a performance test after being taught for a semester under a particular method. The results are:

Teaching Method		
T_1	T_2	T_3
20	10	40
40	10	60
30	10	

There are three populations that are being considered. The first is that of all individuals who might undergo treatment 1 with respect to the scores on the performance test. The second is of all of those individuals who might undergo treatment 2, and the third is of all of those that might undergo treatment 3.

The null hypothesis is $H_0 : \mu_1 = \mu_2 = \mu_3$ and the other conditions of the model, which have already been discussed, are:

2) $\sigma_{X_1}^2 = \sigma_{X_2}^2 = \sigma_{X_3}^2$
3) X_1, X_2, X_3 all normal
4) Sampling random and independent
5) $df = k - 1, N - k = 2,5$

Conditions 2 and 3 are not known to be met. In many situations this is the case. The extent to which they affect the sampling distribution of F of course depends on how far the actual conditions are from the ideal. In most situations these conditions are not critical, especially if the samples are of equal size. Increasing the sample size also decreases the necessity for adhering strictly to these conditions.

The alternative hypothesis is $H_A : \mu_1 \neq \mu_2$ and/or $\neq \mu_3$ and α will be taken as .01.

The computation of the F ratio proceeds as follows:

The numerator:

where $\bar{X}_1 = 30, \bar{X}_2 = 10, \bar{X}_3 = 50$

$$\bar{X}_{\bar{x}} = \frac{n_1 \bar{X}_1 + n_2 \bar{X}_2 + n_3 \bar{X}_3}{n_1 + n_2 + n_3} = \frac{90 + 30 + 100}{8} = \frac{220}{8} = 27.5$$

So,
$$\frac{\sum_{i=1}^{k} n_i (\bar{X}_i - \bar{X}_{\bar{x}})^2}{k - 1} = \frac{3(30 - 27.5)^2 + 3(10 - 27.5)^2 + 2(50 - 27.5)^2}{2}$$

$$= \frac{\frac{3(25)}{4} + \frac{3(1225)}{4} + \frac{2(2025)}{4}}{2}$$

$$= \frac{\frac{75}{4} + \frac{3675}{4} + \frac{4050}{4}}{2}$$

$$= \frac{7800}{4} \times \frac{1}{2} = \frac{7800}{8} = 975$$

The denominator:

where
$$SD_1^2 = \frac{200}{3}, \; SD_2^2 = 0, \; SD_3^2 = \frac{200}{2}$$

Therefore,

$$\frac{\sum\limits_{i=1}^{k} n_i SD_i^2}{N-k} = \frac{3 \times \frac{200}{3} + 3(0) + 2 \times \frac{200}{2}}{5} = \frac{400}{5} = 80$$

So

$$F_{2,5_o} = \frac{\sum\limits_{i=1}^{k}(\bar{X}_i - \bar{X}_{\bar{x}})^2}{k-1} \bigg/ \frac{\sum\limits_{i=1}^{k} n_i SD_i^2}{N-k} = \frac{975}{80} = 12.19$$

The evaluation of the probability is:

$$p(F_{2,5} \geq 12.19) > p(F_{2,5} \geq 13.27) = .01 = \alpha$$

Therefore the conclusion must be to fail to reject the null hypothesis. This means that the evidence was insufficient to reject the hypothesis that the methods did not differ in effectiveness. In terms of the sampling theory the conclusion is that the F ratio was not sufficiently greater than 1 to be considered to have been unlikely to have occurred by chance from the assumed populations. In this problem, with $\alpha = .01$, the observed ratio would have had to have been possible by chance less than one time in a hundred.

The diagram of the results is given in Figure 11.3. The symbol $F_{(\nu_1, \nu_2)\alpha}$ is the value of $F_{(\nu_1, \nu_2)}$ such that $p\,[F_{(\nu_1, \nu_2)} \geq F_{(\nu_1, \nu_2)\alpha}] = \alpha$.

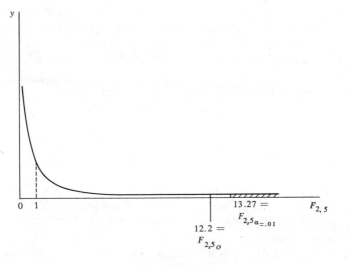

Figure 11.3

12

SUMMARY

The main objective of this text has been to develop the logic and some techniques for making inferences about populations on the basis of evidence from samples. In order to be able to accomplish this a long and detailed development was necessary.

The analysis began with a realization that populations of elements were rarely measured in their entirety. In order to gain information about the population, then, it seemed reasonable to take a sample of the elements. This sample had to be representative of the population. This was interpreted to mean that the elements had to be selected randomly and independently, since this process of selection gave every unique sample an equal chance of occurring. However, the fact that the number of unique samples that might be selected was frequently very large (so large, in fact, that even an astronomer would be at a loss for words) meant that samples would differ from each other. It, therefore, could not be expected that the particular sample that was selected would reflect precisely the population.

Instead of giving up (which would have resulted in a very short book), this problem was attacked with a vengeance (wreaked mostly on the student).

The procedure developed involved selecting a sample and examining the value of a statistic to determine if this result was consistent with the hypotheses.

Since the hypotheses led to an expected value of the statistic, it seemed reasonable to conclude that the further the observed result was from this expected result, the less consistent it should be considered to be with those hypotheses.

Because the models that have been dealt with are statistical in nature, no observation is impossible. Consistency was, therefore, defined in terms of probabilities. Results that defined classes of events that had a high probability of occurring were considered consistent with the model and those that defined classes of events that had a low probability were considered inconsistent with the model. The α level defined how unlikely results had to be before they were considered inconsistent. Although an inconsistent result implied that some aspect of the model was an inaccurate abstraction of the real world situation, a consistent result did not imply that the model was an accurate abstraction. Further, decisions about the models always carried the risk of error. Inconsistent results led to rejection of the model but carried the risk of rejecting true models because sometimes unlikely results do occur by chance. Consistent results led to a failure to reject the model but carried the risk of failing to reject a false model because the true situation may have been different from that which was hypothesized.

After this logical framework had been completed, including the mathematical background necessary for determining probabilities, it was possible to investigate several situations and problems for which a statistical model was an appropriate abstraction. Naturally, this text included only a few of the problem-situations that are amenable to statistical analysis. And many more problem-situations exist for which there currently is no appropriate statistical abstraction. Nevertheless, a limited but useful set of the amenable ones was examined in detail.

The starting point for this examination was the recognition that a decision about a specific hypothesis could only be made if the conditions specified by the other hypotheses in the model had actually been met. Frequently, it was not possible to ascertain that these conditions had been precisely met. The pragmatic solution to this situation was to use the model if the actual sampling distribution of the statistic approximated the theoretical one. The specific aspect of the situation that was being studied then became the null hypothesis. The conclusion that was to be made if the null hypothesis were rejected became abstracted as the alternative hypothesis.

The student, and other interested parties, may wish to be able to analyze the properties of real world situations for which statistical tests have been presented. Among the abstractable properties that have been examined are the number of populations of elements, the level of scaling of the elements on the attribute being considered, and the number of variables on which the elements have been scored. In addition, there have been several different questions that might be asked in each situation. For example, if one population is being dealt with in which the elements have been scored on a single variable that is intervally scaled, and the question being asked concerns the value of the population mean, the appropriate statistical model may be either the z test for the true mean or the t test for the true mean. Which model is appropriate, of course, depends on whether the population variance is known or must be estima-

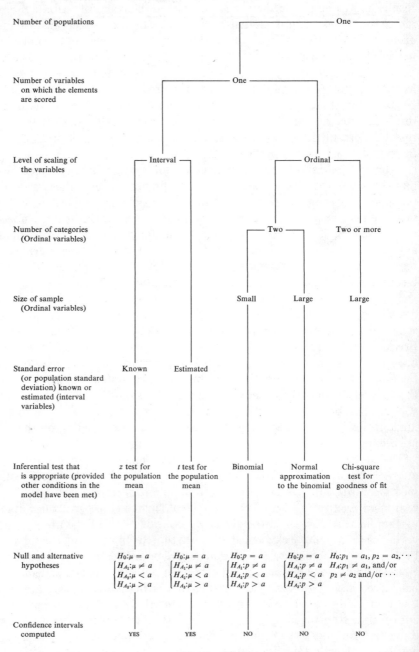

Figure 12.1

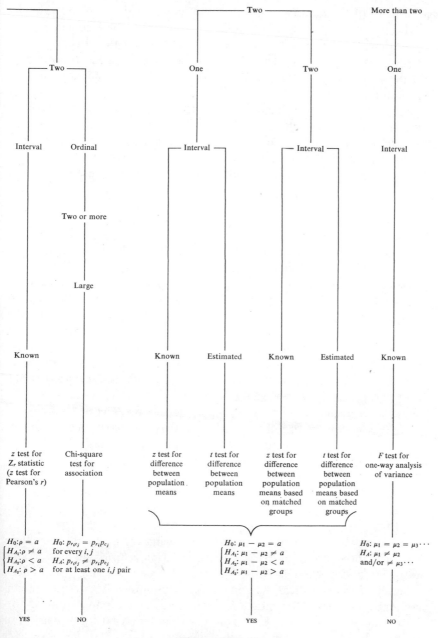

Figure 12.1

ted. In either of these cases the alternative may be two-tailed or one-tailed. That is, depending on the question that is orginally posed, rejection of the hypothesis about the parameter may lead to a conclusion that the true value of the parameter is simply not equal to the assumed value or that it is a value in one direction or the other from the true value.

Further, some situations have been presented in which it is not necessary to test a hypothesis about the population but instead the value of the parameter may be estimated. The construction of confidence intervals accomplished this.

Figure 12.1 shows in detail the properties of the real world that have been abstracted for each of the models in the text. In addition, the null hypothesis, the various form of the alternative hypothesis, and whether the model has been used to construct a confidence interval are indicated. Figure 12.2 summarizes the models that have been presented in this text.

Limitations

It seems appropriate at the end of a text such as this to again indicate limitations of the material presented.

First, not only have a limited number of types of problems been examined but very restricted aspects of these have been investigated. In almost all of the cases, only questions about the population mean were asked. There are, of course, a large number of measures that could be used to describe a population, for example, the standard deviation of the population, its mode, its median, the square root of its mean, the cube root of its mean, and many other creative possibilities. Questions about these parameters have not been examined. For some of these, statistical analyses are available. For most of the others — no. The reason may be clear. The models are useful abstractions if they lead to deductions which allow predictions to be made about the data that is to be collected. The ability to do this has depended on being able to deduce the sampling distribution of the statistic. This was necessary in order to be able to determine the probability for the class of events defined by the observed result. For many parameters that might be defined, the sampling distribution of the appropriate statistic is not known.

In the case of a normal distribution, knowing the mean and the standard deviation results in being able to determine probabilities for any stated interval of events. Thus, it should not be surprising that underlying all of the statistical tests involving continuous distributions is an assumption of normality either for the scores in the population or for the values of the statistic. For example, χ^2 is based on the square of a normal distribution. Additionally, $t^2_{n_1 + n_2 - 2} = F_{1, N-2}$. However, F

Models for Generating Sampling Distributions

1. *An Abstract Model*	2. *z test for True Mean*	3. *t test for True Mean*	4. *z test Difference Between Means*
Parameter's value = a SE of statistic = b Statistic normally distributed Random and independent sampling	$H_0: \mu = a$ $\sigma_{\bar{x}} = b$ $\bar{X}$ normal R and I (Random and independent sampling)	$H_0: \mu = a$ est $\sigma_{\bar{x}} = b$ X normal [$\bar{X}$ normal] $df = n - 1 = c$ R and I	$H_0: \mu_1 - \mu_2 = a$ $\sigma_{(\bar{X}_1 - \bar{X}_2)} = b$ $(\bar{X}_1 - \bar{X}_2)$ normal R and I

5. *t test Difference Between Means*	6. *z test Difference Between Means Using Matched Groups*	7. *t test Difference Between Means Using Matched Groups*

$H_0: \mu_1 - \mu_2 = a$
 est $\sigma_{(\bar{X}_1 - \bar{X}_2)} = b$
 X_1, X_2 normal
 [$\bar{X}_1 - \bar{X}_2$ normal]
 $\sigma^2_{X_1} = \sigma^2_{X_2}$
 $df = n_1 + n_2 - 2$, R and I
	$H_0: \mu_1 - \mu_2 = a$
	 $\sigma_{(\bar{X}_1 - \bar{X}_2)} = b$
	 $(\bar{X}_1 - \bar{X}_2)\,\bar{D}$ normal
	 R and I
		$H_0: \mu_1 - \mu_2 = a$
		 est $\sigma_{(\bar{X}_1 - \bar{X}_2)} = b =$
		   est $\sigma_{\bar{D}} = b$
		 D normal [$(\bar{X}_1 - \bar{X}_2) =$
		   $\bar{D}$ normal]
		 $df = n - 1$
		 R and I

8. *F test for One-Way Analysis of Variance*	9. *z test for Z_r*	10. *Binomial*	11. *z Approx. to Binomial*

$H_0: \mu_1 = \mu_2 =$
   $\mu_3 = \cdots$
 $\sigma^2_{X_1} = \sigma^2_{X_2} =$
   $\sigma^2_{X_3} = \cdots$
 $X_1, X_2, X_3, \cdots$
   normal
 $df = k - 1, n - k$
   $= c, d$
 R and I
	$H_0: \rho = a,$
	   $(Z_\rho = a')$
	 $\sigma_{Z_r} = b$
	 Z_r normal
	 Bivariate normal
	   population
	 R and I
		$H_0: p = a$
		   $(q = 1 - a)$
		 $p(S \cap F) = 0$
		 $p(S \cup F) = 1$
		 R and I
			$H_0: p = a$
			   $(q = 1 - a)$
			 $p(S \cap F) = 0$
			 $p(S \cup F) = 1$
			 f normal
			 R and I

12. *χ^2 Goodness of Fit*	13. *χ^2 Association*
$H_0: p_1 = a, p_2 = b, \cdots, p_k = q$ $p_1 + p_2 + \cdots + p_k = 1$ $p(S_i \cap S_j) = 0$, for every $i \neq j$ $df = k - 1 = c$ f_i normal about F_i for every i R and I	$H_0: p_{c_i r_j} = p_{c_i} \cdot p_{r_j}$ for all i and j $\sum_{i=1}^{r} \sum_{j=1}^{k} p_{c_i r_j} = 1$ $p(r_i \cap r_k) = 0$ for every $i \neq k$ $p(c_i \cap c_j) = 0$ for every $i \neq j$ $df = (r - 1)(k - 1) = c$ f_{ij} normal about F_{ij} for every ij, R and I

Note: Distinguish these models from *Decision Models* which include H_A and α.

Figure 12.2

can also be defined in terms of χ^2 distributions. Thus F is the ratio of two χ^2's, each divided by its degrees of freedom,

$$F_{k-1,N-k} = \frac{\chi^2{}_{k-1}/k-1}{\chi^2{}_{N-k}/N-k}$$

Consequently, the t ratio can also be defined in terms of χ^2. Thus

$$t_{n_1+n_2-2} = \frac{\text{normal deviation}}{\sqrt{\dfrac{\chi^2{}_{n_1+n_2-2}}{n_1 + n_2 - 2}}}$$

t is the ratio of a normal deviate over the square root of a chi-square divided by its degrees of freedom.

As a final precaution, it should again be noted that the statistical significance or lack of significance does not allow one to determine why the results occurred the way they did. It is quite easy to do an experiment, the results of which may be statistically significant, that is poorly designed in terms of the theory or problem that is being investigated. An example of this was noted in Chapter 5.

In spite of these and other limitations, the student may be confident that he now has the tools that will allow him to give objective quantitative answers to many important types of questions that arise in the behavioral sciences.

REFERENCES

Adams, E. W., R. F. Fagot, and R. E. Robinson, A theory of appropriate statistics. *Psychometrika 30*, No. 2, 1965, 99–127.

Birkhoff, G., and S. MacLane, *A survey of modern algebra*. New York: Macmillan, 1953.

Blommers, P., and E. F. Lindquist, *Elementary statistical methods in psychology and education*. Boston: Houghton Mifflin, 1960.

Coombs, C. H., H. Raiffa, and R. M. Thrall, Some views on mathematical models and measurement theory, *Psych. Rev. 61*, 1954, 132–144.

Copi, I. M. *Introduction to logic*. New York: Macmillan, 1953.

Feller, W. *An introduction to probability theory and its applications* (ed. 2). New York: Wiley, 1957

Goodman, L. A., and W. H. Kruskal, Measures of association for cross-classifications. *J. Amer. Stat. Ass. 49*, 1954, 732–764.

Hays, W. L. *Statistics for psychologists*. New York: Holt, Rinehart, and Winston, Inc., 1963.

Parzen, E. *Modern probability theory and its applications*. New York: Wiley, 1960.

Sherwood, G. and A. Taylor, *Calculus*. Englewood Cliffs, New Jersey Prentice-Hall, 1946.

Walker, H. M., and J. Lev, *Statistical inference*. New York: Holt, Rinehart and Winston, Inc., 1953.

Wilder, R. L. *Introduction to the foundations of mathematics*. New York: Wiley, 1956.

APPENDIX

Table I

Table of Areas of the Normal Probability Curve

$$\int_0^z F(z)dz$$

z	0.00	0.01	0.02	0.03	0.04	0.05	0.06	0.07	0.08	0.09
0.0	.0000	.0040	.0080	.0120	.0160	.0199	.0239	.0279	.0319	.0359
0.1	.0398	.0438	.0478	.0517	.0557	.0596	.0636	.0675	.0714	.0753
0.2	.0793	.0832	.0871	.0910	.0948	.0987	.1026	.1064	.1103	.1141
0.3	.1179	.1217	.1255	.1293	.1331	.1368	.1406	.1443	.1480	.1517
0.4	.1554	.1591	.1628	.1664	.1700	.1736	.1772	.1808	.1844	.1879
0.5	.1915	.1950	.1985	.2019	.2054	.2088	.2123	.2157	.2190	.2224
0.6	.2257	.2291	.2324	.2357	.2389	.2422	.2454	.2486	.2517	.2549
0.7	.2580	.2611	.2642	.2673	.2704	.2734	.2764	.2794	.2823	.2852
0.8	.2881	.2910	.2939	.2967	.2995	.3023	.3051	.3078	.3106	.3133
0.9	.3159	.3186	.3212	.3238	.3264	.3289	.3315	.3340	.3365	.3389
1.0	.3413	.3438	.3461	.3485	.3508	.3531	.3554	.3577	.3599	.3621
1.1	.3643	.3665	.3686	.3708	.3729	.3749	.3770	.3790	.3810	.3830
1.2	.3849	.3869	.3888	.3907	.3925	.3944	.3962	.3980	.3997	.4015
1.3	.4032	.4049	.4066	.4082	.4099	.4115	.4131	.4147	.4162	.4177
1.4	.4192	.4207	.4222	.4236	.4251	.4265	.4279	.4292	.4306	.4319
1.5	.4332	.4345	.4357	.4370	.4382	.4394	.4406	.4418	.4429	.4441
1.6	.4452	.4463	.4474	.4484	.4495	.4505	.4515	.4525	.4535	.4545
1.7	.4554	.4564	.4573	.4582	.4591	.4599	.4608	.4616	.4625	.4633
1.8	.4641	.4649	.4656	.4664	.4671	.4678	.4686	.4693	.4699	.4706
1.9	.4713	.4719	.4726	.4732	.4738	.4744	.4750	.4756	.4761	.4767
2.0	.4773	.4778	.4783	.4788	.4793	.4798	.4803	.4808	.4812	.4817
2.1	.4821	.4826	.4830	.4834	.4838	.4842	.4846	.4850	.4854	.4857
2.2	.4861	.4864	.4868	.4871	.4875	.4878	.4881	.4884	.4887	.4890
2.3	.4893	.4896	.4898	.4901	.4904	.4906	.4909	.4911	.4913	.4916
2.4	.4918	.4920	.4922	.4925	.4927	.4929	.4931	.4932	.4934	.4936
2.5	.4938	.4940	.4941	.4943	.4945	.4946	.4948	.4949	.4951	.4952
2.6	.4953	.4955	.4956	.4957	.4959	.4960	.4961	.4962	.4963	.4964
2.7	.4965	.4966	.4967	.4968	.4969	.4970	.4971	.4972	.4973	.4974
2.8	.4974	.4975	.4976	.4977	.4977	.4978	.4979	.4979	.4980	.4981
2.9	.4981	.4982	.4983	.4983	.4984	.4984	.4985	.4985	.4986	.4986
3.0	.4987	.4987	.4987	.4988	.4988	.4989	.4989	.4989	.4989	.4990
3.1	.4990	.4991	.4991	.4991	.4992	.4992	.4992	.4992	.4993	.4993
3.2	.4993	.4993	.4994	.4994	.4994	.4994	.4994	.4995	.4995	.4995
3.3	.4995	.4995	.4996	.4996	.4996	.4996	.4996	.4996	.4996	.4997
3.4	.4997	.4997	.4997	.4997	.4997	.4997	.4997	.4997	.4997	.4998
3.5	.4998	.4998	.4998	.4998	.4998	.4998	.4998	.4998	.4998	.4998
3.6	.4998	.4998	.4999	.4999	.4999	.4999	.4999	.4999	.4999	.4999
3.7	.4999	.4999	.4999	.4999	.4999	.4999	.4999	.4999	.4999	.4999
3.8	.4999	.4999	.4999	.4999	.4999	.4999	.4999	.4999	.4999	.5000
3.9	.5000	.5000	.5000	.5000	.5000	.5000	.5000	.5000	.5000	.5000
z	0.00	0.01	0.02	0.03	0.04	0.05	0.06	0.07	0.08	0.09

Table II

Table of t^*

Degrees of Freedom	Probability				
	0.50	0.10	0.05	0.02	0.01
1	1.000	6.34	12.71	31.82	63.66
2	0.816	2.92	4.30	6.96	9.92
3	.765	2.35	3.18	4.54	5.84
4	.741	2.13	2.78	3.75	4.60
5	.727	2.02	2.57	3.36	4.03
6	.718	1.94	2.45	3.14	3.71
7	.711	1.90	2.36	3.00	3.50
8	.706	1.86	2.31	2.90	3.36
9	.703	1.83	2.26	2.82	3.25
10	.700	1.81	2.23	2.76	3.17
11	.697	1.80	2.20	2.72	3.11
12	.695	1.78	2.18	2.68	3.06
13	.694	1.77	2.16	2.65	3.01
14	.692	1.76	2.14	2.62	2.98
15	.691	1.75	2.13	2.60	2.95
16	.690	1.75	2.12	2.58	2.92
17	.689	1.74	2.11	2.57	2.90
18	.688	1.73	2.10	2.55	2.88
19	.688	1.73	2.09	2.54	2.86
20	.687	1.72	2.09	2.53	2.84
21	.686	1.72	2.08	2.52	2.83
22	.686	1.72	2.07	2.51	2.82
23	.685	1.71	2.07	2.50	2.81
24	.685	1.71	2.06	2.49	2.80
25	.684	1.71	2.06	2.48	2.79
26	.684	1.71	2.06	2.48	2.78
27	.684	1.70	2.05	2.47	2.77
28	.683	1.70	2.05	2.47	2.76
29	.683	1.70	2.04	2.46	2.76
30	.683	1.70	2.04	2.46	2.75
35	.682	1.69	2.03	2.44	2.72
40	.681	1.68	2.02	2.42	2.71
45	.680	1.68	2.02	2.41	2.69
50	.679	1.68	2.01	2.40	2.68
60	.678	1.67	2.00	2.39	2.66
70	.678	1.67	2.00	2.38	2.65
80	.677	1.66	1.99	2.38	2.64
90	.677	1.66	1.99	2.37	2.63
100	.677	1.66	1.98	2.36	2.63
125	.676	1.66	1.98	2.36	2.62
150	.676	1.66	1.98	2.35	2.61
200	.675	1.65	1.97	2.35	2.60
300	.675	1.65	1.97	2.34	2.59
400	.675	1.65	1.97	2.34	2.59
500	.674	1.65	1.96	2.33	2.59
1000	.674	1.65	1.96	2.33	2.58
∞	.674	1.64	1.96	2.33	2.58

This table is taken from Fisher: *Statistical Methods for Research Workers*, published by Oliver & Boyd Ltd., Edinburgh, and by permission of the author and publishers.

Source: Reproduced by permission from C. H. Goulden, *Methods of Statistical Analysis* (New York: John Wiley & Sons, 1939).

Table III

Table of Z_r for Values of r from .00 to 1.00

$$Z_r = \tfrac{1}{2}[\log_e(1 + r) - \log_e(1 - r)] = 1.1513\left[\log \frac{1 + r}{1 - r}\right]$$

Table A. r from Zero to 0.89 by Hundredths

r	.00	.01	.02	.03	.04	.05	.06	.07	.08	.09
.0	.0000	.0100	.0200	.0300	.0400	.0500	.0601	.0701	.0802	.0902
.1	.1003	.1104	.1206	.1307	.1409	.1511	.1614	.1717	.1820	.1923
.2	.2027	.2132	.2237	.2342	.2448	.2554	.2661	.2769	.2877	.2986
.3	.3095	.3205	.3316	.3428	.3541	.3654	.3769	.3884	.4001	.4118
.4	.4236	.4356	.4477	.4599	.4722	.4847	.4973	.5101	.5230	.5361
.5	.5493	.5627	.5763	.5901	.6042	.6184	.6328	.6475	.6625	.6777
.6	.6931	.7089	.7250	.7414	.7582	.7753	.7928	.8107	.8291	.8480
.7	.8673	.8872	.9076	.9287	.9505	.9730	.9962	1.0203	1.0454	1.0714
.8	1.0986	1.1270	1.1568	1.1881	1.2212	1.2562	1.2933	1.3331	1.3758	1.4219

Table B. r from 0.900 to 0.999 by Thousandths

r	.000	.001	.002	.003	.004	.005	.006	.007	.008	.009
.90	1.4722	1.4775	1.4828	1.4882	1.4937	1.4992	1.5047	1.5103	1.5160	1.5217
.91	1.5275	1.5334	1.5393	1.5453	1.5513	1.5574	1.5636	1.5798	1.5762	1.5826
.92	1.5890	1.5956	1.6022	1.6089	1.6157	1.6226	1.6296	1.6366	1.6438	1.6510
.93	1.6584	1.6658	1.6734	1.6811	1.6888	1.6967	1.7047	1.7129	1.7211	1.7295
.94	1.7380	1.7467	1.7555	1.7645	1.7736	1.7828	1.7923	1.8019	1.8117	1.8216
.95	1.8318	1.8421	1.8527	1.8635	1.8745	1.8857	1.8972	1.9090	1.9210	1.9333
.96	1.9459	1.9588	1.9721	1.9857	1.9996	2.0139	2.0287	2.0439	2.0595	2.0756
.97	2.0923	2.1095	2.1273	2.1457	2.1649	2.1847	2.2054	2.2269	2.2494	2.2729
.98	2.2976	2.3235	2.3507	2.3796	2.4101	2.4427	2.4774	2.5147	2.5550	2.5987
.99	2.6467	2.6996	2.7587	2.8257	2.9031	2.9945	3.1063	3.2504	3.4534	3.8002

Source: Reproduced by permission from A. E. Treloar, *Elements of Statistical Reasoning* (New York: John Wiley & Sons, 1939).

Table IV

Table of r for Values of Z_r from 0 to 5*

z	.00	.01	.02	.03	.04	.05	.06	.07	.08	.09
.0	.0000	.0100	.0200	.0300	.0400	.0500	.0599	.0699	.0798	.0898
.1	.0997	.1096	.1194	.1293	.1391	.1489	.1587	.1684	.1781	.1878
.2	.1974	.2070	.2165	.2260	.2355	.2449	.2543	.2636	.2729	.2821
.3	.2913	.3004	.3095	.3185	.3275	.3364	.3452	.3540	.3627	.3714
.4	.3800	.3885	.3969	.4053	.4136	.4219	.4301	.4382	.4462	.4542
.5	.4621	.4700	.4777	.4854	.4930	.5005	.5080	.5154	.5227	.5299
.6	.5370	.5441	.5511	.5581	.5649	.5717	.5784	.5850	.5915	.5980
.7	.6044	.6107	.6169	.6231	.6291	.6352	.6411	.6469	.6427	.6584
.8	.6640	.6696	.6751	.6805	.6858	.6911	.6963	.7014	.7064	.7114
.9	.7163	.7211	.7259	.7306	.7352	.7398	.7443	.7487	.7531	.7574
1.0	.7616	.7658	.7699	.7739	.7779	.7818	.7857	.7895	.7932	.7969
1.1	.8005	.8041	.8076	.8110	.8144	.8178	.8210	.8243	.8275	.8306
1.2	.8337	.8367	.8397	.8426	.8455	.8483	.8511	.8538	.8565	.8591
1.3	.8617	.8643	.8668	.8693	.8717	.8741	.8764	.8787	.8810	.8832
1.4	.8854	.8875	.8896	.8917	.8937	.8957	.8977	.8996	.9015	.9033
1.5	.9052	.9069	.9087	.9104	.9121	.9138	.9154	.9170	.9186	.9202
1.6	.9217	.9232	.9246	.9261	.9275	.9289	.9302	.9316	.9329	.9342
1.7	.9354	.9367	.9379	.9391	.9402	.9414	.9425	.9436	.9447	.9458
1.8	.9468	.9478	.9488	.9498	.9508	.9518	.9527	.9536	.9545	.9554
1.9	.9562	.9571	.9579	.9587	.9595	.9603	.9611	.9619	.9626	.9633
2.0	.9640	.9647	.9654	.9661	.9668	.9674	.9680	.9687	.9693	.9699
2.1	.9705	.9710	.9716	.9722	.9727	.9732	.9738	.9743	.9748	.9753
2.2	.9757	.9762	.9767	.9771	.9776	.9780	.9785	.9789	.9793	.9797
2.3	.9801	.9805	.9809	.9812	.9816	.9820	.9823	.9827	.9830	.9834
2.4	.9837	.9840	.9843	.9846	.9849	.9852	.9855	.9858	.9861	.9863
2.5	.9866	.9869	.9871	.9874	.9876	.9879	.9881	.9884	.9886	.9888
2.6	.9890	.9892	.9895	.9897	.9899	.9901	.9903	.9905	.9906	.9908
2.7	.9910	.9912	.9914	.9915	.9917	.9919	.9920	.9922	.9923	.9925
2.8	.9926	.9928	.9929	.9931	.9932	.9933	.9935	.9936	.9937	.9938
2.9	.9940	.9941	.9942	.9943	.9944	.9945	.9946	.9947	.9949	.9950
3.0	.9951									
4.0	.9993									
5.0	.9999									

*The figures in the body of the table are values of r corresponding to z-values read from the scales on the left and top of the table.

Source: Reproduced from F. C. Mills, *Statistical Methods* (New York: Holt, Rinehart and Winston, Inc., 1924), p. 702.

Table V

χ^2 Probability Scale
Table of Values of χ^2 Corresponding to Certain Chances of Exceeding χ^2

Degrees of Freedom	$P=.90$	.70	.50	.30	.20	.10	.05	.02	.01
1	0.02	0.15	0.45	1.07	1.64	2.71	3.84	5.41	6.63
2	0.21	0.71	1.39	2.41	3.22	4.60	5.99	7.82	9.21
3	0.58	1.42	2.37	3.66	4.64	6.25	7.81	9.84	11.34
4	1.06	2.19	3.36	4.88	5.99	7.78	9.49	11.67	13.28
5	1.61	3.00	4.35	6.06	7.29	9.24	11.07	13.39	15.09
6	2.20	3.83	5.35	7.23	8.56	10.64	12.59	15.03	16.81
7	2.83	4.67	6.35	8.38	9.80	12.02	14.07	16.62	18.47
8	3.49	5.53	7.34	9.52	11.03	13.36	15.51	18.17	20.09
9	4.17	6.39	8.34	10.66	12.24	14.68	16.92	19.68	21.67
10	4.86	7.27	9.34	11.78	13.44	15.99	18.31	21.16	23.21
11	5.58	8.15	10.34	12.90	14.63	17.27	19.67	22.62	24.72
12	6.30	9.03	11.34	14.01	15.81	18.55	21.03	24.05	26.22
13	7.04	9.93	12.34	15.12	16.98	19.81	22.36	25.47	27.69
14	7.79	10.82	13.34	16.22	18.15	21.06	23.68	26.87	29.14
15	8.55	11.72	14.34	17.32	19.31	22.31	25.00	28.26	30.58
16	9.31	12.62	15.34	18.42	20.46	23.54	26.30	29.63	32.00
17	10.08	13.53	16.34	19.51	21.61	24.77	27.59	30.99	33.41
18	10.86	14.44	17.34	20.60	22.76	25.99	28.87	32.35	34.80
19	11.65	15.35	18.34	21.69	23.90	27.20	30.14	33.69	36.19
20	12.44	16.27	19.34	22.77	25.04	28.41	31.41	35.02	37.57
21	13.24	17.18	20.34	23.86	26.17	29.61	32.67	36.34	38.93
22	14.04	18.10	21.34	24.94	27.30	30.81	33.92	37.66	40.29
23	14.85	19.02	22.34	26.02	28.43	32.01	35.17	38.97	41.64
24	15.66	19.94	23.34	27.10	29.55	33.20	36.41	40.27	42.98
25	16.47	20.87	24.34	28.17	30.67	34.38	37.65	41.57	44.31
26	17.29	21.79	25.34	29.25	31.79	35.56	38.88	42.86	45.64
27	18.11	22.72	26.34	30.32	32.91	36.74	40.11	44.14	46.96
28	18.94	23.65	27.34	31.39	34.03	37.92	41.34	45.42	48.28
29	19.77	24.58	28.24	32.46	35.14	39.09	42.56	46.69	49.59
30	20.60	25.51	29.34	33.53	36.25	40.26	43.77	47.96	50.89
Degrees of Freedom	$P=.90$	.70	.50	.30	.20	.10	.05	.02	.01

χ^2 Probability Scale

Table VI

5% (Roman Type) and 1% (Bold Face Type) Points for the Distribution of F

n_1 degrees of freedom (for greater mean square)

n_2	1	2	3	4	5	6	7	8	9	10	11	12	14	16	20	24	30	40	50	75	100	200	500	∞
1	161 / 4,052	200 / 4,999	216 / 5,403	225 / 5,625	230 / 5,764	234 / 5,859	237 / 5,928	239 / 5,981	241 / 6,022	242 / 6,056	243 / 6,082	244 / 6,106	245 / 6,142	246 / 6,169	248 / 6,208	249 / 6,234	250 / 6,258	251 / 6,286	252 / 6,302	253 / 6,323	253 / 6,334	254 / 6,352	254 / 6,361	254 / 6,366
2	18.51 / 98.49	19.00 / 99.00	19.16 / 99.17	19.25 / 99.25	19.30 / 99.30	19.33 / 99.33	19.36 / 99.34	19.37 / 99.36	19.38 / 99.38	19.39 / 99.40	19.40 / 99.41	19.41 / 99.42	19.42 / 99.43	19.43 / 99.44	19.44 / 99.45	19.45 / 99.46	19.46 / 99.47	19.47 / 99.48	19.47 / 99.48	19.48 / 99.49	19.49 / 99.49	19.49 / 99.49	19.50 / 99.50	19.50 / 99.50
3	10.13 / 34.12	9.55 / 30.82	9.28 / 29.46	9.12 / 28.71	9.01 / 28.24	8.94 / 27.91	8.88 / 27.67	8.84 / 27.49	8.81 / 27.34	8.78 / 27.23	8.76 / 27.13	8.74 / 27.05	8.71 / 26.92	8.69 / 26.83	8.66 / 26.69	8.64 / 26.60	8.62 / 26.50	8.60 / 26.41	8.58 / 26.35	8.57 / 26.27	8.56 / 26.23	8.54 / 26.18	8.54 / 26.14	8.53 / 26.12
4	7.71 / 21.20	6.94 / 18.00	6.59 / 16.69	6.39 / 15.98	6.26 / 15.52	6.16 / 15.21	6.09 / 14.98	6.04 / 14.80	6.00 / 14.66	5.96 / 14.54	5.93 / 14.45	5.91 / 14.37	5.87 / 14.24	5.84 / 14.15	5.80 / 14.02	5.77 / 13.93	5.74 / 13.83	5.71 / 13.74	5.70 / 13.69	5.68 / 13.61	5.66 / 13.57	5.65 / 13.52	5.64 / 13.48	5.63 / 13.46
5	6.61 / 16.26	5.79 / 13.27	5.41 / 12.06	5.19 / 11.39	5.05 / 10.97	4.95 / 10.67	4.88 / 10.45	4.82 / 10.27	4.78 / 10.15	4.74 / 10.05	4.70 / 9.96	4.68 / 9.89	4.64 / 9.77	4.60 / 9.68	4.56 / 9.55	4.53 / 9.47	4.50 / 9.38	4.46 / 9.29	4.44 / 9.24	4.42 / 9.17	4.40 / 9.13	4.38 / 9.07	4.37 / 9.04	4.36 / 9.02
6	5.99 / 13.74	5.14 / 10.92	4.76 / 9.78	4.53 / 9.15	4.39 / 8.75	4.28 / 8.47	4.21 / 8.26	4.15 / 8.10	4.10 / 7.98	4.06 / 7.87	4.03 / 7.79	4.00 / 7.72	3.96 / 7.60	3.92 / 7.52	3.87 / 7.39	3.84 / 7.31	3.81 / 7.23	3.77 / 7.14	3.75 / 7.09	3.72 / 7.02	3.71 / 6.99	3.69 / 6.94	3.68 / 6.90	3.67 / 6.88
7	5.59 / 12.25	4.74 / 9.55	4.35 / 8.45	4.12 / 7.85	3.97 / 7.46	3.87 / 7.19	3.79 / 7.00	3.73 / 6.84	3.68 / 6.71	3.63 / 6.62	3.60 / 6.54	3.57 / 6.47	3.52 / 6.35	3.49 / 6.27	3.44 / 6.15	3.41 / 6.07	3.38 / 5.98	3.34 / 5.90	3.32 / 5.85	3.29 / 5.78	3.28 / 5.75	3.25 / 5.70	3.24 / 5.67	3.23 / 5.65
8	5.32 / 11.26	4.46 / 8.65	4.07 / 7.59	3.84 / 7.01	3.69 / 6.63	3.58 / 6.37	3.50 / 6.19	3.44 / 6.03	3.39 / 5.91	3.34 / 5.82	3.31 / 5.74	3.28 / 5.67	3.23 / 5.56	3.20 / 5.48	3.15 / 5.36	3.12 / 5.28	3.08 / 5.20	3.05 / 5.11	3.03 / 5.06	3.00 / 5.00	2.98 / 4.96	2.96 / 4.91	2.94 / 4.88	2.93 / 4.86
9	5.12 / 10.56	4.26 / 8.02	3.86 / 6.99	3.63 / 6.42	3.48 / 6.06	3.37 / 5.80	3.29 / 5.62	3.23 / 5.47	3.18 / 5.35	3.13 / 5.26	3.10 / 5.18	3.07 / 5.11	3.02 / 5.00	2.98 / 4.92	2.93 / 4.80	2.90 / 4.73	2.86 / 4.64	2.82 / 4.56	2.80 / 4.51	2.77 / 4.45	2.76 / 4.41	2.73 / 4.36	2.72 / 4.33	2.71 / 4.31
10	4.96 / 10.04	4.10 / 7.56	3.71 / 6.55	3.48 / 5.99	3.33 / 5.64	3.22 / 5.39	3.14 / 5.21	3.07 / 5.06	3.02 / 4.95	2.97 / 4.85	2.94 / 4.78	2.91 / 4.71	2.86 / 4.60	2.82 / 4.52	2.77 / 4.41	2.74 / 4.33	2.70 / 4.25	2.67 / 4.17	2.64 / 4.12	2.61 / 4.05	2.59 / 4.01	2.56 / 3.96	2.55 / 3.93	2.54 / 3.91
11	4.84 / 9.65	3.98 / 7.20	3.59 / 6.22	3.36 / 5.67	3.20 / 5.32	3.09 / 5.07	3.01 / 4.88	2.95 / 4.74	2.90 / 4.63	2.86 / 4.54	2.82 / 4.46	2.79 / 4.40	2.74 / 4.29	2.70 / 4.21	2.65 / 4.10	2.61 / 4.02	2.57 / 3.94	2.53 / 3.86	2.50 / 3.80	2.47 / 3.74	2.45 / 3.70	2.42 / 3.66	2.41 / 3.62	2.40 / 3.60
12	4.75 / 9.33	3.88 / 6.93	3.49 / 5.95	3.26 / 5.41	3.11 / 5.06	3.00 / 4.82	2.92 / 4.65	2.85 / 4.50	2.80 / 4.39	2.76 / 4.30	2.72 / 4.22	2.69 / 4.16	2.64 / 4.05	2.60 / 3.98	2.54 / 3.86	2.50 / 3.78	2.46 / 3.70	2.42 / 3.61	2.40 / 3.56	2.36 / 3.49	2.35 / 3.46	2.32 / 3.41	2.31 / 3.38	2.30 / 3.36
13	4.67 / 9.07	3.80 / 6.70	3.41 / 5.74	3.18 / 5.20	3.02 / 4.86	2.92 / 4.62	2.84 / 4.44	2.77 / 4.30	2.72 / 4.19	2.67 / 4.10	2.63 / 4.02	2.60 / 3.96	2.55 / 3.85	2.51 / 3.78	2.46 / 3.67	2.42 / 3.59	2.38 / 3.51	2.34 / 3.42	2.32 / 3.37	2.28 / 3.30	2.26 / 3.27	2.24 / 3.21	2.22 / 3.18	2.21 / 3.16

5% (Roman Type) and 1% (Bold Face Type) Points for the Distribution of F

n_1 degrees of freedom (for greater mean square)

n_2	1	2	3	4	5	6	7	8	9	10	11	12	14	16	20	24	30	40	50	75	100	200	500	∞	n_2
14	4.60 **8.86**	3.74 **6.51**	3.34 **5.56**	3.11 **5.03**	2.96 **4.69**	2.85 **4.46**	2.77 **4.28**	2.70 **4.14**	2.65 **4.03**	2.60 **3.94**	2.56 **3.86**	2.53 **3.80**	2.48 **3.70**	2.44 **3.62**	2.39 **3.51**	2.35 **3.43**	2.31 **3.34**	2.27 **3.26**	2.24 **3.21**	2.21 **3.14**	2.19 **3.11**	2.16 **3.06**	2.14 **3.02**	2.13 **3.00**	14
15	4.54 **8.68**	3.68 **6.36**	3.29 **5.42**	3.06 **4.89**	2.90 **4.56**	2.79 **4.32**	2.70 **4.14**	2.64 **4.00**	2.59 **3.89**	2.55 **3.80**	2.51 **3.73**	2.48 **3.67**	2.43 **3.56**	2.39 **3.48**	2.33 **3.36**	2.29 **3.29**	2.25 **3.20**	2.21 **3.12**	2.18 **3.07**	2.15 **3.00**	2.12 **2.97**	2.10 **2.92**	2.08 **2.89**	2.07 **2.87**	15
16	4.49 **8.53**	3.63 **6.23**	3.24 **5.29**	3.01 **4.77**	2.85 **4.44**	2.74 **4.20**	2.66 **4.03**	2.59 **3.89**	2.54 **3.78**	2.49 **3.69**	2.45 **3.61**	2.42 **3.55**	2.37 **3.45**	2.33 **3.37**	2.28 **3.25**	2.24 **3.18**	2.20 **3.10**	2.16 **3.01**	2.13 **2.96**	2.09 **2.89**	2.07 **2.86**	2.04 **2.80**	2.02 **2.77**	2.01 **2.75**	16
17	4.45 **8.40**	3.59 **6.11**	3.20 **5.18**	2.96 **4.67**	2.81 **4.34**	2.70 **4.10**	2.62 **3.93**	2.55 **3.79**	2.50 **3.68**	2.45 **3.59**	2.41 **3.52**	2.38 **3.45**	2.33 **3.35**	2.29 **3.27**	2.23 **3.16**	2.19 **3.08**	2.15 **3.00**	2.11 **2.92**	2.08 **2.86**	2.04 **2.79**	2.02 **2.76**	1.99 **2.70**	1.97 **2.67**	1.96 **2.65**	17
18	4.41 **8.28**	3.55 **6.01**	3.16 **5.09**	2.93 **4.58**	2.77 **4.25**	2.66 **4.01**	2.58 **3.85**	2.51 **3.71**	2.46 **3.60**	2.41 **3.51**	2.37 **3.44**	2.34 **3.37**	2.29 **3.27**	2.25 **3.19**	2.19 **3.07**	2.15 **3.00**	2.11 **2.91**	2.07 **2.83**	2.04 **2.78**	2.00 **2.71**	1.98 **2.68**	1.95 **2.62**	1.93 **2.59**	1.92 **2.57**	18
19	4.38 **8.18**	3.52 **5.93**	3.13 **5.01**	2.90 **4.50**	2.74 **4.17**	2.63 **3.94**	2.55 **3.77**	2.48 **3.63**	2.43 **3.52**	2.38 **3.43**	2.34 **3.36**	2.31 **3.30**	2.26 **3.19**	2.21 **3.12**	2.15 **3.00**	2.11 **2.92**	2.07 **2.84**	2.02 **2.76**	2.00 **2.70**	1.96 **2.63**	1.94 **2.60**	1.91 **2.54**	1.90 **2.51**	1.88 **2.49**	19
20	4.35 **8.10**	3.49 **5.85**	3.10 **4.94**	2.87 **4.43**	2.71 **4.10**	2.60 **3.87**	2.52 **3.71**	2.45 **3.56**	2.40 **3.45**	2.35 **3.37**	2.31 **3.30**	2.28 **3.23**	2.23 **3.13**	2.18 **3.05**	2.12 **2.94**	2.08 **2.86**	2.04 **2.77**	1.99 **2.69**	1.96 **2.63**	1.92 **2.56**	1.90 **2.53**	1.87 **2.47**	1.85 **2.44**	1.84 **2.42**	20
21	4.32 **8.02**	3.47 **5.78**	3.07 **4.87**	2.84 **4.37**	2.68 **4.04**	2.57 **3.81**	2.49 **3.65**	2.42 **3.51**	2.37 **3.40**	2.32 **3.31**	2.28 **3.24**	2.25 **3.17**	2.20 **3.07**	2.15 **2.99**	2.09 **2.88**	2.05 **2.80**	2.00 **2.72**	1.96 **2.63**	1.93 **2.58**	1.89 **2.51**	1.87 **2.47**	1.84 **2.42**	1.82 **2.38**	1.81 **2.36**	21
22	4.30 **7.94**	3.44 **5.72**	3.05 **4.82**	2.82 **4.31**	2.66 **3.99**	2.55 **3.76**	2.47 **3.59**	2.40 **3.45**	2.35 **3.35**	2.30 **3.26**	2.26 **3.18**	2.23 **3.12**	2.18 **3.02**	2.13 **2.94**	2.07 **2.83**	2.03 **2.75**	1.98 **2.67**	1.93 **2.58**	1.91 **2.53**	1.87 **2.46**	1.84 **2.42**	1.81 **2.37**	1.80 **2.33**	1.78 **2.31**	22
23	4.28 **7.88**	3.42 **5.66**	3.03 **4.76**	2.80 **4.26**	2.64 **3.94**	2.53 **3.71**	2.45 **3.54**	2.38 **3.41**	2.32 **3.30**	2.28 **3.21**	2.24 **3.14**	2.20 **3.07**	2.14 **2.97**	2.10 **2.89**	2.04 **2.78**	2.00 **2.70**	1.96 **2.62**	1.91 **2.53**	1.88 **2.48**	1.84 **2.41**	1.82 **2.37**	1.79 **2.32**	1.77 **2.28**	1.76 **2.26**	23
24	4.26 **7.82**	3.40 **5.61**	3.01 **4.72**	2.78 **4.22**	2.62 **3.90**	2.51 **3.67**	2.43 **3.50**	2.36 **3.36**	2.30 **3.25**	2.26 **3.17**	2.22 **3.09**	2.18 **3.03**	2.13 **2.93**	2.09 **2.85**	2.02 **2.74**	1.98 **2.66**	1.94 **2.58**	1.89 **2.49**	1.86 **2.44**	1.82 **2.36**	1.80 **2.33**	1.76 **2.27**	1.74 **2.23**	1.73 **2.21**	24
25	4.24 **7.77**	3.38 **5.57**	2.99 **4.68**	2.76 **4.18**	2.60 **3.86**	2.49 **3.63**	2.41 **3.46**	2.34 **3.32**	2.28 **3.21**	2.24 **3.13**	2.20 **3.05**	2.16 **2.99**	2.11 **2.89**	2.06 **2.81**	2.00 **2.70**	1.96 **2.62**	1.92 **2.54**	1.87 **2.45**	1.84 **2.40**	1.80 **2.32**	1.77 **2.29**	1.74 **2.23**	1.72 **2.19**	1.71 **2.17**	25
26	4.22 **7.72**	3.37 **5.53**	2.98 **4.64**	2.74 **4.14**	2.59 **3.82**	2.47 **3.59**	2.39 **3.42**	2.32 **3.29**	2.27 **3.17**	2.22 **3.09**	2.18 **3.02**	2.15 **2.96**	2.10 **2.86**	2.05 **2.77**	1.99 **2.66**	1.95 **2.58**	1.90 **2.50**	1.85 **2.41**	1.82 **2.36**	1.78 **2.28**	1.76 **2.25**	1.72 **2.19**	1.70 **2.15**	1.69 **2.13**	26

Table VI (*Continued*)

5% (Roman Type) and 1% (Bold Face Type) Points for the Distribution of F

n_1 degrees of freedom (for greater mean square)

n_2	1	2	3	4	5	6	7	8	9	10	11	12	14	16	20	24	30	40	50	75	100	200	500	∞	n_2
27	4.21 **7.68**	3.35 **5.49**	2.96 **4.60**	2.73 **4.11**	2.57 **3.79**	2.46 **3.56**	2.37 **3.39**	2.30 **3.26**	2.25 **3.14**	2.20 **3.06**	2.16 **2.98**	2.13 **2.93**	2.08 **2.83**	2.03 **2.74**	1.97 **2.63**	1.93 **2.55**	1.88 **2.47**	1.84 **2.38**	1.80 **2.33**	1.76 **2.25**	1.74 **2.21**	1.71 **2.16**	1.68 **2.12**	1.67 **2.10**	27
28	4.20 **7.64**	3.34 **5.45**	2.95 **4.57**	2.71 **4.07**	2.56 **3.76**	2.44 **3.53**	2.36 **3.36**	2.29 **3.23**	2.24 **3.11**	2.19 **3.03**	2.15 **2.95**	2.12 **2.90**	2.06 **2.80**	2.02 **2.71**	1.96 **2.60**	1.91 **2.52**	1.87 **2.44**	1.81 **2.35**	1.78 **2.30**	1.75 **2.22**	1.72 **2.18**	1.69 **2.13**	1.67 **2.09**	1.65 **2.06**	28
29	4.18 **7.60**	3.33 **5.42**	2.93 **4.54**	2.70 **4.04**	2.54 **3.73**	2.43 **3.50**	2.35 **3.33**	2.28 **3.20**	2.22 **3.08**	2.18 **3.00**	2.14 **2.92**	2.10 **2.87**	2.05 **2.77**	2.00 **2.68**	1.94 **2.57**	1.90 **2.49**	1.85 **2.41**	1.80 **2.32**	1.77 **2.27**	1.73 **2.19**	1.71 **2.15**	1.68 **2.10**	1.65 **2.06**	1.64 **2.03**	29
30	4.17 **7.56**	3.32 **5.39**	2.92 **4.51**	2.69 **4.02**	2.53 **3.70**	2.42 **3.47**	2.34 **3.30**	2.27 **3.17**	2.21 **3.06**	2.16 **2.98**	2.12 **2.90**	2.09 **2.84**	2.04 **2.74**	1.99 **2.66**	1.93 **2.55**	1.89 **2.47**	1.84 **2.38**	1.79 **2.29**	1.76 **2.24**	1.72 **2.16**	1.69 **2.13**	1.66 **2.07**	1.64 **2.03**	1.62 **2.01**	30
32	4.15 **7.50**	3.30 **5.34**	2.90 **4.46**	2.67 **3.97**	2.51 **3.66**	2.40 **3.42**	2.32 **3.25**	2.25 **3.12**	2.19 **3.01**	2.14 **2.94**	2.10 **2.86**	2.07 **2.80**	2.02 **2.70**	1.97 **2.62**	1.91 **2.51**	1.86 **2.42**	1.82 **2.34**	1.76 **2.25**	1.74 **2.20**	1.69 **2.12**	1.67 **2.08**	1.64 **2.02**	1.61 **1.98**	1.59 **1.96**	32
34	4.13 **7.44**	3.28 **5.29**	2.88 **4.42**	2.65 **3.93**	2.49 **3.61**	2.38 **3.38**	2.30 **3.21**	2.23 **3.08**	2.17 **2.97**	2.12 **2.89**	2.08 **2.82**	2.05 **2.76**	2.00 **2.66**	1.95 **2.58**	1.89 **2.47**	1.84 **2.38**	1.80 **2.30**	1.74 **2.21**	1.71 **2.15**	1.67 **2.08**	1.64 **2.04**	1.61 **1.98**	1.59 **1.94**	1.57 **1.91**	34
36	4.11 **7.39**	3.26 **5.25**	2.86 **4.38**	2.63 **3.89**	2.48 **3.58**	2.36 **3.35**	2.28 **3.18**	2.21 **3.04**	2.15 **2.94**	2.10 **2.86**	2.06 **2.78**	2.03 **2.72**	1.98 **2.62**	1.93 **2.54**	1.87 **2.43**	1.82 **2.35**	1.78 **2.26**	1.72 **2.17**	1.69 **2.12**	1.65 **2.04**	1.62 **2.00**	1.59 **1.94**	1.56 **1.90**	1.55 **1.87**	36
38	4.10 **7.35**	3.25 **5.21**	2.85 **4.34**	2.62 **3.86**	2.46 **3.54**	2.35 **3.32**	2.26 **3.15**	2.19 **3.02**	2.14 **2.91**	2.09 **2.82**	2.05 **2.75**	2.02 **2.69**	1.96 **2.59**	1.92 **2.51**	1.85 **2.40**	1.80 **2.32**	1.76 **2.22**	1.71 **2.14**	1.67 **2.08**	1.63 **2.00**	1.60 **1.97**	1.57 **1.90**	1.54 **1.86**	1.53 **1.84**	38
40	4.08 **7.31**	3.23 **5.18**	2.84 **4.31**	2.61 **3.83**	2.45 **3.51**	2.34 **3.29**	2.25 **3.12**	2.18 **2.99**	2.12 **2.88**	2.07 **2.80**	2.04 **2.73**	2.00 **2.66**	1.95 **2.56**	1.90 **2.49**	1.84 **2.37**	1.79 **2.29**	1.74 **2.20**	1.69 **2.11**	1.66 **2.05**	1.61 **1.97**	1.59 **1.94**	1.55 **1.88**	1.53 **1.84**	1.51 **1.81**	40
42	4.07 **7.27**	3.22 **5.15**	2.83 **4.29**	2.59 **3.80**	2.44 **3.49**	2.32 **3.26**	2.24 **3.10**	2.17 **2.96**	2.11 **2.86**	2.06 **2.77**	2.02 **2.70**	1.99 **2.64**	1.94 **2.54**	1.89 **2.46**	1.82 **2.35**	1.78 **2.26**	1.73 **2.17**	1.68 **2.08**	1.64 **2.02**	1.60 **1.94**	1.57 **1.91**	1.54 **1.85**	1.51 **1.80**	1.49 **1.78**	42
44	4.06 **7.24**	3.21 **5.12**	2.82 **4.26**	2.58 **3.78**	2.43 **3.46**	2.31 **3.24**	2.23 **3.07**	2.16 **2.94**	2.10 **2.84**	2.05 **2.75**	2.01 **2.68**	1.98 **2.62**	1.92 **2.52**	1.88 **2.44**	1.81 **2.32**	1.76 **2.24**	1.72 **2.15**	1.66 **2.06**	1.63 **2.00**	1.58 **1.92**	1.56 **1.88**	1.52 **1.82**	1.50 **1.78**	1.48 **1.75**	44
46	4.05 **7.21**	3.20 **5.10**	2.81 **4.24**	2.57 **3.76**	2.42 **3.44**	2.30 **3.22**	2.22 **3.05**	2.14 **2.92**	2.09 **2.82**	2.04 **2.73**	2.00 **2.66**	1.97 **2.60**	1.91 **2.50**	1.87 **2.42**	1.80 **2.30**	1.75 **2.22**	1.71 **2.13**	1.65 **2.04**	1.62 **1.98**	1.57 **1.90**	1.54 **1.86**	1.51 **1.80**	1.48 **1.76**	1.46 **1.72**	46
48	4.04 **7.19**	3.19 **5.08**	2.80 **4.22**	2.56 **3.74**	2.41 **3.42**	2.30 **3.20**	2.21 **3.04**	2.14 **2.90**	2.08 **2.80**	2.03 **2.71**	1.99 **2.64**	1.96 **2.58**	1.90 **2.48**	1.86 **2.40**	1.79 **2.28**	1.74 **2.20**	1.70 **2.11**	1.64 **2.02**	1.61 **1.96**	1.56 **1.88**	1.53 **1.84**	1.50 **1.78**	1.47 **1.73**	1.45 **1.70**	48

254

5% (Roman Type) and 1% (Bold Face Type) Points for the Distribution of F

n_1 degrees of freedom (for greater mean square)

n_2	1	2	3	4	5	6	7	8	9	10	11	12	14	16	20	24	30	40	50	75	100	200	500	∞
50	4.03 **7.17**	3.18 **5.06**	2.79 **4.20**	2.56 **3.72**	2.40 **3.41**	2.29 **3.18**	2.20 **3.02**	2.13 **2.88**	2.07 **2.78**	2.02 **2.70**	1.98 **2.62**	1.95 **2.56**	1.90 **2.46**	1.85 **2.39**	1.78 **2.26**	1.74 **2.18**	1.69 **2.10**	1.63 **2.00**	1.60 **1.94**	1.55 **1.86**	1.52 **1.82**	1.48 **1.76**	1.46 **1.71**	1.44 **1.68**
55	4.02 **7.12**	3.17 **5.01**	2.78 **4.16**	2.54 **3.68**	2.38 **3.37**	2.27 **3.15**	2.18 **2.98**	2.11 **2.85**	2.05 **2.75**	2.00 **2.66**	1.97 **2.59**	1.93 **2.53**	1.88 **2.43**	1.83 **2.35**	1.76 **2.23**	1.72 **2.15**	1.67 **2.06**	1.61 **1.96**	1.58 **1.90**	1.52 **1.82**	1.50 **1.78**	1.46 **1.71**	1.43 **1.66**	1.41 **1.64**
60	4.00 **7.08**	3.15 **4.98**	2.76 **4.13**	2.52 **3.65**	2.37 **3.34**	2.25 **3.12**	2.17 **2.95**	2.10 **2.82**	2.04 **2.72**	1.99 **2.63**	1.95 **2.56**	1.92 **2.50**	1.86 **2.40**	1.81 **2.32**	1.75 **2.20**	1.70 **2.12**	1.65 **2.03**	1.59 **1.93**	1.56 **1.87**	1.50 **1.79**	1.48 **1.74**	1.44 **1.68**	1.41 **1.63**	1.39 **1.60**
65	3.99 **7.04**	3.14 **4.95**	2.75 **4.10**	2.51 **3.62**	2.36 **3.31**	2.24 **3.09**	2.15 **2.93**	2.08 **2.79**	2.02 **2.70**	1.98 **2.61**	1.94 **2.54**	1.90 **2.47**	1.85 **2.37**	1.80 **2.30**	1.73 **2.18**	1.68 **2.09**	1.63 **2.00**	1.57 **1.90**	1.54 **1.84**	1.49 **1.76**	1.46 **1.71**	1.42 **1.64**	1.39 **1.60**	1.37 **1.56**
70	3.98 **7.01**	3.13 **4.92**	2.74 **4.08**	2.50 **3.60**	2.35 **3.29**	2.23 **3.07**	2.14 **2.91**	2.07 **2.77**	2.01 **2.67**	1.97 **2.59**	1.93 **2.51**	1.89 **2.45**	1.84 **2.35**	1.79 **2.28**	1.72 **2.15**	1.67 **2.07**	1.62 **1.98**	1.56 **1.88**	1.53 **1.82**	1.47 **1.74**	1.45 **1.69**	1.40 **1.62**	1.37 **1.56**	1.35 **1.53**
80	3.96 **6.96**	3.11 **4.88**	2.72 **4.04**	2.48 **3.56**	2.33 **3.25**	2.21 **3.04**	2.12 **2.87**	2.05 **2.74**	1.99 **2.64**	1.95 **2.55**	1.91 **2.48**	1.88 **2.41**	1.82 **2.32**	1.77 **2.24**	1.70 **2.11**	1.65 **2.03**	1.60 **1.94**	1.54 **1.84**	1.51 **1.78**	1.45 **1.70**	1.42 **1.65**	1.38 **1.57**	1.35 **1.52**	1.32 **1.49**
100	3.94 **6.90**	3.09 **4.82**	2.70 **3.98**	2.46 **3.51**	2.30 **3.20**	2.19 **2.99**	2.10 **2.82**	2.03 **2.69**	1.97 **2.59**	1.92 **2.51**	1.88 **2.43**	1.85 **2.36**	1.79 **2.26**	1.75 **2.19**	1.68 **2.06**	1.63 **1.98**	1.57 **1.89**	1.51 **1.79**	1.48 **1.73**	1.42 **1.64**	1.39 **1.59**	1.34 **1.51**	1.30 **1.46**	1.28 **1.43**
125	3.92 **6.84**	3.07 **4.78**	2.68 **3.94**	2.44 **3.47**	2.29 **3.17**	2.17 **2.95**	2.08 **2.79**	2.01 **2.65**	1.95 **2.56**	1.90 **2.47**	1.86 **2.40**	1.83 **2.33**	1.77 **2.23**	1.72 **2.15**	1.65 **2.03**	1.60 **1.94**	1.55 **1.85**	1.49 **1.75**	1.45 **1.68**	1.39 **1.59**	1.36 **1.54**	1.31 **1.46**	1.27 **1.40**	1.25 **1.37**
150	3.91 **6.81**	3.06 **4.75**	2.67 **3.91**	2.43 **3.44**	2.27 **3.14**	2.16 **2.92**	2.07 **2.76**	2.00 **2.62**	1.94 **2.53**	1.89 **2.44**	1.85 **2.37**	1.82 **2.30**	1.76 **2.20**	1.71 **2.12**	1.64 **2.00**	1.59 **1.91**	1.54 **1.83**	1.47 **1.72**	1.44 **1.66**	1.37 **1.56**	1.34 **1.51**	1.29 **1.43**	1.25 **1.37**	1.22 **1.33**
200	3.89 **6.76**	3.04 **4.71**	2.65 **3.88**	2.41 **3.41**	2.26 **3.11**	2.14 **2.90**	2.05 **2.73**	1.98 **2.60**	1.92 **2.50**	1.87 **2.41**	1.83 **2.34**	1.80 **2.28**	1.74 **2.17**	1.69 **2.09**	1.62 **1.97**	1.57 **1.88**	1.52 **1.79**	1.45 **1.69**	1.42 **1.62**	1.35 **1.53**	1.32 **1.48**	1.26 **1.39**	1.22 **1.33**	1.19 **1.28**
400	3.86 **6.70**	3.02 **4.66**	2.62 **3.83**	2.39 **3.36**	2.23 **3.06**	2.12 **2.85**	2.03 **2.69**	1.96 **2.55**	1.90 **2.46**	1.85 **2.37**	1.81 **2.29**	1.78 **2.23**	1.72 **2.12**	1.67 **2.04**	1.60 **1.92**	1.54 **1.84**	1.49 **1.74**	1.42 **1.64**	1.38 **1.57**	1.32 **1.47**	1.28 **1.42**	1.22 **1.32**	1.16 **1.24**	1.13 **1.19**
1000	3.85 **6.66**	3.00 **4.62**	2.61 **3.80**	2.38 **3.34**	2.22 **3.04**	2.10 **2.82**	2.02 **2.66**	1.95 **2.53**	1.89 **2.43**	1.84 **2.34**	1.80 **2.26**	1.76 **2.20**	1.70 **2.09**	1.65 **2.01**	1.58 **1.89**	1.53 **1.81**	1.47 **1.71**	1.41 **1.61**	1.36 **1.54**	1.30 **1.44**	1.26 **1.38**	1.19 **1.28**	1.13 **1.19**	1.08 **1.11**
∞	3.84 **6.64**	2.99 **4.60**	2.60 **3.78**	2.37 **3.32**	2.21 **3.02**	2.09 **2.80**	2.01 **2.64**	1.94 **2.51**	1.88 **2.41**	1.83 **2.32**	1.79 **2.24**	1.75 **2.18**	1.69 **2.07**	1.64 **1.99**	1.57 **1.87**	1.52 **1.79**	1.46 **1.69**	1.40 **1.59**	1.35 **1.52**	1.28 **1.41**	1.24 **1.36**	1.17 **1.25**	1.11 **1.15**	1.00 **1.00**

Table VII

Table of Random Numbers (8.000 numbers)

	1-4	5-8	9-12	13-16	17-20	21-24	25-28	29-32	33-36	37-40
					First Thousand					
1	23 15	75 48	59 01	83 72	59 93	76 24	97 08	86 95	23 03	67 44
2	05 54	55 50	43 10	53 74	35 08	90 61	18 37	44 10	96 22	13 43
3	14 87	16 03	50 32	40 43	62 23	50 05	10 03	22 11	54 38	08 34
4	38 97	67 49	51 94	05 17	58 53	78 80	59 01	94 32	42 87	16 95
5	97 31	26 17	18 99	75 53	08 70	94 25	12 58	41 54	88 21	05 13
6	11 74	26 93	81 44	33 93	08 72	32 79	73 31	18 22	64 70	68 50
7	43 36	12 88	59 11	01 64	56 23	93 00	90 04	99 43	64 07	40 36
8	93 80	62 04	78 38	26 80	44 91	55 75	11 89	32 58	47 55	25 71
9	49 54	01 31	81 08	42 98	41 87	69 53	82 96	61 77	73 80	95 27
10	36 76	87 26	33 37	94 82	15 69	41 95	96 86	70 45	27 48	38 80
11	07 09	25 23	92 24	62 71	26 07	06 55	84 53	44 67	33 84	53 20
12	43 31	00 10	81 44	86 38	03 07	52 55	51 61	48 89	74 29	46 47
13	61 57	00 63	60 06	17 36	37 75	63 14	89 51	23 35	01 74	69 93
14	31 35	28 37	99 10	77 91	89 41	31 57	97 64	48 62	58 48	69 19
15	57 04	88 65	26 27	79 59	36 82	90 52	95 65	46 35	06 53	22 54
16	09 24	34 42	00 68	72 10	71 37	30 72	97 57	56 09	29 82	76 50
17	97 95	53 50	18 40	89 48	83 29	52 23	08 25	21 22	53 26	15 87
18	93 73	25 95	70 43	78 19	88 85	56 67	16 68	26 95	99 64	45 69
19	72 62	11 12	25 00	92 26	82 64	35 66	65 94	34 71	68 75	18 67
20	61 02	07 44	18 45	37 12	07 94	95 91	73 78	66 99	53 61	93 78
21	97 83	98 54	74 33	05 59	17 18	45 47	35 41	44 22	03 42	30 00
22	89 16	09 71	92 22	23 29	06 37	35 05	54 54	89 88	43 81	03 61
23	25 96	68 82	20 62	87 17	92 65	02 82	35 28	62 84	91 95	48 83
24	81 44	33 17	19 05	04 95	48 06	74 69	00 75	67 65	01 71	65 45
25	11 32	25 49	31 42	36 23	43 86	08 62	49 76	67 42	24 52	32 45
					Second Thousand					
1	64 75	58 38	85 84	12 22	59 20	17 69	61 56	55 95	04 59	59 47
2	10 30	25 22	89 77	43 63	44 30	38 11	24 90	67 07	34 82	33 28
3	71 01	79 84	95 51	30 85	03 74	66 59	10 28	87 53	76 56	91 49
4	60 01	25 56	05 88	41 03	48 79	79 65	59 01	69 78	80 00	36 66
5	37 33	09 46	56 49	16 14	28 02	48 27	45 47	55 44	55 36	50 90
6	47 86	98 70	01 31	59 11	22 73	60 62	61 28	22 34	69 16	12 12
7	38 04	04 27	37 64	16 78	95 78	39 32	34 93	24 88	43 43	87 06
8	73 50	83 09	08 83	05 48	00 78	36 66	93 02	95 56	46 04	53 36
9	32 62	34 64	74 84	06 10	43 24	20 62	83 73	19 32	35 64	39 69
10	97 59	19 95	49 36	63 03	51 06	62 06	99 29	75 95	32 05	77 34
11	74 01	23 19	55 59	79 09	69 82	66 22	42 40	15 96	74 90	75 89
12	56 75	42 64	57 13	35 10	50 14	90 96	63 36	74 69	09 63	34 88
13	49 80	04 99	08 54	83 12	19 98	08 52	82 63	72 92	92 36	50 26
14	43 58	48 96	47 24	87 85	66 70	00 22	15 01	93 99	59 16	23 77
15	16 65	37 96	64 60	32 57	13 01	35 74	28 36	36 73	05 88	72 29
16	48 50	26 90	55 65	32 25	87 48	31 44	68 02	37 31	25 29	63 67
17	96 76	55 46	92 36	31 68	62 30	48 29	63 83	52 23	81 66	40 94
18	38 92	36 15	50 80	35 78	17 84	23 44	41 24	63 33	99 22	81 28
19	77 95	88 16	94 25	22 50	55 87	51 07	30 10	70 60	21 86	19 61
20	17 92	82 80	65 25	58 60	87 71	02 64	18 50	64 65	79 64	81 70
21	94 03	68 59	78 02	31 80	44 99	41 05	41 05	31 87	43 12	15 96
22	47 46	06 04	79 56	23 04	84 17	14 37	28 51	67 27	55 80	03 68
23	47 85	65 60	88 51	99 28	24 39	40 64	41 71	70 13	46 31	82 88
24	57 61	63 46	53 92	29 86	20 18	10 37	57 65	15 62	98 69	07 56
25	08 30	09 27	04 66	75 26	66 10	57 18	87 91	07 54	22 22	20 13

Source: Reproduced from M. G. Kendall and B. B. Smith, *Tables of Random Sampling Numbers*. Tracts for Computers XXIV (London: Cambridge University Press, 1939), pp. 2–5. By permission of the Biometrika Trustees and the Department of Statistics, University College, London.

Table VII (*continued*)

Random Numbers

Third Thousand

	1-4	5-8	9-12	13-16	17-20	21-24	25-28	29-32	33-36	37-40
1	89 22	10 23	62 65	78 77	47 33	51 27	23 02	13 92	44 13	96 51
2	04 00	59 98	18 63	91 82	90 32	94 01	24 23	63 01	26 11	06 50
3	98 54	63 80	66 50	85 67	50 45	40 64	52 28	41 53	25 44	41 25
4	41 71	98 44	01 59	22 60	13 14	54 58	14 03	98 49	98 86	55 79
5	28 73	37 24	89 00	78 52	58 43	24 61	34 97	97 85	56 78	44 71
6	65 21	38 39	27 77	76 20	30 86	80 74	22 43	95 68	47 68	37 92
7	65 55	31 26	78 90	90 69	04 66	43 67	02 62	17 69	90 03	12 05
8	05 66	86 90	80 73	02 98	57 46	58 33	27 82	31 45	98 69	29 98
9	39 30	29 97	18 49	75 77	95 19	27 38	77 63	73 47	26 29	16 12
10	64 59	23 22	53 45	87 92	94 31	38 32	00 59	81 18	06 78	71 37
11	07 51	34 87	92 47	31 48	36 60	68 90	70 53	36 82	57 99	15 82
12	86 59	36 85	01 56	63 89	98 00	82 83	93 51	48 56	54 10	72 32
13	83 73	52 25	99 97	97 78	12 48	36 83	89 95	60 32	41 06	76 14
14	08 59	52 18	26 54	65 50	82 04	87 99	01 70	33 56	25 80	53 84
15	41 27	32 71	49 44	29 36	94 58	16 82	86 39	62 15	86 43	54 31
16	00 47	37 59	08 56	23 81	22 42	72 63	17 63	14 47	25 20	63 47
17	86 13	15 37	89 81	38 30	78 68	89 13	29 61	82 07	00 98	64 32
18	33 84	97 83	59 04	40 20	35 86	03 17	68 86	63 08	01 82	25 46
19	61 87	04 16	57 07	46 80	86 12	98 08	39 73	49 20	77 54	50 91
20	43 89	86 59	23 25	07 88	61 29	78 49	19 76	53 91	50 08	07 86
21	29 93	93 91	23 04	54 84	59 85	60 95	20 66	41 28	72 64	64 73
22	38 50	58 55	55 14	38 85	50 77	18 65	79 48	87 67	83 17	08 19
23	31 82	43 84	31 67	12 52	55 11	72 04	41 15	62 53	27 98	22 68
24	91 43	00 37	67 13	56 11	55 97	06 75	09 25	52 02	39 13	87 53
25	38 63	56 89	76 25	49 89	75 26	96 45	80 38	05 04	11 66	35 14

Fourth Thousand

	1-4	5-8	9-12	13-16	17-20	21-24	25-28	29-32	33-36	37-40
1	02 49	05 41	22 27	94 43	93 64	04 23	07 20	74 11	67 95	40 82
2	11 96	73 64	69 60	62 78	37 01	09 25	33 02	08 01	38 53	74 82
3	48 25	68 34	65 49	69 92	40 79	05 40	33 51	54 39	61 30	31 36
4	27 24	67 30	80 21	48 12	35 36	04 88	18 99	77 49	48 49	30 71
5	32 53	27 72	65 72	43 07	07 22	86 52	91 84	57 92	65 71	00 11
6	66 75	79 89	55 92	37 59	34 31	43 20	45 58	25 45	44 36	92 65
7	11 26	63 45	45 76	50 59	77 46	34 66	82 69	99 26	74 29	75 16
8	17 87	23 91	42 45	56 18	01 46	93 13	74 89	24 64	25 75	92 84
9	62 56	13 03	65 03	40 81	47 54	51 79	80 81	33 61	01 09	77 30
10	62 79	63 07	70 35	49 77	05 01	30 10	50 81	33 00	99 79	19 70
11	75 51	02 17	71 04	33 93	36 60	42 75	76 22	23 87	56 54	84 68
12	87 43	90 16	91 63	51 72	65 90	44 43	70 72	17 98	70 63	90 32
13	97 74	20 26	21 10	74 87	88 03	38 33	76 52	26 92	14 95	90 51
14	98 81	10 60	01 21	57 10	28 75	21 82	88 39	12 85	18 86	16 24
15	51 26	40 18	52 64	60 79	25 53	29 00	42 66	95 78	58 36	29 98
16	40 23	99 33	76 10	41 96	86 10	49 12	00 29	41 80	03 59	93 17
17	26 93	65 91	86 51	66 72	76 45	46 32	94 46	81 94	19 06	66 47
18	88 50	21 17	16 98	29 94	09 74	42 39	46 22	00 69	09 48	16 46
19	63 49	93 80	93 25	59 36	19 95	79 86	78 05	69 01	02 33	83 74
20	36 37	98 12	06 03	31 77	87 10	73 82	83 10	83 60	50 94	40 91
21	93 80	12 23	22 47	47 95	70 17	59 33	43 06	47 43	06 12	66 60
22	29 85	68 71	20 56	31 15	00 53	25 36	58 12	65 22	41 40	24 31
23	97 72	08 79	31 88	26 51	30 50	71 01	71 51	77 06	95 79	29 19
24	85 23	70 91	05 74	60 14	63 77	59 93	81 56	47 34	17 79	27 53
25	75 74	67 52	68 31	72 79	57 73	72 36	48 73	24 36	87 90	68 02

Table VII (*continued*)

Random Numbers

Fifth Thousand

	1-4	5-8	9-12	13-16	17-20	21-24	25-28	29-32	33-36	37-40
1	29 93	50 69	71 63	17 55	25 79	10 47	88 93	79 61	42 82	13 63
2	15 11	40 71	26 51	89 07	77 87	75 51	01 31	03 42	94 24	81 11
3	03 87	04 32	25 10	58 98	76 29	22 03	99 41	24 38	12 76	50 22
4	79 39	03 91	88 40	75 64	52 69	65 95	92 06	40 14	28 42	29 60
5	30 03	50 69	15 79	19 65	44 28	64 81	95 23	14 48	72 18	15 94
6	29 03	99 98	61 28	75 97	98 02	68 53	13 91	98 38	13 72	43 73
7	78 19	60 81	08 24	10 74	97 77	09 59	94 35	69 84	82 09	49 56
8	15 84	78 54	93 91	44 29	13 51	80 13	07 37	52 21	53 91	09 86
9	36 61	46 22	48 49	19 49	72 09	92 58	79 20	53 41	02 18	00 64
10	40 54	95 48	84 91	46 54	38 62	35 54	14 44	66 88	89 47	41 80
11	40 87	80 89	97 14	28 60	99 82	90 30	87 80	07 51	58 71	66 58
12	10 22	94 92	82 41	17 33	14 68	59 45	51 87	56 08	90 80	66 60
13	15 91	87 67	87 30	62 42	59 28	44 12	42 50	88 31	13 77	16 14
14	13 40	31 87	96 49	90 99	44 04	64 97	94 14	62 18	15 59	83 35
15	66 52	39 45	96 74	90 89	02 71	10 00	99 86	48 17	64 06	89 09
16	91 66	53 64	69 68	34 31	78 70	25 97	50 46	62 21	27 25	06 20
17	67 41	58 75	15 08	20 77	37 29	73 20	15 75	93 96	91 76	96 99
18	76 52	79 69	96 23	72 43	34 48	63 39	23 23	94 60	88 79	06 17
19	19 81	54 77	89 74	34 81	71 47	10 95	43 43	55 81	19 45	44 07
20	25 59	25 35	87 76	38 47	25 75	84 34	76 89	18 05	73 95	72 22
21	55 90	24 55	39 63	64 63	16 09	95 99	98 28	87 40	66 66	66 92
22	02 47	05 83	76 79	79 42	24 82	42 42	39 61	62 47	49 11	72 64
23	18 63	05 32	63 13	31 99	76 19	35 85	91 23	50 14	63 28	86 59
24	89 67	33 82	30 16	06 39	20 07	59 50	33 84	02 76	45 03	33 33
25	62 98	66 73	64 06	59 51	74 27	84 62	31 45	65 82	86 05	73 00

Sixth Thousand

	1-4	5-8	9-12	13-16	17-20	21-24	25-28	29-32	33-36	37-40
1	27 50	13 05	46 34	63 85	87 60	35 55	05 67	88 15	47 00	50 92
2	02 31	57 57	62 98	41 09	66 01	69 88	92 83	35 70	76 59	02 58
3	37 43	12 83	66 39	77 33	63 26	53 99	48 65	23 06	94 29	53 04
4	83 56	65 54	19 33	35 42	92 12	37 14	70 75	18 58	98 57	12 52
5	06 81	56 27	49 32	12 42	92 42	05 96	82 94	70 25	45 49	18 16
6	39 15	03 60	15 56	73 16	48 74	50 27	43 42	58 36	73 16	39 90
7	84 45	71 93	10 27	15 83	84 20	57 42	41 28	42 06	15 90	70 47
8	82 47	05 77	06 89	47 13	92 85	60 12	32 89	25 22	42 38	87 37
9	98 04	06 70	24 21	69 02	65 42	55 33	11 95	72 35	73 23	57 26
10	18 33	49 04	14 33	48 50	15 64	58 26	14 91	46 02	72 13	48 62
11	33 92	19 93	38 27	43 40	27 72	79 74	86 57	41 83	58 71	56 99
12	48 66	74 30	44 81	06 80	29 09	50 31	69 61	24 64	28 89	97 79
13	85 85	07 54	21 50	31 80	10 19	56 65	82 52	26 58	55 12	26 34
14	08 27	08 08	35 87	96 57	33 12	01 77	52 76	09 89	71 12	17 69
15	59 61	22 14	26 09	96 75	17 94	51 08	41 91	45 94	80 48	59 92
16	17 45	77 79	31 66	36 54	92 85	65 60	53 98	63 50	11 20	96 63
17	11 26	37 08	07 71	95 95	39 75	92 48	99 78	23 33	19 56	06 67
18	48 08	13 98	16 52	41 15	73 96	32 55	03 12	38 30	88 77	17 03
19	76 27	72 22	99 61	72 15	00 25	21 54	47 79	18 41	58 50	57 66
20	98 89	22 25	72 92	53 55	07 98	66 71	53 29	61 71	56 96	41 78
21	88 69	61 63	01 67	61 88	58 79	35 65	08 45	63 38	69 86	79 47
22	12 58	13 75	80 98	01 35	91 16	18 36	90 54	99 17	68 36	85 06
23	08 86	96 36	14 09	43 85	51 20	65 18	06 40	52 17	48 10	68 97
24	33 81	05 51	32 48	60 12	32 44	08 12	89 00	98 82	79 17	97 22
25	05 15	99 28	87 15	07 08	66 92	53 81	69 42	02 27	65 33	57 69

Table VII (*continued*)

Random Numbers

	1-4	5-8	9-12	13-16	17-20	21-24	25-28	29-32	33-36	37-40
1	80 30	23 64	67 96	21 33	36 90	03 91	69 33	90 13	34 48	02 19
2	61 29	89 61	32 08	12 62	26 08	42 00	31 73	31 30	30 61	34 11
3	23 33	61 01	02 21	11 81	51 32	36 10	23 74	50 31	90 11	73 52
4	94 21	32 92	93 50	72 67	23 20	74 59	30 30	48 66	75 32	27 97
5	87 61	92 69	01 60	28 79	74 76	86 06	39 29	73 85	03 27	50 57
6	37 56	19 18	03 42	86 03	85 74	44 81	86 45	71 16	13 52	35 56
7	64 86	66 31	55 04	88 40	10 30	84 38	06 13	58 83	62 04	63 52
8	22 69	58 45	49 23	09 81	98 84	05 04	75 99	27 70	72 79	32 19
9	23 22	14 22	64 90	10 26	74 23	53 91	27 73	78 19	92 43	68 10
10	42 38	59 64	72 96	46 57	89 67	22 81	94 56	69 84	18 31	06 39
11	17 18	01 34	10 98	37 48	93 86	88 59	69 53	78 86	37 26	85 48
12	39 45	69 53	94 89	58 97	29 33	29 19	50 94	80 57	31 99	38 91
13	43 18	11 42	56 19	48 44	45 02	84 29	01 78	65 77	76 84	88 85
14	59 44	06 45	68 55	16 65	66 13	38 00	95 76	50 67	67 65	18 83
15	01 50	34 32	38 00	37 57	47 82	66 59	19 50	87 14	35 59	79 47
16	79 14	60 35	47 95	90 71	31 03	85 37	38 70	34 16	64 55	66 49
17	01 56	63 68	80 26	14 97	23 88	59 22	82 39	70 83	48 34	46 48
18	25 76	18 71	29 25	15 51	92 96	01 01	28 18	03 35	11 10	27 84
19	23 52	10 83	45 06	49 85	35 45	84 08	81 13	52 57	21 23	67 02
20	91 64	08 64	25 74	16 10	97 31	10 27	24 48	89 06	42 81	29 10
21	80 86	07 27	26 70	08 65	85 20	31 23	28 99	39 63	32 03	71 91
22	31 71	37 60	95 60	94 95	54 45	27 97	03 67	30 54	86 04	12 41
23	05 83	50 36	09 04	39 15	66 55	80 36	39 71	24 10	62 22	21 53
24	98 70	02 90	30 63	62 59	26 04	97 20	00 91	28 80	40 23	09 91
25	82 79	35 45	64 53	93 24	86 55	48 72	18 57	05 79	20 09	31 46

	1-4	5-8	9-12	13-16	17-20	21-24	25-28	29-32	33-36	37-40
1	37 52	49 55	40 65	27 61	08 59	91 23	26 18	95 04	98 20	99 52
2	48 16	69 65	69 02	08 83	08 83	68 37	00 96	13 59	12 16	17 93
3	50 43	06 59	56 53	30 61	40 21	29 06	49 60	90 38	21 43	19 25
4	89 31	62 79	45 73	71 72	77 11	28 80	72 35	75 77	24 72	98 43
5	63 29	90 61	86 39	07 38	38 85	77 06	10 23	30 84	07 95	30 76
6	71 68	93 94	08 72	36 27	85 89	40 59	83 37	93 85	73 97	84 05
7	05 06	96 63	58 24	05 95	56 64	77 53	85 64	15 95	93 91	59 03
8	03 35	58 95	46 44	25 70	31 66	01 05	44 44	62 91	36 31	45 04
9	13 04	57 67	74 77	53 35	93 51	82 83	27 38	63 16	04 48	75 23
10	49 96	43 94	56 04	02 79	55 78	01 44	75 26	85 54	01 81	32 82
11	24 36	24 08	44 77	57 07	54 41	04 56	09 44	30 58	25 45	37 56
12	55 19	97 20	01 11	47 45	79 79	06 72	12 81	86 97	54 09	06 53
13	02 28	54 60	28 35	32 94	36 74	51 63	96 90	04 13	30 43	10 14
14	90 50	13 78	22 20	37 56	97 95	49 95	91 15	52 73	12 93	78 94
15	33 71	32 43	29 58	47 38	39 96	67 51	64 47	49 91	64 58	93 07
16	70 58	28 49	54 32	97 70	27 81	64 69	71 52	02 56	61 37	04 58
17	09 68	96 10	57 78	85 00	89 81	98 30	19 40	76 28	62 99	99 83
18	19 36	60 85	35 04	12 87	83 88	66 54	32 00	30 20	05 30	42 63
19	04 75	44 49	64 26	51 46	80 50	53 91	00 55	67 36	68 66	08 29
20	79 83	32 39	46 77	56 83	42 21	60 03	14 47	07 01	66 85	49 22
21	80 99	42 43	08 58	54 41	98 05	54 39	34 42	97 47	38 35	59 40
22	48 83	64 99	86 94	48 78	79 20	62 23	56 45	92 65	56 36	83 02
23	28 45	35 85	22 20	13 01	73 96	70 05	84 50	68 59	96 58	16 63
24	52 07	63 15	82 30	66 23	14 26	66 61	17 80	41 97	40 27	24 80
25	39 14	52 18	35 87	48 55	48 81	03 11	26 99	03 80	08 86	50 42

INDEX

J